# Trees and Shrubs
## for the
## Southeast

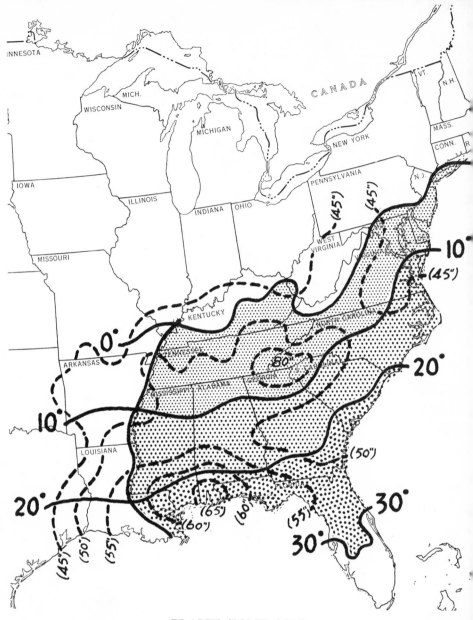

## PLANT ZONE MAP

The map of the Southeastern States is divided into three zones referred to in the text as (1) the Southern Coastal Plain, (2) the Southern Piedmont, and (3) the Upper South. The zonal boundaries correspond closely to those of the "Plant Hardiness Zone Map" of the Agricultural Research Service of the U. S. D. A. (Miscellaneous Publication No. 814) where the Coastal Plain is in Zone 9 with average minimum temperatures of 30 to 20 degrees, the Piedmont is in Zone 8 with average minimums of 20 to 10 degrees, and the Upper South is in Zone 7 with minimums of 10 to 0 degrees. Average annual precipitation is indicated by dashed lines taken from the U. S. D. A. Yearbook for 1941, "Climate and Man."

# Trees and Shrubs

# for the

# Southeast

By
BROOKS E. WIGGINTON

UNIVERSITY OF GEORGIA PRESS
ATHENS

# Contents

# Acknowledgments

THIS volume has been prepared while the author was the recipient of the Garden Research Fellowship awarded by the Trustees for Harvard University at the Dumbarton Oaks Research Library, Washington, D. C. The generous assistance of the Garden Advisory Committee of Dumbarton Oaks, under whose guidance the work has been developed, and of the staff of the Library is gratefully acknowledged. The author is especially indebted to Mr. and Mrs. Robert Woods Bliss who created the house, the garden, and the collection at Dumbarton Oaks, and who have made them available for use by himself as well as by the profession of Landscape Architecture.

Grateful acknowledgment is made also for the invaluable personal assistance of many landscape architects and nurserymen of the Southeast, and particularly to Mrs. Marion T. Brawley of Southern Pines, Miss Clermont Lee of Savannah, Mr. T. Miesse Baumgardner of Sea Island, Mr. Walter A. J. Ewald of Memphis, Mr. Campbell E. Miller of Louisville, Mr. Doan R. Ogden and Mr. William Pitkin of Ashville, Mr. Lallie T. Richter of Nashville, Mr. John D. Scruggs of Lexington, and Mr. William S. Wiedorn of New Orleans. Professor Hubert B. Owens of the Department of Landscape Architecture of the University of Georgia was most encouraging and helpful from the beginning of this undertaking and throughout its course. Dr. Wilbur H. Duncan of the Herbarium of the University of Georgia, and Dr. Frederick G. Meyer, Taxonomic Botanist of the U. S. D. A. Research Service at Beltsville, Md., have been most generous with their knowledge in clearing problems of plant identification.

The plant names used in this work are taken from *Standardized Plant Names*, Second Edition. The system employed in organizing and presenting the material was devised by Professor L. C. Chadwick of Ohio State University, and it is used with his permission. Reference is made to existing works on the botany and horticulture of this region as much as possible, and a partial list of these is given in the Bibliography.

# Introduction

In its origin this book had the simple purpose of suggesting a limited basic palette of plant materials which could be recommended confidently to satisfy most normal requirements in landscape design in the southeastern United States.

Prior to this, studies covering two of the three sections into which this region has been divided have been published as preliminaries. These are *Trees and Shrubs for the Southern Piedmont* and *Trees and Shrubs for the Southern Coastal Plain* (University of Georgia Press, 1949 and 1957). Materials from these, revised and corrected as experience suggests, have been included here, with additional notes on the Upper South to make what, it is hoped, will prove to be a comprehensive survey for the region.

Major emphasis in this study is placed on the use of plants as materials for landscape design. The basic purpose is to present a designer's manual and not a guide to horticultural practice. There is a difference, despite some overlapping, between the attitude of approach to these two. In this case the problems of landscape design are outlined and the means to solve them simply and effectively through the proper selection of plant materials are suggested. Ideally these selections should give satisfaction without recourse to intensive horticultural practices. In landscape architecture today, when the services of good gardeners are ever more scarce, the aim of the designer is to dispose his materials so skillfully that they will flourish in their appointed places without major alterations of soil or excessive recourse to sprays, fertilizers, or pruning shears, remaining even at maturity part of a pleasing predetermined composition in which all components take their natural form in proper scale relationship to each other.

The reader must not expect, therefore, to find here recipes for becoming the envy of his neighbors through introducing and fostering some exotic species. Interesting as it is, this kind of activity has little to do with the creation of a garden which is functionally fit and aesthetically delightful. A garden full of the rarest and most exotic

1

of plants may leave the observer with nothing more than a sense of restlessness and dissatisfaction if the materials have not been put together in a way that accentuates their design qualities.

More detailed remarks on these qualities follow. In pursuit of the argument, it follows that for the average person it is more important to select a few basic plants which grow well under a variety of circumstances to fulfill certain definite requirements such as screening, shading, and groundcovering. Therefore the emphasis here is on use. The kinds of questions one might expect to find answered are: "What kind of shade tree should be planted in the narrow dry strip between the sidewalk and the street? What shrub which will not grow over 3 feet tall might be planted under the bay window on the shaded north side of the house? What plant would cover the bare ground under the Oak tree? What are some good evergreens for providing screening?"

These are elementary problems which confront every gardener, every homeowner, and it is hoped that these pages will offer suggestions and ideas which will stimulate the imagination and prove genuinely helpful. At the same time it is hoped that the experienced gardener, and even the professional who may not be as familiar with the rich flora of this region as he would like to be, may find this a useful reference manual. For this reason, the design qualities of the materials, their ranges of adaptability, and their character under different conditions have been rather carefully studied and outlined.

## THE SOUTHEAST — PHYSICAL CHARACTERISTICS

The region covered in this study is outlined on the frontispiece map. It lies between Virginia and Kentucky on the north, and the Gulf of Mexico and subtropical Florida on the south, between the Atlantic Ocean on the east and the Mississippi River on the west. Ecologists term this the "Southern Rain Forest" region. In a broad sense it is characterized by some unity in the composition of the native flora, and it has, as well, a common social, economic, and historical background.

This area is subdivided into three parts which are called (1) the Coastal Plain, (2) the Piedmont, and (3) the Upper South. The first two names are in common parlance, but the third is selected arbitrarily for lack of a better one. It is possibly unfortunate that the first two names, which do possess definite geographic connotations, should be employed here in a slightly different sense, being more particularly related to climatic than to geologic boundaries. Indeed, these subregional names as they are employed here correspond closely to those outlined in the "Plant Hardiness Zone Map" of the U. S. Department of Agriculture (1960) as follows: the Southern Coastal Plain lies in Zone 9 in which average minimum temperatures range from 20 to

30 degrees; the Southern Piedmont is in Zone 8 with minimums of 10 to 20 degrees; and the Upper South is in Zone 7 with minimums of 0 to 10 degrees. The questionable validity of the above subregional titles is acknowledged. Possibly it would have been better to have chosen something like Lower South, Middle South, and Upper South. The justification for their use lay in that they do evoke mental pictures of locales which are much more clear than climatic zone numbers alone could be, and they are at least as descriptive as less familiar titles manufactured for the occasion might be.

These designations are employed here also in an attempt to overcome a possible source of confusion which zone numbers alone do not clarify. The latter, being defined by temperature isotherms, do not take into account rainfall which is a climatic factor of significance to plant adaptation almost equal to that of temperature. Failure to take this into account can be misleading, and thus planting problems in Mobile can be quite different from those in Corpus Christi, both in Zone 9. Consequently, on the map a pattern of lines representing Average Annual Precipitation is superimposed on the temperature zones. From this pattern it will be seen that all of this region receives at least 45 inches of rainfall annually.

The recommendations made here are intended to apply neither to areas farther west where the precipitation is less although temperatures are comparable, nor to localities farther north where temperatures are lower but the rainfall is equal. Variations in both temperature as well as rainfall norms are considered to be limiting factors. This does not imply that zonal references are not helpful, but simply that this work is intended to supplement and sharpen the information usually provided through them. In a number of works on plant materials and even in some nursery catalogues, zone numbers are employed to suggest hardiness range. Their use is widely accepted and, to a large extent, understood. But a statement to the effect that the Strawberry Madrone (Arbutus) is adapted to Zone 8 does not reveal the fact that this is a fine tree in the portion of the zone located in California but not in the part in the Piedmont of Georgia. This study is thus more restricted in its scope, attempting to show what plants are grown in the Southeast and how they behave there.

Although temperature and rainfall limits of the three proposed subregions can be rather clearly defined, generalizations on the adaptability of plants are both difficult and dangerous. Topography or altitude, exposure, drainage, and proximity to large bodies of water or the shelter provided in congested urban centers, exercise strong local influences on temperatures and plant reactions to them. Much can be accomplished through a careful study of "micro-climates" in siting plants to increase their range of adaptability. Upon approaching the northern and southern limits of any one zone as outlined, there appears, of course, a gradual merging of many of the typical plants of that zone with those plants characteristic of the next cooler or warmer belt respectively. However, under normal conditions the ultimate survival of any species depends on the most unfavorable combinations of circumstances and not on the best or even the average. The landscape designer does well to bear in mind this basic axiom of the plant ecologist because gardeners in general find a constant challenge in growing the exotics. These can often be handled satisfactorily in cutting gardens or in hobby collections, but the permanent structure of a landscape must always be built of reliable materials.

Soil compositions also strongly influence matters of plant selection, second to climatic factors in importance only because they can be altered. With relative ease light soils can be made more retentive of moisture and nutrients, heavy soils can be lightened, drainage can be corrected, and acidity or alkalinity can be altered. All this requires time and work and money, however. The best practice is to acknowledge the limitations of the existing conditions and to work within them sympathetically. It is well known that Azaleas do not take well to alkaline soils, for example. To make them flourish on such soils is difficult, expensive, and often discouraging. Happier results might be achieved with another choice of material.

The major soil areas of this region may be summarized as follows: the Coastal Plain is made up largely of sandy soils and silts, usually well drained, occasionally swampy, acid in reaction except for large chalky areas in southwest Louisiana and southeast Texas, and in parts of the seacoast strip which may contain deposits of shells or corals. The Piedmont is made up primarily of red clays, occasional sandy loams, predominantly acid in reaction. The mountain sections of the Upper South are granitic through north Georgia, western North Carolina and Virginia; sandstones and shales prevail in eastern Kentucky and most of West Virginia. These soils are usually acid. Alkaline soils are found in large limestone areas of central and western Kentucky and central Tennessee, in smaller sections of northeast Tennessee and western Virginia, and also in the chalky "black belt" of central Alabama and east Mississippi. The great river valley areas are made up of silts which may be alkaline as in the Mississippi delta. There are important bands of loess soils on either side of the Mississippi River in west Tennessee and Mississippi and east Arkansas.

For more detailed information on the soil classifications and the related plant pattern as a more accurate reflection of the geological structure of this region, reference may be made to the interesting study of F. L. Mulford called *The Plant Growth Regions of the United States*, published by the U. S. Department of Agriculture in 1937. In this study a map of the United States is divided into regions, and lists of native plants which are typical of each region are given. According to Mulford's classification, the Southeast is subdivided into sections called the Swampy Coastal Plain (corresponding very closely to our "Southern Coastal Plain"), the Upper Coastal Plain, the Piedmont, the Appalachians, and the Ohio-Tennessee River Valleys. Our "Southern Piedmont" includes roughly half of Mulford's Piedmont and most of his Upper Coastal Plain. Our "Upper South" embraces the upper half of his Piedmont, a small part of his Upper Coastal Plain, and large portions of his Appalachian and River Valley sections. Mulford's regions correspond to accepted geographic definitions, and they reflect some consideration for rainfall. However, as the author himself suggests, they are hardly sufficiently sensitive to temperature variations. Since the latter are considered to be of prime importance as far as present purposes are concerned, the temperature zones are used as the basis for this study in preference to the geographic areas.

## ORGANIZATION OF THE PLANT LISTS

Any gardener or designer who has a thorough knowledge of about a dozen very good species in several size classifications—such as trees, shrubs, and vines that were quite reliable in his locality—will have a solid basis for undertaking planting problems in his own yard. He will also have a sound foundation on which to enlarge his acquaintance with more exotic and unusual materials.

Ultimate size of the materials under discussion is accepted as the criterion upon which the following information is organized. Next to suitability to growing conditions of any certain locale, the factor of ultimate size of a plant material is the most basic consideration in planting design. Because, when one is planning for any planting, he thinks of a tree or shrub first of all in terms of how big it will grow, the following lists are made up in "Size Groups." These are: I. Vines, II. Groundcovers (under 1 foot in height), III. Dwarf Shrubs (1 to 4 feet), IV. Small Shrubs (4 to 6 feet), V. Medium-sized Shrubs (6 to 10 feet), VI. Large Shrubs (over 10 feet), VII. Small Trees (to 40 feet), and VIII. Large Trees (over 40 feet). For purposes of preliminary discussion of landscape uses for materials within these categories, this organization is further simplified by grouping the Dwarf and Small Shrubs into one division of Lesser Shrubs, under eye level (6 feet) in height; the Medium and Large Shrubs under the heading of Major Shrubs, above eye level in height (over 6 feet); and the two minor subdivisions of the Tree group together. Thus the above list of eight size classes can be thought of in simpler form, consisting of five major divisions. These are Vines (1), Groundcovers (II), Lesser Shrubs (III-IV), Major Shrubs (V-VI), and Trees (VII-VIII).

While size is the basic organizing theme of these plant lists within their respective geographic areas, and while it is also true in theory that these sizes should be capable of accurate determination, it is the matter of placing plants in their proper size categories that has been most difficult in the preparation of this manuscript. On the one hand there are those who take what might be called the "practical" viewpoint, saying that some of the very slow-growing plants might as well be used as if they would not reach their full stature, that they can be maintained with very little care in sizes less than those they might reach unrestrained. Where one wants a small shrub, it may be difficult to find just the right thing, especially since dependable low-growing materials are comparatively rare. Therefore, it may be reasonable to choose some slow-growing plant from the next larger size group to satisfy the need. This point of view has always had its stout defenders, particularly among those who seek to create an immediate effect of some "finish." This practice, however, often leads to overcrowding, high maintenance cost, and to the eventual necessity of removing overgrown materials and replacing them with new ones.

Opposed to this view are the more strict interpreters of fact. In preparing these lists the writer has been inclined to side with the latter point of view although, it must be confessed, not entirely consistently. The result of much inner struggle on this matter appears in the lists which represent the opinion of one person as to the most helpful way of presenting the information. However one may feel on this subject, there are always borderline cases. In several instances a material may fall in one class in a certain locality, and in another in a warmer or cooler zone. Even within one small area, the height and character of a single species may show considerable variation in different exposures, soil conditions, and under different management. Generalizations are always risky and must be studied in the light of modifications which may be imposed by peculiar local circumstances. The astute designer with plants takes advantage of these modifications, of course, and it is a mark of his skill and knowledge when he does so successfully. Trouble arises when he is tempted to reach too far out of line or when, without adequate consideration, he makes a miscalculation. Sometimes it is too much easier to take readily available material than to try to find the right material. Gardens and foundation plantings everywhere show how easy it is to step into these pitfalls.

Following each "Size Group" chapter heading there are two lists of plants for each of the subregions, the Coastal Plain, the Piedmont, and the Upper South. In each case the first or recommended list attempts to include about a dozen "best" species, considered highly desirable and, within reasonable limits, thoroughly reliable for most needs. The second list of species for limited use includes those which are judged inferior in general adaptability or which may not be so well known. It should be emphasized, however, that the secondary list may contain the "just right" plant for some particular spot or unusual circumstance; and, since it includes things not as widely tested, it may cover some plants of the greatest potential interest—the favorites of tomorrow.

In comparing the plant lists for the different subregions, one will note that some overlapping occurs because a plant is often useful in more than one of these areas. The Willow Oak, for example, is judged to be a first-class Large Tree for all, the Coastal Plain, the Piedmont, and the Upper South. The Southern Magnolia, on the other hand, is ranked high in the Coastal Plain and the Piedmont, but it is somewhat questionable in parts of the Upper South where it is listed with the materials for limited use. It will survive throughout the latter area, and excellent specimens of it will be found in favored spots, but it probably should not be counted on, certainly not as a Large Tree, in severe exposures or at higher elevations. A similar case in reverse is the Sugar Maple which is superb in the Upper South, good in cooler sections of the Piedmont, and not at all to be recommended in the Coastal Plain. In this connection, it is worth noting that hardiness is not entirely a matter of enduring cold, but that tolerance to heat and length of growing season must also be considered.

The boundaries of the plant regions and the zones of tolerance of the species growing within them are fluid rather than fixed. In an effort to suggest this and to portray the range of the recommended species, a graphic chart for each size class follows the three subregional lists. On the chart, each subregion is divided into two sections representing its cooler and warmer extremes, and bars made of x's following the plant names indicate the range of the species. Within the recommended range x's are shown; in the less favorable areas the broken bar is shown. Referring to the Magnolia and the Maple cited as examples above, the former is presented with a x's through the Coastal Plain, the Piedmont, and into the Upper South where the bar becomes broken; and the latter shows x's in the Upper South and into the Piedmont where the bar is broken and finally disappears in the Coastal Plain.

Following the plant lists and the graphic range chart which

head each chapter, there is a brief descriptive paragraph on each of the listed species, alphabetically arranged. This descriptive matter is also presented as a composite of the three subregions so that, for example, all of the material on the Willow Oak, advocated for all sections, appears in one place and repetition is eliminated.

## Selecting the Recommended Plants

An effort is made to be perfectly impartial in ranking the plants in their respective categories. Nevertheless, it is difficult at times to eliminate purely personal preferences which may conflict with those of others. Therefore, it may be well to enumerate here some of the points on which such choices are made. Roughly in order of importance these are form, foliage, ease of cultivation, flowers or fruits, and rate of growth. It will be noted that displays of flowers or fruits, which are temporary, should be considered less important than the more permanent qualities of foliage and form even though the former frequently become the prime bases of choice for the average person.

### Form

Form is scarcely less important to the designer of plant compositions than size. The vegetable world offers a broad range of shapes varying from the vertical columnar through the round oval to the flat horizontal. The compactness or density of habit of growth makes some difference in the impact of these forms. Clipping can modify them to a great extent. Under this heading also must come a consideration of those fascinating forms of twisted, gnarled, sculpturesque trunks and branches which only nature can produce. These are high in interest value, and their wispy lines and contorted bulks can be played against the neutral backgrounds of foliage masses or masonry walls with telling advantage. A good plant vocabulary should include a variety of forms along with an assortment of massive, as opposed to light, picturesque materials.

### Foliage

Foliage frames the permanent background of the garden, providing the screen for privacy and the restful refreshing green foil for colorful flowers. This is the strong foundation on which, with architectural features, the garden structure must be built. This structural foundation must be good. Here one must consider the qualities of plants which are evergreen and those which are deciduous, losing their leaves in winter. The latter exhibit, during the dormant season, those colorful, intricate, and often bizarre traceries of branch and twig which are mentioned above.

Foliage colors grade from gray and blue-greens to yellow-greens in both dark and light tones; in a few species there are more extreme variations to golden yellow, dull red, and to various combinations of these.

Finally, leafage shows a wide range in what the landscape architect calls texture. This term refers to the coarse, rich, exciting effect of the Magnolia as opposed to the fine, light, soothing appearance of something like the Albizzia. The texture quality depends often on the size of the individual leaf, ranging from coarse through medium, to fine, although this is modified somewhat by the density and the compactness of the foliage. Thus some shrubs, such as the dwarf Japanese Hollies which bear very small leaves, may have a rugged and rather coarse effect because of their dense block-like forms and their decisive heavy shades in bright sunlight.

*Ease of Cultivation*

Ease of cultivation is again a matter of prime importance in the selection of any list of recommended plants, and it becomes increasingly important as skilled garden helpers become more rare. Theoretically, any species enumerated here among the "best" should be almost immune to disease and insect attack and capable of thriving under any average conditions. But this is not possible by any means, largely because there are a good many things which are well worth growing despite an occasional spraying chore. The petal blossom blight of Azaleas, to cite one example, would not remove this gorgeous beauty from its pre-eminent place although this disease is widespread, destructive, and stubborn to control. And although scales, "die-back," untimely freezes, and need for special growing conditions harass the fancier of Camellias, he would be the last to begrudge the time consumed in the tasks associated with the pursuit of his hobby.

However, unless a species does possess some unusual merit, it might well be relegated to a minor place in its size group on account of cultural difficulties. If special problems may be expected with the highly rated plants, these problems are discussed sufficiently that one may know what troubles to expect. These problems will consist usually in (a) exacting requirements as to sunny or shaded sites, (b) soils swampy or well drained, sandy or heavy, acid or alkaline, etc., (c) susceptibility to diseases and/or damage from common insect pests, and (d) excessive pruning demands.

Hardiness or the adaptability of a plant to any particular climate zone is a factor involved in the "ease of cultivation" and is, of course, taken into account in the first formulation of these lists. But it is a matter which might be discussed further chiefly because current garden literature is constantly tempting one with invitations to grow

Camellias in Connecticut or something equally doubtful as far as good garden design is concerned. Such feats may challenge the hobbyists, but unsuccessful attempts to equal them will probably discourage the person who simply wants a good garden.

A plant's reaction to climate is affected by its condition as well as the latitude of its location. For example, a young fast-growing Zelkova tree, unquestionably hardy to Cleveland, Ohio, may be killed by a cold snap in Atlanta, Georgia. This kind of loss, common throughout the South and particularly with introduced materials, may be due to the plant's being in active growing condition when cold weather arrives suddenly after a warm, rainy autumn. Wherever there is doubt as to hardiness, such materials should be grown on well-drained sites, and water and food should be withheld late in the growing season so that hardening off is encouraged. Boxwoods, the evergreen Viburnums, Loquats, Oriental and English Hollies are typical examples of plants needing such treatment.

Losses of this kind must not be confused with those associated with burning of foliage during the midwinter, common on most broad-leaved evergreens throughout much of the Southeast. During any sunny windy period in the winter, foliage of these plants gives off water vapor in the process of transpiration. Moisture lost in this fashion must be replaced from the soil through the roots. To make up this loss, the roots must be in growing condition and in contact with free moisture. They must not be locked in a frozen condition. For this reason it is a general rule that evergreens should be planted in places where their foliage has some protection from exposure to winter sun and wind, and their roots should be somewhat insulated by mulch coverings which temper sudden atmospheric changes. This also explains why the selection of broad-leaved evergreens narrows in colder sections where the ground freezes deep.

Introduced plants coming chiefly from the temperate climates of Japan and western Europe, as many of our ornamentals do, frequently adapt with difficulty to the continental climate of parts of the Southeast, characterized as it is by severe fluctuations, whereas these oriented plants might endure quite easily the cold alone. On the other hand, native materials often show a surprising tolerance, the Devilwood Osmanthus and the Inkberry being two outstanding examples in the evergreen class. This is another reason for knowing native American materials. This is not to say, however, that native plants can take the place in landscape design of those introduced. Native materials too can have a very close tolerance, chiefly in the matter of soil preferences, as in the instance of many Rhododendrons, the Mountain Pieris, Bearberry, etc. Each planting choice must be decided on its own merits. If the designer understands how plants are likely to react to cold and exposure, his latitude of successful choice is greatly increased. These lists can hardly be used effectively without some appreciation of these points.

*Flowers and Fruits*

In all too many cases plants are selected solely for their seasonal displays of flowers and fruits rather than for their more permanent values of form and foliage in a well-organized plant composition. The seasonal displays have their place certainly, but in many cases a gaudy flower simply masks for a time an awkward form or a problem in upkeep. Plants for the main garden structure and for the year-round effect should be selected first on the basis of a well-integrated pattern of forms, textures, and colors of foliage as well as for flowers. But for those extra bloomers which one may desire in spite of practicability, there should be a cutting garden on every place which can possibly afford the space. Such a plot is doubly advisable because one hesitates sometimes to cut as much as he might like from the shrubs and trees in the important garden areas.

*Speed of Growth*

Speed of growth and development are important factors in planting design when an early appearance of maturity is desirable. When one builds a garden, he likes to think he is working on a permanent thing. But the fact is that in this day of mobile populations, people frequently do not live long in any one house, and it is becoming quite rare for the home of one generation to be occupied by the next generation of the same family. In recognition of this situation, the demand for "immediate effect" becomes ever more insistent. There are three ways in which this may be achieved: (1) to purchase full-grown specimens from the nurseryman, (2) to plant the species which will grow more rapidly, or (3) to overplant, using a good many filler plants which may be discarded when the more choice ones begin to take up their allotted spaces. A point which might be noted here is that every precaution should be taken to preserve existing trees or other valuable growth when one is building a new place. Sometimes these are irreplaceable at any price, and, properly cared for, they can often give a new garden an appearance of maturity.

In any event, fast-growing materials are of some importance in landscape design, and plant lists such as are proposed here should include at least a few of them. Unfortunately the softwooded subjects have several faults as a class. Trees of the group are susceptible to bad breakage in storms and usually are short-lived. The shrubs, in order to support their vigorous growths frequently rob the soil of food and water to the detriment of other plants. These shrubs also tend to fill up with dead wood and consequently require a good deal of pruning and care to keep them in presentable condition. Since they are easily and quickly grown, they are usually very common.

## PLANTING DESIGN

It might be logical to discuss here the aesthetics of planting design. But since that is not within the purpose of this study, and there are many good references available on the subject, suffice it to call attention to some fundamental ideals which bear on the organization and content of the material which follows.

Planting design and landscape design are, in a large degree, inseparable. It is difficult to conceive of a work of landscape architecture which is not expressed somehow in terms of plants. It has become customary, however, to make the distinction in which landscape design is more particularly the process of determining areas and their functions and planting design is that of choosing materials which will carry out those functions in the most satisfying way. Thus in a work of landscape architecture, plants have their proper place insofar as they fulfill a function, a definite purpose. In a very real sense a thing of beauty, as a well-grown shrub may be, is not necessarily a joy forever in a garden unless it fits appropriately into a larger scheme and contributes to, or functions effectively in, an artistic whole. It is possible that a good basic design can be largely destroyed by poor use of plants. An indifferent design, even an ugly situation, can gain a measure of quality from an inspired planting arrangement.

This study attempts to treat plants as functioning units in landscape design. The major functions which they fulfill may be suggested in the outline on the opposite page.

One should note first that the landscape designer begins with establishing the structural functions of the materials which will execute the main lines of his design. Then he will proceed to study the decorative qualities of form, texture, and color of the plants listed within the particular Size Group or Groups fulfilling the structural requirements. In dealing with plants as structural units, he is handling materials with integral decorative qualities of infinite capacity. All plants have some decorative potential. A major task of the designer is to control, unify, and harmonize these decorative features, subordinating them to a major theme, yet employing them in those enriching contrasts which give life and interest to the composition. In order to suggest some of these potentials, a set of garden photographs is included herein to show, not primarily plants as specimens, but plants as design materials combined in a manner to suggest their value for artistic expression.

Good planting design is based, to some extent at least, on a certain

## I. STRUCTURAL

A. Canopy - (shelter, shade, overhead enclosure)

Here are Shade trees for garden or street, Small or Large (Groups VII-VIII) in proportion to available space. Vines (Group I) trained on arbors may be included also.

B. Division - (space definition, horizontal enclosure or framing)

1. High boundary - (not blocking vision or circulation)

Trees (Groups VII-VIII) or Major Shrubs (Groups V-VI) permitting vision under, between, or through.

2. High boundary - (blocking vision and circulation)

Low-branched trees, mostly of Group VII, Major Shrubs (Groups V-VI), and Vines (Group I) trained on fences.

3. Low boundary - (possibly blocking circulation but not vision)

Lesser Shrubs (Groups III-IV) and Groundcovers (Group II).

C. Groundcovering - (for soil protection, erosion control, circulation direction)

Materials of Group II and occasionally Vines (Group I) or Lesser Shrubs (Groups III-IV).

## II. DECORATIVE

A. Sculpture

All Groups.

1. Clipped forms, topiary, hedges

2. Natural forms

B. Color

C. Texture

sensitivity to the quality or character of the material. There is always the "right" plant for each situation, and it should be allowed to develop in its individual way with a minimum of restraint and, incidentally, care. This philosophy of planting design may be said to be consistent with that basic tenet of contemporary architectural design calling for "honest" expression in the use of materials. Perhaps the word "honesty" is not altogether appropriate here because an artistic creation is not necessarily defended on moral grounds. Deceit has often been a respected resource of the artist. Still the ideal of selecting the right thing for the right place and letting it do the job in its own way with a minimum of encouragement might well enrich our work, and it can certainly lighten the burden of landscape maintenance. In all public and institutional projects the latter is vital. For the average gardener, to whom ordinary garden chores ought to be a pleasure, it is desirable that upkeep does not become burdensome.

Finally, it may be well to call attention to some of the common pitfalls which beset the enthusiastic gardener. First of all, nearly everyone buys too many varieties. A good planting composition is an art product, and its design is governed still by the old principles of unity, harmony, and order. No one can make a harmony of a "hodge-podge." Second, the general tendency to plant too much material, generally resulting from a lack of appreciation of the ultimate sizes which may be reasonably expected, brings about crowding, then damage to the plants themselves, and eventually to an appearance of stuffiness which oftentimes can be relieved only by clearing and starting anew. Third, too many good gardeners in the South have turned their attentions almost entirely to the Azaleas and Camellias, with a few other broad-leaved evergreens, to the neglect of many other good materials. The Southeast is rich in its selection of evergreens which may very well form the principal structure of the garden, but there are times when masses of them have a somber and funereal effect. The lightness of deciduous trees and shrubs with their fresh greens in spring, their varied autumn tints, their colorful flowers and their intricate traceries of twig structure, these will always have their place. A well-chosen few can give any garden the distinctive and individual quality which should be sought.

With these preliminary and explanatory notes on the selection and use of these lists, let it be said that the ultimate purpose in presenting them is to enrich the enjoyment of the increasing number of people who are turning to gardening for pleasure and relaxation. It is too much to be hoped that they will not receive criticism. There is always something new to be learned. But, perhaps even so, this work can serve as a skeleton of organization about which one can build other observations—a sort of stepping stone to new conquests in this rich and varied world of plants. A study of this kind makes one realize how very great is the need within this area for adequate arboretums or botanical gardens, equipped to make and maintain trial plantings for comparison and study.

Carolina Jessamine

# 1

# VINES

VINES are wonderful mellowing agents in the landscape. To newly-built walls and fences their twining and clinging growth adds both an element of harmony with the environment and a new decorative interest in texture, the play of light and shadow, and the incidental color of flower and fruit.

Vines cling to their supports and climb by three devices: (1) by means of rootlets or modified tendrils by which they attach themselves to masonry or woodwork, (2) by twining around various supports such as arbors, trellises, or tree trunks, and (3) by means of tendrils which clasp sustaining structures. Still another group of plants, not vining in the strict sense, climbs by scrambling over supports of one kind or another. The Climbing Roses are of this type, needing training, and many shrubs, such as the Elaeagnus and Jasmines, can be treated as vines in this manner. An elementary factor influencing the choice of vine species is the method of support.

Nearly all vines require some upkeep. This may be reduced to the minimum by: first, making allowance for the proper kind of support; second, selecting a small or large-growing species which normally remains in proper scale relation to the space at hand; and third, it goes without saying, studying the adaptability of desired species to existing soil and exposure conditions. Even when all this is done, however, at least a certain amount of training and pruning must be anticipated to guide the growth in desired directions and to develop the wished-for effect. Usually wall surfaces should not be entirely blanked out with growth, and arbors are more attactive when they are not entirely engulfed in masses of foliage.

Vine growths can be quite destructive in places. Wistarias are

15

common offenders, pulling down gutters from houses and wrecking flimsy arbors. The Ivies, if not restrained, will prod into window openings, between clapboards, and may cover screens and woodwork, doing considerable damage. However, there seems to be little reason to fear that vine growths on masonry will weaken mortar joints if the joints are reasonably sound. Plant roots can absorb nutrients, such as the lime in mortar, only if they are in solution. Unless the wall is continuously wet, there should be little of the absorption of "strength" so widely dreaded. Rather it would seem more reasonable to suppose that such growths would protect the masonry from sudden freezes and thaws which are major foes of all stone and brickwork.

In terms of design function, vines are primarily curtain and canopy materials. Some are useful as groundcovers, but this aspect is discussed more fully in Group II. By effective use of vines, ugly wall surfaces can be transfigured with richly varied, glare-softening tapestries to enclose or form the background for the garden. Evergreen materials might be desired for this use, but deciduous vines are scarcely less attractive because they give an interesting pattern effect of stems and shadows even in winter after the foliage has fallen. Some of these are brilliant in fall color too. Often the two types mix happily as, for example, the English Ivy and Virginia Creeper. These two seem to positively assist each other culturally, and, of course, their decorative qualities happily supplement one another.

Free-standing curtains of foliage are often desirable for the sake of privacy within narrow quarters. The harsh and forbidding steel fences around school grounds, factories, and parks or cemeteries may be given a more humane appearance if they support Climbing Roses. Covered with Ivy or Honeysuckle, such fences can provide year-round protection from intruding eyes as well as from trespassing persons and neighbors' animals. These screens can be made to fit into spaces of approximately a foot in width, while shrub borders, to do the same job, require many times as much space.

Vines serving as canopies must have the artificial support of arbors. The construction of these can be ambitious or simple according to the character of the general design and the ambitions of the garden owner. Ever since gardening began, such bowers of foliage and flower have been favorite outdoor retreats. In the South, the Scuppernong arbor has long tradition. The most crude construction beside the farmer's cottage becomes a cool and fabulous summer resort as sheltering vines cover it.

This group of plants could be employed more frequently than it is in foundation plantings, especially in the treatment of small houses on small lots, since vines occupy less space than most shrubs. Under certain conditions, vines may also fit the much larger scale of institutional problems. On the college campus, for example, one usually sees the many buildings, often of disconnected architectural character, surrounded by heavy foundation plantings of shrubs, a design that is a vain attempt to meet the scale of the surroundings. Generally such plantings fail to achieve the harmony, intimacy, and domesticity which appear to be their purpose, and their folly is only accentuated by the attempts of untrained, underpaid, overworked maintenance men to keep order in the brushy masses of growth. In many cases, turf on the ground, well-placed trees, and a harmonious planting of vines on the large buildings would bring about a more dignified result. The upkeep? Of course the vines must be prevented from coming into the windows and from pulling down the gutters. But this work is no more demanding than pruning a large number of shrubs, weeding, and trimming around them. In addition, no special qualifications are required for this type of work. A good resistance to vertigo qualifies a man to carry it out with some measure of success!

## I. Vines for the SOUTHERN COASTAL PLAIN

### RECOMMENDED FOR GENERAL USE

| *Botanical Name* | *Common Name* |
| --- | --- |
| Bignonia capreolata | Crossvine |
| Ficus pumila | Climbing Fig |
| Gelsemium sempervirens | Carolina Jessamine |
| Hedera canariensis | Algerian Ivy |
| Rosa banksiae | Banks Rose |
| Rosa laevigata | Cherokee Rose |
| Smilax lanceolata | Lanceleaf Greenbrier |
| Solanum jasminoides | Jasmine Nightshade |
| Trachelospermum jasminoides | Chinese Starjasmine |

### RECOMMENDED FOR RESTRICTED USE

| | |
| --- | --- |
| Akebia quinata | Fiveleaf Akebia |
| Ampelopsis brevipedunculata | Amur Ampelopsis |
| Antigonon leptopus | Mountainrose Coralvine |
| Clematis paniculata | Sweetautumn Clematis |
| Clytostoma callistegioides | Argentine Trumpetvine |
| Decumaria barbara | Southeast Decumaria |
| Doxantha unguis-cati | Catclaw Funnelcreeper |
| Hedera helix | English Ivy |
| Jasminum humile | Italian Jasmine |
| Jasminum multiflorum | Furry Jasmine |
| Jasminum officinale | Common Jasmine |

| *Botanical Name* | *Common Name* |
|---|---|
| Kadsura japonica | Scarlet Kadsura |
| Lonicera heckrotti | Everblooming Honeysuckle |
| Parthenocissus henryana | Silvervein Creeper |
| Parthenocissus quinquefolia | Virginia Creeper |
| Parthenocissus tricuspidata | Japanese Creeper |
| Passiflora incarnata | Maypop Passionflower |
| Pileostegia viburnoides | |
| Plumbago capensis | Cape Plumbago |
| Rosa bracteata, "Mermaid" | Mermaid Climbing Rose |
| Rosa chinensis, "Louis Philippe" | Louis Philippe Climbing Rose |
| Rosa hybrids | Climbing Tea and Hybrid Tea Rose |
| Tecomaria capensis | Cape Honeysuckle |
| Vitis rotundifolia hybrids | Muscadine Grape |
| Wistaria floribunda | Japanese Wistaria |
| Wistaria frutescens | American Wistaria |
| Wistaria sinensis | Chinese Wistaria |

## I. Vines for the SOUTHERN PIEDMONT

### RECOMMENDED FOR GENERAL USE

| Akebia quinata | Fiveleaf Akebia |
|---|---|
| Ampelopsis brevipedunculata | Amur Ampelopsis |
| Bignonia capreolata | Crossvine |
| Clematis jackmani | Jackman Clematis |
| Clematis paniculata | Sweetautumn Clematis |
| Gelsemium sempervirens | Carolina Jessamine |
| Hedera helix | English Ivy |
| Rosa banksiae | Banks Rose |
| Rosa laevigata | Cherokee Rose |
| Smilax lanceolata | Lanceleaf Greenbrier |
| Wistaria sinensis | Chinese Wistaria |

### RECOMMENDED FOR RESTRICTED USE

| Actinidia arguta | Bower Actinidia |
|---|---|
| Antigonon leptopus | Mountainrose Coralvine |
| Aristolochia durior | Common Dutchmanspipe |
| Campsis radicans | Common Trumpetcreeper |
| Celastrus orbiculata | Oriental Bittersweet |
| Celastrus scandens | American Bittersweet |
| Clematis species | Clematis |
| Decumaria barbara | Southeast Decumaria |
| Euonymus fortunei | Wintercreeper Euonymus |

| *Botanical Name* | *Common Name* |
|---|---|
| Ficus pumila | Climbing Fig |
| Hedera canariensis | Algerian Ivy |
| Hydrangea petiolaris | Climbing Hydrangea |
| Kadsura japonica | Scarlet Kadsura |
| Lonicera heckrotti | Everblooming Honeysuckle |
| Lonicera japonica | Japanese Honeysuckle |
| Parthenocissus quinquefolia | Virginia Creeper |
| Parthenocissus tricuspidata | Japanese Creeper |
| Passiflora incarnata | Maypop Passionflower |
| Pileostegia viburnoides | |
| Polygonum auberti | Silvervine Fleeceflower |
| Pueraria thunbergiana | Kudzubean |
| Rosa bracteata, "Mermaid" | Mermaid Climbing Rose |
| Rosa chinensis, "Louis Philippe" | Louis Philippe Climbing Rose |
| Rosa hybrids | Climbing Hybrid Tea Rose |
| Solanum jasminoides | Jasmine Nightshade |
| Trachelospermum jasminoides | Chinese Starjasmine |
| Vitis labrusca | Fox Grape |
| Vitis rotundifolia | Muscadine Grape |
| Wistaria floribunda | Japanese Wistaria |
| Wistaria frutescens | American Wistaria |

## I. Vines for the UPPER SOUTH

### RECOMMENDED FOR GENERAL USE

| | |
|---|---|
| Actinidia arguta | Bower Actinidia |
| Akebia quinata | Fiveleaf Akebia |
| Ampelopsis brevipedunculata | Amur Ampelopsis |
| Clematis jackmani | Jackman Clematis |
| Clematis paniculata | Sweetautumn Clematis |
| Euonymus fortunei | Wintercreeper Euonymus |
| Hedera helix | English Ivy |
| Parthenocissus quinquefolia | Virginia Creeper |
| Rosa hybrids | Climbing Rose |
| Wistaria sinensis | Chinese Wistaria |

### RECOMMENDED FOR RESTRICTED USE

| | |
|---|---|
| Aristolochia durior | Common Dutchmanspipe |
| Bignonia capreolata | Crossvine |
| Campsis radicans | Common Trumpetcreeper |
| Celastrus orbiculata | Oriental Bittersweet |
| Celastrus scandens | American Bittersweet |

| Botanical Name | Common Name |
|---|---|
| Clematis species | Clematis |
| Hydrangea petiolaris | Climbing Hydrangea |
| Lonicera heckrotti | Everblooming Honeysuckle |
| Lonicera japonica | Japanese Honeysuckle |
| Parthenocissus tricuspidata | Japanese Creeper |
| Passiflora incarnata | Maypop Passionflower |
| Polygonum auberti | Silvervine Fleeceflower |
| Pueraria thunbergiana | Kudzubean |
| Vitis labrusca | Fox Grape |
| Wistaria floribunda | Japanese Wistaria |
| Wistaria frutescens | American Wistaria |

### RANGE CHART FOR GROUP I. THE VINES*

| | Coastal Plain | Piedmont | Upper South |
|---|---|---|---|
| Actinidia arguta | | - - -   x x x | x x x   x x x |
| Akebia quinata | - - -   x x x | x x x   x x x | x x x   x x x |
| Ampelopsis brevipedunculata | - - -   x x x | x x x   x x x | x x x   x x x |
| Bignonia capreolata | x x x   x x x | x x x   x x x | - - -   - - - |
| Clematis jackmani | | - - -   x x x | x x x   x x x |
| Clematis paniculata | - - -   x x x | x x x   x x x | x x x   x x x |
| Euonymus fortunei | | - - - | x x x   x x x |
| Ficus pumila | x x x   x x x | x x x   - - - | |
| Gelsemium sempervirens | x x x   x x x | x x x   x x x | - - - |
| Hedera canariensis | x x x   x x x | - - - | |
| Hedera helix | | x x x   x x x | x x x   x x x |
| Parthenocissus quinquefolia | - - -   - - - | - - -   x x x | x x x   x x x |
| Rosa banksiae | x x x   x x x | x x x   x x x | - - - |
| Rosa laevigata | x x x   x x x | x x x   x x x | - - - , |
| Rosa hybrids | - - - | - - -   x x x | x x x   x x x |
| Smilax lanceolata | x x x   x x x | x x x   x x x | - - - |
| Solanum jasminoides | x x x   x x x | x x x   - - - | |
| Trachelospermum jasminoides | x x x   x x x | - - - | |
| Wistaria sinensis | - - -   x x x | x x x   x x x | x x x   x x x |

Of the vines in the recommended list, only four (*Bignonia, Gelsemium, Parthenocissus,* and *Smilax*) are natives. Except for the *Parthenocissus* which has a very wide range, all of these are distinctly southern species. The range of the *Bignonia* can be extended to the Ohio River, but it may freeze back here on occasion. Concerning the remainder on the list, there should be little question of hardiness within the limits indicated. Also, there are few special soil requirements to be considered although the hybrid *Clematis* and the *Hedera,* even within their proper zones, need to be placed with some allowance for exposure. The Euonymus may be grown farther south than

---

*For explanation of Range Charts, *see* page 7, paragraph 3.

is indicated here. But, being liable to scale attacks which are worse in milder zones, this can hardly be called a first-rate material in any but colder areas where no other evergreens except the Ivy—which can take little sun—will thrive.

*Actinidia arguta*, Bower Actinidia. The Actinidia is valuable chiefly in cooler sections of the Upper South and the Piedmont where its clean, dark green, deciduous, pest-free foliage in decorative contrast with the red petioles is excellent for coarse and luxurious effect. It is a twining vine capable of reaching great size on arbors or on supports against buildings in either sun or shade. This rampant habit limits its use on the average small place. There are no flowers or fruits of note; this will be used chiefly for screening and texture contrast on a large scale. The Chinese Actinidia, *A. chinensis*, is a more tender species of similar rampant growth habit said to be preferable, where available, for the Piedmont and the cooler Coastal Plain. The Actinidias bear inconspicuous flowers on separate male and female plants, and the latter produce edible gooseberry-like fruits after pollination.

*Akebia quinata*, Fiveleaf Akebia. This is a twining vine of medium, relatively restrained growth which may reach large size in time. Yet it has a rather delicate character imparted by its lovely five-parted leaves which are deciduous in the north and almost evergreen in the Piedmont and the Coastal Plain. Male and female flowers of interesting form but inconspicuous size and purplish brown color, quite fragrant, appear on the same plant in late spring. This is, without doubt, one of the finest of materials in cooler sections, perfectly hardy, entirely free of pests, and quite at home in sun or shade in even the poorest and driest of soils. Its tendency to run along the ground, rooting as it goes, makes it also a fairly good groundcover. This habit must be restrained in many areas, however, or it becomes overly aggressive.

*Ampelopsis brevipedunculata*, Amur Ampelopsis. Often called the Porcelain Vine, this is outstanding for its fruits which develop in clusters of small berries colored creamy white, rosy lilac, and bright green-blue. Often all of these colors are present in each cluster, making this a beautiful and out-of-the-ordinary material for cutting. The Ampelopsis is best adapted to the Upper South and the Piedmont where it is first rate, but it does well enough in a more restrained way almost to the Florida border, wherever it can sink its roots into a good, reasonably well-watered subsoil. This is a vigorous grower of medium size with dense deciduous foliage of medium effect. In the rather common variety, *A. b. maximowiczi*, the leaves are more finely divided; in *A. b. elegans*, they are variegated with stripes of creamy-white and pink. The plant prefers a sunny location in good soils. However, it will stand neglect, after being established, and considerable shade, but will produce less fruit. It has no pests, but, being a Grape relative, it will need spraying for Japanese Beetles where these are common.

*Antigonon leptopus,* Mountainrose Coralvine. The Coralvine is a favorite of the Coastal Plain for its bright coral-pink or white flowers produced almost continuously throughout the year. In warmer sections it grows to large size, scrambling over arbors and up to second story balconies, but it will survive and bloom as far north as Atlanta where cold will cut it down occasionally to the ground, an event not always to be regretted. It appears to thrive in the driest and poorest of soils without any care, luxuriating in heat and full exposure to sunshine. The foliage is light green in color and rather coarse. Its rather unattractive appearance, weedy habit of growth, and difficult flower color make this a material to be employed with some restraint.

*Aristolochia durior,* Common Dutchmanspipe. Often listed as *A. sipho,* this is an interesting material because it is native to the Upper South, because of its coarse-textured rounded leaves up to 10 inches in diameter, and for its curious although not very showy flowers shaped like a gooseneck pipe. This vine is twining, making a dense, deciduous, pest-free screen in good soils in half-shaded locations. It is somewhat weedy in habit and large-growing. Its exotic character makes its use difficult for general situations but its very coarse texture may give just the right touch in others.

*Bignonia capreolata,* Crossvine. A common native creeper of this region, this vine gets its name from the cross-shaped pith which is seen when a stem is cut. It is valuable for its handsome, coarse, evergreen foliage, and for its clusters of yellowish-red tubular flowers which are quite showy for a brief time in early spring. The plant clings tightly to walls, tree trunks, or wood surfaces by means of little discs at the ends of the tendrils which accompany each pair of leaves. It is a very strong grower in good soil, one of the most effective in making a quick cover in either sunny or shaded places. It is entirely free from insect or disease troubles. It is safe for hardiness in the Coastal Plain and the Piedmont, and will grow as far north as the Ohio River Valley where it may be cut down by occasional hard freezes. While it is not one of the most colorful of vines, there are few which will provide such a clean, clinging evergreen cover over a large space in such a short time.

*Campsis radicans,* Common Trumpetcreeper. This is often listed under the name of *Bignonia radicans.* It attaches itself to walls of masonry or wood, growing rapidly to a height of 30 feet or more. With its rather attractive, deciduous, compound foliage of medium texture, this vine is a suitable material, absolutely trouble-free, for rare use in large-scale plantings, but its weedy habit renders it unfit for most situations. In July to August it produces clusters of large tubular flowers of a strong orange-red color at the ends of long side branches. There are rarely seen varieties with yellow or purplish flowers, and a hybrid, *B. tagliabuana* Mme. Galen, can be obtained for more compact habit of growth and superior bloom. The Trumpet-creeper is native to the entire Southeast, and it is easily grown in all parts.

*Celastrus orbiculata*, Oriental Bittersweet. *Celastrus scandens*, American Bittersweet. Because of their rampant growth, neither of the Bittersweets ought to be recommended for general planting. They are particularly destructive when they escape into woodlands. Occasionally, however, they may be desirable because of their fine autumnal displays of yellow foliage and the characteristic orange fruits which appear in bunches (of the American) at roadside stands and are sought for dried winter bouquets. The deciduous foliage is medium in texture and the plant is pest-free, well suited to the climates and the soils of both the Upper South and the Piedmont. The two species are distinguished easily because the berries of the Oriental Bittersweet occur along the stems in the leaf axils, while those of the American appear in bunches at the ends of the branchlets. The former may be somewhat the more showy of the two. It makes a fairly good groundcover where it can be controlled. These plants are mono-sexual, and for fruit production, both males and females must be set in reasonable proximity. This characteristic also militates against the general desirability of the Bittersweets for the average place where space is at a premium.

*Clematis* species, Clematis. Volumes are written on the many species and hybrids of Clematis. Only a cursory survey of the chief types and their uses is attempted here. Some are difficult to grow, but, as a group, they are most rewarding for a succession of outstanding flowers from spring until fall. Most of them belong in the flower garden where their usually restrained and delicate growth fits in very well, and where they can be given the desired pruning, watering, and other care. All species climb by scrambling, some clasping by means of leaflets which twist like tendrils, and all save one are deciduous with fine-textured foliage. They bloom best when the top growth reaches full exposure to the sun, but they like their roots to be in cool, moist shade in fertile soils of neutral to alkaline reaction where they are not disturbed by cultivation. Generally they do not like heat, preferring the cooler sections of the Piedmont and the Upper South where they are a choice garden material.

*Clematis jackmani*, the Jackman Clematis, is a large-flowered hybrid which is very common, and, next to the above, probably the most easily grown of all. It is highly recommended throughout the Upper South and the cooler Piedmont for a truly gorgeous show of rich purple flowers in mid-spring. It is excellent for trellises up to about 15 feet in height or for scrambling over walls and fences.

Other Clematis of note, most of them somewhat more rare and restricted in their use to gardening enthusiasts who are willing to give some care to their needs, may be considered in two broad classes: (1) some of the lesser known species, and (2) the large-flowered hybrids.

Outstanding among the former is the Scarlet Clematis, *C. texensis,* which is a slight thing, growing only to about 8 feet, with scarlet, urn-shaped flowers through the summer. For a delicate picket fence or for ornamenting a small gate, this is quite choice. The Viorna, *C. viorna,* bearing purple blossoms of a similar shape, is a fairly common native of the Upper South having less garden value. The Pink Anemone Clematis, *C. montana rubens,* is a showy form with medium-sized blooms, white to pinkish in color in May, reaching about 15 feet in height. The Golden Clematis, *C. tangutica,* a re-strained grower, bears clusters of small yellow flowers in June. The Virgin's Bower, *C. virginiana,* is a common native of the Upper South with small white flowers in late summer, similar in many ways but inferior to the *C. paniculata.* It could be a fairly good material for naturalizing. The Armand Clematis, *C. armandi,* is unusual in bearing coarse linear leaves up to 5 inches in length which are ever-green or nearly so. This is quite tender, but it thrives with some protection in Washington, D. C., and its large white flowers are showy in late spring. This is one of the few species flowering on wood of the previous year. Consequently it is pruned in mid-summer if at all, while other species are cut back annually in early spring.

The numerous large-flowered hybrid Clematis furnish a rich palette of form and color ranging from white through red-violet and violet-blue during the long summer season. Some of the best known of these are the Belle of Woking and Duchess of Edinburgh, white; Ramona, blue; Nelly Moser, mauve. In general these are garden subjects which call for care throughout the year.

*Clematis paniculata,* the Sweetautumn Clematis, is the most com-mon, robust, and generally useful of the genus. It is a strong and rapid grower—even at times weedy—in any soil, pest free, tolerat-ing heat and drought better than any other variety. In early autumn it is literally covered with its small white, intensely fragrant flowers, to make a fine show; still later its plumed seeds are quite interesting. This should have an annual pruning to thin out old wood, but other-wise it requires no care. This is excellent throughout the Upper

South and the Piedmont, and it is probably the one species which
can be recommended for cooler sections of the Coastal Plain.

*Clytostoma callistegioides,* Argentine Trumpetvine. This is a
well-known vine of the Deep South, usually carried in the nursery
trade as *Bignonia speciosa* or *B. violacea* and called the Lavender
Trumpet. In the spring the lovely three-inch violet, trumpet-form
flowers of this vine make a very beautiful display, but the evergreen
foliage is quite as attractive the year around. The handsome leaves are
fairly large, oval in outline, with a rich green color and a waxy sheen.
This is a twining vine which has the added advantage of a rather
modest growing habit, amenable to small places. It will grow in sunny
or lightly shaded spots in almost any soil, but its hardiness in the
upper limits of the Coastal Plain is questionable. Within its growing
range, this is one of the most choice of all for flower and foliage.

*Decumaria barbara,* Southeast Decumaria. This is a native of the
moist woodlands of this region from Virginia to Florida and Louisiana.
It is not often found grown as an ornamental, but it might well be
considered for naturalistic plantings at least. This is closely related
to the Hydrangeas, and it bears some resemblance to them. The
rather coarse foliage is semi-evergreen. The leaves are arranged
in opposite pairs along the stems, which attach themselves to tree
trunks by means of rootlets. The flat-headed clusters of white
flowers appear in early summer.

*Doxantha unguis-cati,* Catclaw Funnelcreeper. This is listed frequently in nursery catalogues as *Bignonia chamberlayni* or *Anemo-
paegma chamberlayni,* the Golden Trumpet. The plant is characterized
by small, linear evergreen leaflets occurring in opposite pairs along
the slender stems, and by tendrils ending in three small hooks or
claws which give rise to the name of "Cat's Claw." These tendrils are
sufficiently probing and tenacious to support the plant on masonry
walls and on rough wood surfaces. The beauty of this vine is in its
large, radiantly golden-yellow, trumpet-like flowers which bloom in
profusion in mid-spring. In some places the plants are grown on the
trunks of Pines where they make an unforgettable show, flaunting
their golden drifts in the midst of the sombre green of the tree
foliage. This use suggests that the Cat's Claw is a large-scale climber
of rapid growth, which, given good conditions, it is. However, it
may also be used in sunny, hot, dry places where, although growing
well, it is more easily controlled. The foliage is fine in texture, yellow-
green in color, and not the most attractive. This plant is used successfully in the sandy alkaline soils of the seaside, but it may be
seen more rarely as far north as Memphis where, although it is
usually frozen to the ground, it recovers quickly from the root and
may bloom in one year out of three to five.

*Euonymus fortunei* varieties, Wintercreeper Euonymus. Many of the Euonymus are unfortunately prone to infestations by scale insects, and gardeners who have had unhappy experiences with them will not recommend this vine for general use. This hazard can be overcome, however, by watching for the first signs of an invasion, and by following up with prompt spraying with DDT in summer to catch the juvenile insects plus an oil application in fall or spring to clean up the hard scales.

*Euonymus fortunei vegetus*, the Bigleaf Wintercreeper, is one of the few evergreen vines reliably hardy throughout the Upper South, and thus it must be given a front ranking for this section. With its rather rugged texture, waxy rich green leaves, and clusters of orange, Bittersweet-like fruits, it is one of the most beautiful vines throughout the year. This is one of the rootlet vines which will cling to masonry, reaching ultimately to a height of 25 feet or more, with strong laterally projecting branchlets which can give it a rather shaggy appearance if permitted to grow out of reach of the pruning shears. Like most vines, this is more attractive if it is kept under firm, but not obvious, control. The Wintercreeper likes sun, and it is not fussy about soils. It may be grown as a shrub, or in mass for ground-cover, reaching a height of about 3 feet. The winter foliage may be burned off the plant in very cold seasons, but this is unusual if the location is sheltered from severe exposure to wind. The plant is hardy in the Piedmont, but scale attacks are likely to be harder to control in warmer sections and thus it is not advocated here.

There are other forms of Wintercreeper which, as vines, are only a little less handsome and valuable than the above. The Common Wintercreeper, *E. fortunei radicans*, often listed simply as *E. radicans*, is also evergreen, with small, dull green leaves of medium texture. It clings close to wall surfaces, making a dense mat, but it does not produce fruits. Of this there are generally available two forms with variegated foliage. These are Purpleleaf, *E. f. coloratus*, with green leaves turning purplish in winter, and Whitevein, *E. f. reticulatus*, with creamy markings. The Glossy Wintercreeper, *E. f. carrieri*, appears to be intermediate in leaf size and ruggedness of character between the Bigleaf and the Common forms. Its excellent foliage and its fruiting habit are good qualities. These varieties appear to be more resistant to scale insects than the Bigleaf Wintercreeper. All of these can reach considerable size, to 20 feet or more, but there are two forms which are true dwarfs in every respect. These are the Baby Wintercreeper, *E. f. minimus*, and the Kew W., *E. f. kewensis*, which are interesting for miniature detail. Most of these are good vines for a wide variety of application, and equally useful as groundcovers. They are particularly valuable in cooler sections for their hardiness and their tolerance of alkaline soils and urban surroundings.

*Ficus pumila*, Climbing Fig. This vine is almost too well known to need description or comment. For clothing any kind of wall with a close fitting, fine-textured, evergreen mantle of greenery, this vine has no equal. As a young plant it sends its long fingers over a surface, turning it into a delicate lacework. With time all the open spaces are filled in with a solid sheet. After this has been achieved, the vine sends out lateral shoots which hang free of the wall, and these bear coarse leaves and inedible green "figs." At this stage the appearance is somewhat brushy and untidy, and so the gardener usually tries to discourage the laterals by cutting back some of the main stems occasionally to forestall maturity. The Climbing Fig is one of the easiest of vines to grow. It tolerates all soils, and loves hot sun, yet succeeds also in full shade in the poorest soils without any trouble from insects or diseases. It is sufficiently hardy throughout the Coastal Plain, but in the Piedmont it should be recommended only for planting on warmer walls with a southern exposure. Under these conditions it is fairly satisfactory to Atlanta. It can be employed for covering large structures, but it can be controlled rather easily in smaller spaces. It lends itself well to clipping into patterns where one wants to indulge in this kind of care. Mention is made of a smaller growing variety called *F. p. minima*. Where this is procurable, it may be superior for the average small place.

*Gelsemium sempervirens*, Carolina Jessamine. This is a native of the Coastal Plain and the Piedmont, found both on the borders of swampy areas and rivers and also on hillsides covered with Oak woods. It is one of the earliest of the native plants to bloom in the spring, and its bright golden masses of trumpet-like flowers floating among the tops of the smaller trees make a lovely decoration along the highways at this season. On closer inspection one finds that the Jessamine has a fine fragrance, and that its evergreen foliage is small and fine-textured on thin, wiry twisting stems. This plant grows equally well in sun or shade in any fair to good soil of neutral to acid reaction, but the stems must be able to reach the light in order to produce flowers. In shaded areas it is habitually thin and spindly, but in exposed sites it grows stocky and quite thick and heavy. The foliage takes on a purplish cast where it receives an abundance of winter sunshine. The plant will grow to heights of 30 feet to reach light, but it can be restrained to small spaces. It makes few cultural demands and has no insect enemies. Being quite hardy, this is, in every respect, one of the choicest vines for its range— to Memphis, Atlanta, and Norfolk.

*Hedera canariensis*, Algerian Ivy. *Hedera helix*, English Ivy. In the

Coastal Plain, the Algerian Ivy is considered to be the superior species of the two, but it is not entirely hardy in the Piedmont and the Upper South where the English Ivy is recommended. In their respective areas both are basic evergreen landscape materials. The former is distinguished chiefly by its larger, more lush foliage and more vigorous growth, but both are rated rather coarse in texture. The English Ivy is one of the oldest of plants in cultivation. There are about forty named varieties, some with dwarf growing habits, others with interesting leaf forms, and color and hardiness variations, so that something is available for almost every purpose or space except salty seacoast areas. The Ivies have no peer for those deeply shaded spots which are encountered frequently in small city plots. They enjoy dampness and shade, and they are easily burned on overexposure to sun and wind. They are unusually pest free, but in warm sections where air circulation is poor, snails and scale insects can give them trouble.

There is almost no limit to the ultimate size the English Ivy will reach, topping house walls and tree trunks, if it is not given the control which transforms it into the handsome garden ornament it can be. Before it is planted, the question must be settled as to whether it will become a nuisance with its probing into window openings or under clapboard siding. Two common queries about Ivy concern (1) hardiness, and (2) starting growth up a wall surface. The first depends largely on exposure. Most of the English forms are perfectly reliable in all but the higher elevations of the Upper South, but they grow better in somewhat protected sites, with some shade, and, most important, shelter from winter sun and wind. They need moisture and prefer neutral to alkaline soils. The second problem is really no problem at all if the above conditions are met and if the plant is set immediately against the wall surface.

The Ivy's curious habit of producing two foliage forms on the same plant sometimes baffles the interested observer of plants. When the plant is growing vertically up a wall surface, the leaves are typically lobed and the foliage clings close. When the stems reach the top of their climb, however, new growth, having no further heights to ascend, comes out in laterals which give the vine quite a different, bushy or shaggy character. Leaves on the laterals become entire and rather heart-shaped, not at all typical, and on the branch ends appear clusters of small green flowers in spring and black fruits in fall. Cuttings taken from these shrubby laterals produce shrubby fruiting plants hardly recognizable as the English Ivy.

*Hydrangea petiolaris*, Climbing Hydrangea. This is a large-growing, wall-clinging, robust, coarse-textured material for large surfaces, preferably in some shade. Its rugged effect is emphasized by its habit of producing heavy laterals extending several feet from the supporting surface. It is on these side branches that the showy, flat, white flower clusters appear in late June, providing a brilliant show for a brief time. Commended chiefly for the Upper South, this plant is perfectly hardy, free from pests, easily grown in cool neutral to alkaline soils containing humus and a good water supply. The shaggy appearance, including its habit of shedding the reddish bark of the older stems, disqualifies this material for tidy environments, and suits it better to those of rustic character—on rough stone chimneys, high walls, and tree trunks. A close relative is the Japanese Hydrangea-vine, *Schizophragma hydrangeoides*. The two may be confused, but the former, more showy in flower and perfectly suited to this region, is the preferred genus.

*Jasminum humile*, Italian Jasmine. *Jasminum multiflorum*, Furry Jasmine. *Jasminum officinale*, Common Jasmine. In the Coastal Plain several Jasmines are grown as small vines although they might be considered properly as scandent shrubs. They are generally desirable for their summer flowers which are, in some cases at least, very fragrant. They are easy to grow and are pest free, tolerant of a wide variety of soils, of heat or drought, of sunny to lightly shaded locations. Some grow to large size, but the species listed here are rather tender. They are consequently best used for restricted decorative growth on fences or on protected arbors. Of these, the Furry Jasmine, often listed as *J. pubescens* or Star Jasmine, is probably the most common and satisfactory. Bearing evergreen foliage of medium texture and fragrant white flowers throughout most of the summer, it will freeze back occasionally, but recovers from the root very readily after a hard pruning. It is best sited in the shade of the north side of a building where it is fine for small-scale detail interest trained on a fence or light support. *J. humile*, the Italian Jasmine, has evergreen compound foliage of nice fine texture and fragrant yellow flowers, but it is rather tender. *J. officinale*, the Common Jasmine, bears fragrant white flowers through the summer. Dr. Wyman recommends it to Zone 7, which includes Memphis, Knoxville, and Washington, D. C. *J. stephanense*, the Stephan Jasmine, is hardy well into the Piedmont, bearing fragrant pink flowers in summer, but it is weedy in habit and has little to recommend it except perhaps as a groundcover. Among the shrub forms discussed below, *J. mesnyi, J. floridum, J. nudiflorum* are reliably hardy in the Coastal Plain and lend themselves nicely to training in vine form.

*Kadsura japonica*, Scarlet Kadsura. This is hard to locate in the nurseries of the region and it seems to be relatively untried. It may prove, however, to be one of the very good small vines (to 12 feet) for the future. It has large, coarse-textured, evergreen leaves with reddish petioles. It is said to bear yellowish flowers in early summer, followed by clusters of scarlet berries in autumn. It should prove perfectly hardy throughout the Coastal Plain and well up into the Piedmont. This is a twining vine which certainly appears to be worth a trial. It can also be useful as a groundcover.

*Lonicera heckrotti*, Everblooming Honeysuckle. *Lonicera japonica*, Japanese Honeysuckle. The Everblooming Honeysuckle is a hybrid descendant of the Trumpet Honeysuckle, *L. sempervirens*, which is native throughout the Southeast and, in itself, a good selection for naturalizing. It is commonly found in nurseries in its form called the "Gold-flame" Honeysuckle, and is nice for a long succession of red-purple and gold flowers produced throughout the summer. The medium-textured foliage is evergreen in the Coastal Plain—partly so to the north—and gray-green in color. The paired leaves often connect around the stem (called perfoliate) in an interesting manner. This is well adapted to the region in any soil, needing sun for best bloom. Its major fault is that it seems to be a favorite of plant lice at certain seasons, but these are controlled easily and do little harm anyway. This is an excellent vine for a spot of detail interest, twining on a balustrade, picket fence, or small trellis.

The Japanese Honeysuckle, or its common Hall's variety, is almost too well known, having become a formidable weed in many areas in the Southeast. This state of affairs should not blind the plantsman, however, to the plant's real value for screening. Trained on a wire fence, it makes a vigorous, pest-free, semi-evergreen cover in sun or shade under the most trying conditions, giving a bonus of fragrant flowers. The chief problem is one of control, and where other materials will suffice, this should be omitted throughout all but the coldest parts of this region.

*Parthenocissus quinquefolia*, Virginia Creeper. *Parthenocissus tricuspidata*, Japanese Creeper. *Parthenocissus henryana*, Silvervein Creeper. The Virginia Creeper is a common native of the Southeast, one of the most widely adapted and fastest growing materials in this class. Unfortunately, where the Japanese Beetles are numerous, the foliage of this plant suffers with that of other members of the Grape family. Still, this is a material of many uses, making a quick and handsome cover for any type of wall or for steep and rocky road cuts to hold soil in place and to soften the raw scar. There are no flowers of consequence, but the clusters of tiny blue fruits, loved by birds, are sometimes effective. Its chief beauty is in the foliage which is palmately divided into five parts, rich and coarse in texture. When, in autumn, this assumes its brilliant rose-red color, it becomes one of the most beautiful things in the landscape. This is not a material for close quarters, but for a bold show in large scale it is excellent. A somewhat more refined variety is the Engleman Creeper, *P. q. engelmanni*, probably to be preferred for most uses. Because of its hardiness and wide suitability, the Virginia Creeper is classed among the best in the Upper South where the selection is not so varied. It is also excellent in warmer sections where it is given a secondary rating because there are others, particularly the evergreens, with greater usefulness available.

The Japanese Creeper, more commonly known as the Boston Ivy, is widely grown for a quick cover on masonry walls. It also is a vigorous, large-size material of coarse texture, hardy and amenable to almost any soil in the Upper South and the Piedmont as long as it has a sunny exposure. Having no fall color nor flowers or fruits of note, it may be considered slightly inferior in beauty to the Virginia Creeper. Its smaller-growing variety, Low's Japanese Creeper, *P. t. lowi*, is better suited to confined areas. With its small, finely-divided, close-packed, and twisted foliage, it makes an interesting pattern and texture effect on wall surfaces which one would not want completely covered with growth.

Another species worth noting for the Coastal Plain is the Silver-vein Creeper, *P. henryana*. Very likely this will not be hardy except in the warmer parts of the Southeast. It is a modest grower, a lover of shade, with deciduous palmately-divided leaves beautifully marked with white veins and purplish undersides.

*Passiflora incarnata*, Maypop Passionflower. This species is native from Virginia to Florida, making an interesting garden subject. The foliage is excellent, rather large and coarse in texture, the individual dark green glossy leaves deeply divided into three finger-like lobes. In warmer sections it is almost evergreen. In colder climates it may freeze back to the ground, but it makes a rapid recovery from its persistent root. The flowers open more or less continuously through midsummer to fall. They are from 2 to 3 inches in diameter, purple in color, and almost incredible in their complicated structure which is said to symbolize various elements of the crucifixion. Although these blooms never make a spectacular show in the garden, they always make interesting objects for conversation and for close examination, and they are handsome in short-lived flower arrangements. Bladder-like yellow fruits, said to be edible, develop immediately after flowering. The Passionflower is useful chiefly for climbing on trellises, fences, and arbors in sunny spots where it rapidly makes a dense screen. It has no common diseases or insect enemies. Its faults would seem to be that its bloom is almost too attractive to bumble bees which always hover about it, and its fleshy underground stems push out in all directions in a way that can be overly ambitious for the small place. The Bluecrown Passionflower, *P. caerulea*, is probably in cultivation in gardens of this area also. This, together with its hybrids, is grown commonly in greenhouses. It is distinguished from the Maypop by having five-lobed leaves instead of three-lobed, and by the edges of the leaves being entire rather than serrate. This species is possibly more tender than the former, but Wyman rates it hardy throughout the Coastal Plain and into the Piedmont.

*Pileostegia viburnoides.* This is relatively unknown in this region although it is being tested with promise of rather attractive results for the Piedmont and Coastal Plain. It is a clinging vine, like the Ivy, growing to large size, with coarse-textured evergreen leaves and Hydrangea-like white flowers through the summer. It is said to serve very well also as a groundcover.

*Plumbago capensis,* Cape Plumbago. In a large portion of the Coastal Plain, especially along the Coast, this is sufficiently hardy to be of value in providing blossom color through the summer and autumn. Its flowers bloom continuously and profusely during this season in white or in a clear, light blue. The Plumbago likes sun, and, best of all, it stands heat and drought extremely well and tolerates sandy acid or alkaline soils. Although it is a scandent shrub rather than a true vine, and needs, therefore, some training, it still makes a most decorative plant for a low wall, fence, or trellis. Since its use is limited by its tenderness, it should be set in protected places such as patios or sheltered flower gardens. Even though the top may freeze, it will usually revive quickly from the root as far north as Charleston, S. C., to make a successful display.

*Polygonum auberti,* Silvervine Fleeceflower. This is popularly grown for quick cover and a showy display of tiny white blossoms in trusses in late summer. Where hiding a large area in a sunny location in the shortest possible time is the major consideration, this has some use. This weedy plant is decidedly inferior by comparison, however, to the Sweetautumn Clematis, which will do the same job better.

*Pueraria thunbergiana,* Kudzubean. Ordinary landscape usage will rarely call for the Kudzu, but it is valuable for soil erosion control. It could be used for quick screening around a shopping center or other such installations, but, once started, it would preclude the planting of anything else more desirable. Rank in growth and coarse in appearance, it is not an attractive subject to work with.

*Rosa* species, Climbing Roses. The subject of climbing roses is too large to be given full treatment here. To bring it down to the simplest terms possible, a word as to the types suitable to the various subregions may be appropriate before discussing some of the individual species.

In the Coastal Plain, the best "landscape" roses are several tender species (*R. banksiae, R. laevigata, R. bracteata*), which are outstanding for foliage that is resistant to disease and often almost evergreen, as well as being valuable for their flowers. The climbing form of *R. chinensis,* called Louis Philippe, has a place of its own. The many fine climbing Teas and Hybrid Teas do well here when the normally thin sandy soils are fortified and when the plants receive care, but they belong more particularly to the garden specialist and receive only a mention here.

In the Piedmont the species roses named above are recommended, and the climbing Hybrid Teas, with some protection in cooler portions, are excellent in most soils. The latter varieties do call for high maintenance, however. The class of so-called Large Flowered Climbers such as New Dawn, Blaze, and Silver Moon is considered superior for landscape purposes such as training on fences, buildings, and arbors. This class is suggested also as the best choice for the Upper South.

*Rosa banksiae,* the Banks or Lady Banks Rose, is very common in the Deep South, and its great massive growth, loaded with creamy yellow flowers tumbling through tree tops and over small out-buildings, makes one of the most characteristic sights of the region in springtime. This rose is especially noteworthy in that its fine-textured foliage is evergreen and its twigs are practically thornless. The blossoms are small and very numerous, making a splendid effect in the landscape, but they are not especially good for cutting. There are both single and double forms in yellow and white, but the double yellow seems to be the best. This "old reliable" grows readily and without care under all kinds of soil conditions, and its only requirement is plenty of space.

*R. laevigata,* the Cherokee Rose, has become so widespread in the South that it has been adopted as the state flower of Georgia although it was introduced there from China. This also is a rank grower, more suitable for thickets and fence rows or for climbing on trees than for more confined areas. Its vicious thorns warn against close quarters. The rich glossy foliage is semi-evergreen, and the single white flowers of pure form and lovely fragrance are borne through a long season in the spring and again occasionally in the fall. There is also a striking pink flowering form, but this is a relatively shy bloomer and the color is harsh. None of the ordinary hazards of rose growing seems to affect either of these hardy vines.

The Mermaid variety of the Macartney Rose, *R. bracteata,* somewhat similar to the Cherokee in its growth, is said to be rather more difficult to establish, but it is worth high mention because of its unusually beautiful flowers. These are single, buff-yellow in color, sometimes 4 inches in diameter. Although this rose seems to prefer to ramble in an unpruned state over fence, wall, or building, it is sometimes seen confined to more narrow quarters on arbor or post in the flower garden. It blooms in spring and also sporadically through the summer and fall.

Totally different in character is the Climbing "Louis Philippe," a scandent form of the common bush rose and a dependable bloomer in many southern gardens. The growth of this plant is more delicate and restrained than any of the above, and so it suits even the smallest garden. There is probably no other rose which produces as many flowers over such a long season as this one. Beginning in early spring, it may never be entirely bare of color until Christmas time—in protected places at least. The plant is easily grown in sunny or lightly shaded locations, requiring no spraying and only occasional feeding to support its prodigious production. The only fault one could find with this wonderful plant is its flower color which is a deep and vivid purplish red and harmonizes with few backgrounds and with few other flowers. The foliage also displays a reddish tinge when it first unfolds. In proper settings this color may not be a drawback, however, and certainly this is a plant of unusual quality for certain places.

The above are adaptable in warmer areas to general landscape use, requiring little or nothing in the way of special care or soil conditions. In the Coastal Plain and the Piedmont the climbing Hybrid Teas are also very fine, but they are placed here on the restricted list because they are exacting in their tastes. They are quite good on fences, on walls that are not too fully exposed to the sun, on arbors, or in some cases against buildings. They do need regular spraying and this limits their use against tidy painted surfaces. Some of the stronger growers may be pruned back and treated as shrubs for the cutting garden. Generally they will bloom better if they are trained in a horizontal plane since vertical stems seldom produce flower buds. Pruning of these climbers is largely confined to the removal of dead or weak wood. Most of the gardener's favorite Hybrid Teas are available in the climbing form, possessing all their beauties of individual blossom in more vigorous form, but unfortunately they are shy on repeating.

In the Upper South the most reliable group of roses is that class called the Large Flowered Climbers, also highly recommended for the Piedmont. These are of complex ancestry, but they are typified by such well-known representatives as Blaze and New Dawn. These make a great show of flowering in May and repeat sporadically through the summer. Some varieties such as the older Paul's Scarlet and Dr. Van Fleet bloom only once. These are grown primarily for their color, and all are deciduous. They do require some pruning and need spraying if they are to look their best. However, they are generally less demanding than most bush roses and make excellent hardy landscape materials for seasonal color.

*Smilax lanceolata,* Lanceleaf Greenbrier. This is a native evergreen vine of the South which is seen often in old gardens but rarely in new ones. The only conceivable reason for this might be its rank habit of growth. It may readily attain 20 or 30 feet in a single season. It also tends to spread by underground shoots which may become something of a nuisance. Still, these faults may well be considered virtues by anyone who likes to cut generous swags of this handsome foliage for decorating and giving to friends at Christmas. The Smilax has no color of flowers or fruits, but its glossy, bright evergreen leafage has always been considered a sufficient recommendation. Its tough tendrils make it a good subject for treillage, for fences, and for trees with rough bark. It makes a dense screen, either in the sun or shade. On smaller places it may be controlled by a heavy annual Christmas pruning. For ease of cultivation, tolerance, freedom from disease and pest troubles, and general presentability, this vine is hard to beat. Those who may be inspired to collect Smilax from the woods should note that there are many variations in leaf size in the native stock, and that those plants with smaller leaflets are considered more choice.

*Solanum jasminoides,* Jasmine Nightshade. This is a twining vine of rather delicate appearance, growing to 10 or 15 feet in height, of first-rate hardiness in the Coastal Plain but occasionally freezing back to the ground in the Piedmont. It makes a dense growth, fine for screening in sunny exposures, and it probably blooms better here, but it succeeds nicely in light shade, preferably in fertile, well-watered soils. It never seems to require any care except for a rare restraining pruning. The evergreen foliage has good color and fine texture but it may be defoliated in colder exposures. It is distinguished by the fact that some of the lower leaves are lobed while the upper are entire. In late summer the attractive clusters of small, white, star-like flowers begin to open, continuing prolifically sometimes until Christmas. These are followed by scattered blue berries.

*Tecomaria capensis,* Cape Honeysuckle. This is another good vine or scandent shrub for long season of bloom, its scarlet, trumpet-shaped flowers being produced over many months during the summer and autumn. Unfortunately it is too tender to be recommended for any but the warmest areas. It can probably be planted safely in sheltered spots along the coast as far north as Charleston, S. C. When it suffers cold injury, it may be expected to recover quickly.

In this area the Tecomaria reaches only small stature, rarely over 8 feet in height, making a colorful ornament with good evergreen foliage for the small patio in full sun. It is especially useful for seaside sites where the selection is restricted.

*Trachelospermum jasminoides*, Chinese Starjasmine. One of the favorite vines of the South, this plant is commonly called the Confederate Jasmine and listed under the name of *Rhynchospermum*. This is a moderate grower with twining stems, making a dense screen of dark glossy evergreen leaves of medium texture. In the late spring the plant is well covered with scattered clusters of small, white, exquisitely fragrant flowers which look very much like those of its close relative, the Periwinkle. The Star Jasmine is much planted in both small and large gardens in shaded places where the soil is fertile and moist. It is somewhat subject to attacks of scale insects and of the white fly, and may require spraying for these at times. It is also rather tender, although it is considered reliable throughout the Coastal Plain and, in protected places, into the Piedmont. A sister species, *T. asiaticum*, which is similar but with creamy yellow flowers, is rarely seen, but it deserves mention because it is said to be somewhat more hardy. Both of these come from China. There is also a native species, *T. difforme*, which is rare in cultivation. This grows along river banks in woodlands of the Coastal region, bearing in early summer inconspicuous flowers of little ornamental value.

*Vitis labrusca* hybrids, Fox Grape. *Vitis rotundifolia* hybrids, Muscadine Grape. Various types of cultivated Grapes often deserve a place in planting design for landscape effect. Most of the so-called "Bunch Grapes" are descended from the Fox Grape, native to the Eastern states from New England to Georgia. Most of these are characterized by vigorous growth and by very coarse-textured and handsomely-shaped leaves which are exceptionally decorative. The fruit clusters also are handsome as well as attractive to the palate. The plants should have sunny exposures and fertile soils, and should be planted with spraying and pruning in mind. Arbors are fitting supports; wire fences or runways are ideal. Grown on the latter, the grape makes a good divider or background for lower plantings. Concord, Delaware, and Niagara are good standard varieties bearing fruits of blue, red, and white respectively, but the local agricultural agent should be consulted with regard to the selection of varieties. Unfortunately these grapes do require spraying, which may make them something of a nuisance if planted too close to houses or outdoor sitting places. They should be pruned each year for fruit production.

While the Fox Grape hybrids are recommended for the Upper South, the Muscadine is generally better adapted to the Piedmont and the Coastal Plain where it is native. This grape is long lived, growing to 50 feet or more with an enormous stem when left in its native state. It does not need the spraying required for the bunch grapes, but it should be carefully pruned. Leaves of the Muscadine are not as coarse or as rich in their decorative value as those of the grape, but they are also handsome. The Muscadine may be planted in the same ways as indicated above. In Southern gardens the old-fashioned Scuppernong Arbor is a valuable tradition which might be preserved in modern home grounds. As to varieties, the old Scuppernong, the patented Never-miss, or the late Yuga may be suggested for bronze fruits; good black types are the prolific Hunt and the sweet Dulcet. Again, the local agricultural agent should be consulted on this choice. One must remember that the sexes are separate in the Muscadines, requiring a male plant in the lot.

*Wistaria floribunda*, Japanese Wistaria. *Wistaria sinensis*, Chinese Wistaria. Wistarias are old favorites in southern gardens, making a splendid display of lilac or white flowers in early spring on arbors and porches or climbing through trees. While they are outstanding for this show, they ought to be planted only after careful study for they are so rampant in growth character that they are destructive to young trees, light structures, downspouts, and gutters. Generally they should be planted where they will be given regular pruning. Where this care is given, there develops a picturesque, knotty trunk, loaded with flowering spurs, which has few equals in garden interest. This plant has no pests, and it will grow in any soil, preferably in a sunny exposure, probably blooming better in poor soils than in fertile ones. In fact the most common complaint about the Wistaria concerns lack of bloom. This will be found to apply generally to young, vigorously growing specimens. Those which are well established, starved, and pruned heavily will flower profusely when late frosts do not kill the buds. Most of the Wistarias seen in this region are of the Chinese species although the Japanese is just as hardy and probably equally adaptable. The flowers of the latter are large, up to 4 feet long, and include pink in their color range. All in all they are not more effective, however, because the individual florets do not open at once but begin at the bottom and develop gradually toward the top of the cluster. The two are easily distinguished by the number of leaflets on a petiole, 7 to 13 in the Chinese and 13 to 19 in the Japanese. The American Wistaria, *W. frutescens*, should be mentioned here as a native of the Southeast, which flowers after the leaves appear and somewhat sporadically through the summer. This variety is little different from the above in growth character, and the flowers never make an effective show. Hence it may be considered inferior.

Lentenrose

# 2

# GROUND-
# COVERS

GROUNDCOVERS are generally popular because, (1) requiring no mowing, they will reduce maintenance costs, and (2) because they will provide year-round evergreen covers of good appearance superior to most of the turfs which turn brown in winter or which are so spotted with Crab Grass and weeds that they are quite unsightly much of the time. Groundcovers serve three important purposes in landscape design: (1) in beds they express and garnish ground patterns with interesting textures and, sometimes, colorful flowers, (2) they protect soil from erosion, especially on banks too steep to mow and maintain in turf, and (3) they can render beautiful both those occasional difficult spots under trees and near buildings where grass will not thrive, and also those odd corners which are difficult to mow and trim.

Lawns have always been and still are difficult and expensive to establish and to maintain in the lower South. It is significant in this connection that old gardens of the region almost never depended on lawn areas for their effect but upon Boxwood patterns which gave an evergreen foil for the house. Good evergreen groundcovers may be particularly important here, especially on smaller places and on city lots. Such plantings combined with low shrubs and areas of pine straw make satisfying, low upkeep settings of informal character under trees in suburban areas. There are still some people who maintain that beds of groundcovers harbor snakes, and there may be some truth in that belief in remote rural areas. There seems to be little to support it, however, in urban, intensively

38

cultivated areas, and groundcovers are becoming increasingly important in landscape work.

As defined here, plants of this class will come under 1 foot in height, but there is no reason why many of the dwarf shrubs, reaching 2 feet or even more, cannot be grown for this same purpose in large-scale designs. Some of those shrubs better suited to this end will be indicated in their proper size groups. Many of the groundcovers treated here are superior for conserving soil, however, because they creep and spread and interweave themselves so that eventually they form a continuous mat, giving complete coverage and a uniform texture appearance which is the ideal for this type of material. Those remaining more or less clumpy are slightly less perfect for the purpose. Some vines also make excellent groundcovers. Some of the more adaptable of these are included in this list, for it is difficult to determine whether, in fact, they are more valuable in one category or another. Employing vines in this manner is limited, however, by the serious consideration of whether the plants will leave the ground surface to escape and climb into shrubs and trees which they might overwhelm later.

Since this is a treatise on trees and shrubs, all of the plants should be woody. But in a discussion of groundcovers, particularly for the South, it would be folly to omit mention of some materials, and some of them the best, which are classed as "herbaceous perennials." The *Hemerocallis* is an excellent illustration. The evergreen varieties of this versatile plant fulfill all the qualifications of an excellent groundcover as far as landscape use is concerned. Others of the same class are listed here, and, no doubt, enterprising gardeners of this region will think of still more.

It is also desirable in many cases to introduce into beds of groundcovers other materials which will give color during certain seasons. The bulbous plants are especially well suited here. Some of the Amaryllis and the *Agapanthus* are practically evergreen in warmer sections, and forms of *Oxalis* may be mentioned here. The common red Spider Lily (*Lycoris radiata*) combines well with plantings of *Hemerocallis* in the Coastal Plain and the Piedmont, providing a splash of color in autumn after the latter have bloomed, and sending up fresh foliage to supplement that of the Daylilies which tends to be sparse through the winter. For cooler sections of the Piedmont and the Upper South, *Lycoris squamigera* and the Narcissus in its almost infinite variety come to mind. Considering the richness of this subject, one can hardly afford to be bound by the technical limitations implied by the title "Trees and Shrubs," and such limitations will be passed over as far as the discussion of groundcovers is concerned.

*General discussion*

While groundcovers have many interesting design possibilities and offer some attractive practical advantages, they cannot be employed indiscriminately. The choice of materials calls for some study. In general these plants are difficult to maintain successfully in sunny areas. No matter how poor the soil or how exposed the site, as soon as the ground surface is somewhat sheltered, the seedlings of various shrubs and trees begin to invade the planting, following the natural course of ecological succession. Therefore, where the site under study is well lighted, the use of groundcovers must be planned with allowance for some weeding. It may well be confined to the very steep and difficult spots with slopes steeper than three to one where grass cutting by machine is impractical. This problem of weeding is not entirely eliminated in shaded areas, but it is much less severe, and the groundcovers gain in value here because there are few southern grasses which are very successful in shade. There are, of course, covers which are suited to either sun or shade, but they cannot be planted thoughtlessly with the impression that all gardening problems will then be solved.

The scale of the area to be covered must also be considered in selecting one of these materials. Large areas will obviously call for lusty growers such as Ivy, *Hypericum* or *Serenoa*, while the slow spreaders (Aspidistra, Ferns) and those of miniature character (Partridgeberry) must be suitably located or they will fail completely to fulfill their purpose. And a final word must be inserted on (a) good ground preparation, which means careful removal of all perennial weed root stocks and Bermuda grass before planting, (b) careful spacing of the new plants so that they will cover in a reasonable length of time, and (c) provision for regular assiduous weeding, feeding, and watering of the new plants until they are established. While these steps are primarily of cultural concern and thus lie outside usual considerations of design, adequate provision for them is essential or the plan will not materialize. Groundcovers are beautiful and they are often economical, but few will say that they are cheap to install.

## II. Groundcovers for the SOUTHERN COASTAL PLAIN

*Botanical Name*                                        *Common Name*

RECOMMENDED FOR GENERAL USE

| Botanical Name | Common Name |
|---|---|
| Aspidistra elatior | Common Aspidistra |
| Cyrtomium falcatum | Holly Fern |
| Hedera canariensis | Algerian Ivy |
| Hemerocallis varieties | Daylily |
| Hypericum calycinum | Aaronsbeard St. Johnswort |
| Liriope muscari | Bigblue Liriope |

| *Botanical Name* | *Common Name* |
|---|---|
| Liriope spicata | Creeping Liriope |
| Mondo japonicum | Dwarf Lilyturf |
| Vinca major | Bigleaf Periwinkle |
| Yucca filamentosa | Adamsneedle Yucca |

### Recommended for Restricted Use

| | |
|---|---|
| Ajuga reptans | Carpet Bugle |
| Akebia quinata | Fiveleaf Akebia |
| Gelsemium sempervirens | Carolina Jessamine |
| Hesperaloe parviflora | Red Hesperaloe |
| Jasminum parkeri | Parker Jasmine |
| Juniperus chinensis varieties | Chinese Juniper varieties |
| Juniperus horizontalis varieties | Creeping Juniper varieties |
| Lantana sellowiana | Trailing Lantana |
| Neomarica gracilis | Slender Falseflag |
| Phlox subulata | Creeping Phlox |
| Pleioblastus pygmaeus | Dwarf Bamboo |
| Serenoa repens | Saw Palmetto |
| Trachelospermum jasminoides nana | Dwarf Chinese Starjasmine |
| Vinca minor | Common Periwinkle |
| Viola odorata | Sweet Violet |
| Zamia integrifolia | Coontie |
| Zephyranthes candida | Autumn Zephyrlily |

## II. Groundcovers for the SOUTHERN PIEDMONT

### Recommended for General Use

| | |
|---|---|
| Hedera helix | English Ivy |
| Helleborus orientalis | Lentenrose |
| Hemerocallis varieties | Daylily |
| Hypericum calycinum | Aaronsbeard St. Johnswort |
| Juniperus chinensis varieties | Chinese Juniper varieties |
| Juniperus horizontalis varieties | Creeping Juniper varieties |
| Liriope muscari | Bigblue Liriope |
| Liriope spicata | Creeping Liriope |
| Mondo japonicum | Dwarf Lilyturf |
| Vinca minor | Common Periwinkle |
| Yucca filamentosa | Adamsneedle Yucca |

### Recommended for Restricted Use

| | |
|---|---|
| Ajuga reptans | Carpet Bugle |
| Akebia quinata | Fiveleaf Akebia |

| Botanical Name | Common Name |
|---|---|
| Aspidistra elatior | Common Aspidistra |
| Cotoneaster dammeri | Bearberry Cotoneaster |
| Cyrtomium falcatum | Holly Fern |
| Euonymus fortunei varieties | Wintercreeper Euonymus varieties |
| Galax aphylla | Galax |
| Gelsemium sempervirens | Carolina Jessamine |
| Hedera canariensis | Algerian Ivy |
| Hesperaloe parviflora | Red Hesperaloe |
| Jasminum parkeri | Parker Jasmine |
| Lonicera japonica | Japanese Honeysuckle |
| Mitchella repens | Partridgeberry |
| Pachysandra terminalis | Japanese Pachysandra |
| Phlox subulata | Creeping Phlox |
| Pleioblastus pygmaeus | Dwarf Bamboo |
| Rosa rugosa Max Graf | Max Graf Rose |
| Rosa wichuraiana | Wichura Rose |
| Trachelospermum jasminoides nana | Dwarf Chinese Starjasmine |
| Vinca major | Bigleaf Periwinkle |
| Zephyranthes candida | Autumn Zephyrlily |

## II. Groundcovers for the UPPER SOUTH

### RECOMMENDED FOR GENERAL USE

| | |
|---|---|
| Ajuga reptans | Carpet Bugle |
| Cotoneaster dammeri | Bearberry Cotoneaster |
| Euonymus fortunei varieties | Wintercreeper Euonymus |
| Hedera helix | English Ivy |
| Helleborus orientalis | Lentenrose |
| Hypericum calycinum | Aaronsbeard St. Johnswort |
| Juniperus chinensis varieties | Chinese Juniper varieties |
| Juniperus horizontalis varieties | Creeping Juniper varieties |
| Pachysandra terminalis | Japanese Pachysandra |
| Vinca minor | Common Periwinkle |
| Yucca filamentosa | Adamsneedle Yucca |

### RECOMMENDED FOR RESTRICTED USE

| | |
|---|---|
| Akebia quinata | Fiveleaf Akebia |
| Arctostaphylos uva-ursi | Bearberry |
| Euonymus obovatus | Running Euonymus |
| Galax aphylla | Galax |
| Gaultheria procumbens | Checkerberry Wintergreen |
| Hemerocallis varieties | Daylily |

| Botanical Name | Common Name |
|---|---|
| Liriope muscari | Bigblue Liriope |
| Liriope spicata | Creeping Liriope |
| Lonicera japonica | Japanese Honeysuckle |
| Lycopodium complanatum | Groundcedar — |
| Mahonia repens | Creeping Mahonia |
| Mitchella repens | Partridgeberry |
| Mondo japonicum | Dwarf Lilyturf |
| Phlox subulata | Creeping Phlox |
| Pleioblastus pygmaeus | Dwarf Bamboo |
| Rosa rugosa Max Graf | Max Graf Rose |
| Rosa wichuraiana | Wichura Rose |
| Xanthorhiza simplicissima | Yellowroot |

## RANGE CHART FOR GROUP II. THE GROUNDCOVERS

|  | Coastal Plain | | Piedmont | | Upper South | |
|---|---|---|---|---|---|---|
| Ajuga reptans | | - - - | - - - | x x x | x x x | x x x |
| Aspidistra elatior | x x x | x x x | x x x | - - - | | |
| Cotoneaster dammeri | | - - - | - - - | x x x | x x x | x x x |
| Cyrtomium falcatum | x x x | x x x | x x x | x x x | - - - | |
| Euonymus fortunei varieties | | | - - - | x x x | x x x | x x x |
| Hedera canariensis | x x x | x x x | - - - | | | |
| Hedera helix | | - - - | x x x | x x x | x x x | x x x |
| Helleborus orientalis | | - - - | x x x | x x x | x x x | x x x |
| Hemerocallis varieties | x x x | x x x | x x x | x x x | x x x | - - - |
| Hypericum calycinum | x x x | x x x | x x x | x x x | x x x | x x x |
| Juniperus chinensis varieties | | - - - | x x x | x x x | x x x | x x x |
| Juniperus horizontalis varieties | | - - - | x x x | x x x | x x x | x x x |
| Liriope muscari | x x x | x x x | x x x | x x x | x x x | - - - |
| Liriope spicata | x x x | x x x | x x x | x x x | - - - | - - - |
| Mondo japonicum | x x x | x x x | x x x | x x x | - - - | |
| Pachysandra terminalis | | | - - - | x x x | x x x | x x x |
| Vinca major | x x x | x x x | - - - | - - - | | |
| Vinca minor | | - - - | x x x | x x x | x x x | x x x |
| Yucca filamentosa | x x x | x x x | x x x | x x x | x x x | x x x |

Of all the recommended groundcovers, only the *Yucca* is native to the Southeast, and it is easily adapted to any of the three zones. The *Juniperus horizontalis* comes from the northern U. S. and Canada, but it will tolerate heat very well in most of the region. Few of the Groundcovers are equally good in all localities, but the *Hypericum* is quite successful although weedy for some uses; the *Yucca* mentioned above is good for its peculiar character; and the *Hemerocallis* grow very well everywhere, although the foliage is poor in colder sections through the winter. All of the materials adapt to acid or to alkaline soils rather well. But the *Aspidistra, Cyrtomium, Hedera, Helleborus,* and *Pachysandra* must have shade, while *Cotoneaster* and *Juniperus* require full exposure to sun. Exposure preferences of the others are not so strict.

*Ajuga reptans,* Carpet Bugle. In the Upper South and the Piedmont the Carpet Bugle makes an excellent cover, and it is only slightly less than the best for cooler sites in the Coastal Plain. Its chief requirement seems to be a site which has good drainage, for it will not endure standing water although neither will it stand prolonged drought. It prefers light shade, especially in hot sections, and is equally at home in light or heavy soils so long as they are reasonably fertile. This is a herbaceous plant, but the foliage is quite evergreen, and the leaves have an attractive purplish tinge and a pleasant texture. The plant grows only about 3 inches high, but in the spring it sends up 6-inch spikes of rich blue or white flowers which are very effective. This is a rapid spreader which quickly will make a dense mat from parent plants set 6 to 8 inches apart. With care it is excellent for quick effect. For permanence and freedom from maintenance it may be less desirable than some other materials.

*Akebia quinata,* Fiveleaf Akebia. Described more fully in the Vine chapter, this should be noted here as a fairly good groundcover in all sections of the Southeast for covering large areas. With the warmth of the soil to protect it, it will remain evergreen in all but the coldest spots, and in time even a single plant may be expected to furnish a considerable area of trouble-free, handsome foliage in the most difficult, droughty sites. Like most vines this one must not be set close to shrubs or trees which it might overrun, unless watchful pruning is assured. This does limit its usefulness.

see pg 21

*Arctostaphylos uva-ursi,* Bearberry. This is restricted to higher, cooler elevations in poor sandy or gravelly acid soils, where it is an excellent groundcover, thriving in infertile situations where little else would survive. Its small evergreen leaves, its white flowers of early summer, and its red fruits all are appealing features. Where humidity is high this does well on sunny exposed banks, and it is sometimes used along roadsides. It is difficult to transplant because of its long rooting stems, but is said to be capable of moving in mats or starting from seed.

*Aspidistra elatior,* Common Aspidistra. This is widely known as a house plant for its lush dark green leaves which rise directly from the soil to a height of 12 to 18 inches. This member of the Lily family produces flowers rarely, and it spreads slowly by means of rhizomes rather in the manner of the Iris. However, because it spreads possibly too slowly for covering extensive plots, its coarse, tropical looking foliage may be best fitted for smaller accent areas or for relief in larger beds of a cover of contrasting texture. The *variegata* form with striped leaves of green and white is a striking plant for occasional punctuation. The Aspidistra is somewhat tender. However, it is evergreen throughout the Coastal Plain, especially where it is not touched by winter sunlight or burned by blasts of wind. Even if the leaves are frostbitten, they will renew themselves promptly the following spring. It is grown successfully out-of-doors as far as Memphis and Atlanta. This plant is not particular as to soil. It stands drought and tight urban surroundings well and is not commonly affected by pests, although it can become infested in warmer localities. It should be fine for planting under wide roof overhangs and in architectural plant boxes which have poor exposure to rain and sun.

*Cotoneaster dammeri*, Bearberry Cotoneaster. This, and its variety *radicans*, are rather good groundcovers of a foot or less in height for the Upper South, for cooler parts of the Piedmont, and even for the Coastal Plain, being adapted to well-drained acid or alkaline soils in full sun. There are white flowers in spring, red fruits in fall, and the evergreen foliage is medium to fine in texture. This will eventually spread to cover quite a large area, the branches rooting as they spread. It is not rated as one of the best of this class except in the Upper South because the Cotoneasters as a genus are subject to attacks of blight, scale, mites, and lace bugs, all of which are more serious in warmer areas. The foliage also is a little too thin to shade out competition effectively and so, while this is excellent on occasion, one uses it with some caution. Two other species are grown somewhat here and thus deserve some mention. *C. conspicua decora*, the Necklace Cotoneaster, is an evergreen type and *C. adpressa*, the Creeping Cotoneaster, is deciduous. This genus is useful in general where exposure to sun, wind, drought, and poor soils presents a problem.

*Cyrtomium falcatum*, Holly Fern. Ferns are generally attractive plants and they are seen in gardens fairly frequently. One of the best of these for warmer sections is the Holly Fern. Indeed, for handsome, glossy evergreen leaves of coarse texture and for enduring, pest-free nature, this is one of the best of groundcovers. There are no flowers and no seeds, but if one looks on the undersides of the leaves in late summer or fall, he finds numerous brown spots which are the "sorii" or clusters of small filaments bearing "spores" which correspond to the seeds of other plants. The spores are distributed by wind and water, and those which fall on congenial spots such as damp mouldering bricks or stones will develop quickly into tiny new plants. The Holly Fern prefers shade, some dampness, and a soil rich in humus, but it is surprising to see how it will endure long periods of drought and low fertility in its rooting medium. This plant also is best used as an accent in larger areas of contrasting textures because it does not spread. It is quite hardy throughout the Coastal Plain but it probably ought to be used with caution in the Piedmont where it might not stand the coldest parts.

While on the subject of ferns, mention may be made of several species which are of secondary importance in the region. In warmer sections of the Coastal Plain the Boston Fern, *Nephrolepis exaltata bostoniensis*, is possibly even more common than the above. It spreads quite rapidly to form mats of considerable extent, requiring little care and serving as a most efficient holder of soil. It is inferior, however, because it is not neat in appearance without cleaning. In cooler stream valleys and on north-facing shaded slopes of the Piedmont and the Upper South, the Christmas Fern, *Polystichum acrostichoides*, may be occasionally useful. While remaining evergreen, the leaves fall flat in winter, and the plant is not very effective for a time. The Common Polypody, *Polypodium vulgare*, has better foliage, indeed one of the most beautiful the year around, but its use would be limited by difficulties in moving and growing since it thrives only on rock surfaces or, occasionally, on tree trunks in environments such as described for the Christmas Fern. Either of these is excellent where the cultural problems can be solved, but cannot be suggested for general purposes.

*Euonymus fortunei*, Wintercreeper Euonymus. *Euonymus obovatus*, Running Euonymus. In the previous chapter is mention of the Euonymus to be employed as vines, but some of them are equally valuable as groundcovers. The Bigleaf Wintercreeper, *E. f. vegetus*, is a possible subject, and a handsome one too, but it is almost impossible to maintain below 3 or 4 feet in height. The Common Wintercreeper, *E. f. radicans*, is a first-rate material, however, well suited for areas of any size in sun or shade in the Upper South and, to a lesser extent, in the Piedmont. The same recommendation applies to its colored foliage varieties, Purpleleaf (*E. f. coloratus*) with rosy-purple foliage in autumn and winter, and Silveredge (*E. f. argenteo-marginatus*) with leaves edged in white. For smaller spots, either one of the two dwarf types, the Kew Wintercreeper (*E. f. kewensis*) or Baby Wintercreeper (*E. f. minimus*), is excellent for very fine texture although they both are slow growers. The evergreen foliage of these Wintercreepers is medium to fine in texture, dull green or variegated as noted, and the plants adapt well to almost any acid or alkaline soils with little attention, making a dense, nearly weed-proof cover. Possibly they are better suited to the cooler than to the warmer parts of the region. Their one serious pest seems to be the scale, which is not so general on the Common Wintercreepers as it is on the Bigleaf form. Plantings should be watched for invasions of this pest. Prompt spraying with DDT at monthly intervals from April to late summer should arrest its spread and keep it from becoming a problem.

The Running Euonymus is a native of damp woodlands of the northeastern states and higher elevations of the southeast. Although it is not evergreen, it is a good cover for shaded areas in some localities, particularly those with alkaline soils, and is notable for its red autumn foliage color and its scarlet fruits of fall and winter.

*Galax aphylla*, Galax. That is known to all familiar with the mountain areas of the Upper South, and it is loved for its glossy evergreen circular leaves with purple undersides as well as for its white flowers. Although a shy spreader and difficult to establish in a solid cover, this plant is especially choice for those spots to which it is suited. It must have acid soils with sharp drainage, moisture, and shade. It will be successful at higher elevations and along moist shaded stream valleys through the Piedmont on banks facing north.

*Gaultheria procumbens*, Checkerberry Wintergreen. Similar to the above in soil requirements, this is another native of the woodlands of higher elevations which will be successful only on rare occasions and in limited expanses. Where it will grow it is interesting for its dark evergreen foliage, mat-like growth, and bright red fruits. The leaves, when chewed, taste like wintergreen.

*Gelsemium sempervirens*, Carolina Jessamine. The Jessamine often covers large areas of abandoned fields and cut-over woodlands in the Piedmont and, to a lesser extent, in the Coastal Plain. This suggests its possible use as a groundcover. Its appearance in beds is likely to be somewhat ragged without occasional light sickling, but it should be nearly ideal in this range for rough banks and road cuts in either sun or shade without care in respect to watering, feeding, or spraying. Being less aggressive, it probably is much superior to the ubiquitous Japanese Honeysuckle for the purpose.

*Hedera canariensis*, Algerian Ivy. *Hedera helix*, English Ivy. These have been discussed at length among the vines, but both must be included also among the best of the groundcovers. Again the former is to be preferred in the Coastal Plain, but the latter is superior in the Piedmont and the Upper South. The Ivies enjoy the considerable advantage of being among the easiest and cheapest of all groundcovers to establish. All that is necessary to start them is to secure runners from a neighbor, cut them into lengths of 8 to 10 inches removing all but one or two leaves per cutting, and insert them, top side up, to a depth of 4 to 6 inches in slits about a foot apart in damp ground. If this work is done early in the winter rainy season, most of the cuttings will have rooted without any further care by the following summer and the planting will be established. It is only fair to say that this process is more successful in heavier soils than in very sandy ones, where additional watering may be necessary, and that perfect rooting can hardly be expected in areas where frosts penetrate deep into the ground. Ivy should be located only in the shade. It spreads rapidly, its runners rooting where they touch the ground, making a dense cover that holds soil in place with the finest evergreen appearance. Interest in the plant for this use has prompted the recent introduction of types of more restrained growth, some of them patented, many with interesting leaf form variations and color. Among these are Hahn's Self-branching, Maple Leaf, Shamrock, etc. These are choice for smaller, refined areas.

*Helleborus orientalis*, Lentenrose. Although little used, this seems to have most of the qualities of a superior cover for the Upper South and the Piedmont. It is not well suited to the thin soils and the heat of the Coastal Plain. The foliage is evergreen, of a handsome palmately compound configuration in coarse texture, standing on foot-high stems which arise directly from the crown. Planted from 12 to 15 inches apart, the clumps will form a complete cover which retains its beauty throughout the year. In January the flowers begin to appear, continuing through March. These are quite showy, bell-like blossoms, sometimes 2 inches across, in colors from white through rose with various markings. They last only fairly well as cut flowers, but they are most welcome for cutting at a season when other materials are scarce. The Helleborus are well adapted to any shaded situation, but they suffer if exposed too much to the summer sun. The soil may be acid or alkaline, and it should be improved deeply with well-decayed humus for the long roots. A mulch is almost imperative. Plants of named varieties and separate colors are expensive for groundcover purposes, but propagation by seed is very easy and blooming plants may be produced from volunteers within three years. An undetermined proportion of plants raised from seed will have green flowers, but these are not unattractive even if they are not the best, and the foliage remains undiminished in beauty. The Christmas-rose, *Helleborus niger*, is a much more widely advertised species. It blooms earlier, from December to January. Its blossoms are white, appearing singly on stems arising directly from the ground, while the Lentenrose bears several blossoms on each stem. The Lentenrose is more vigorous and more easily established, and it is the better for this purpose.

*Hemerocallis* varieties, Daylily. Southern gardeners have been coming to rely increasingly on the Daylily for summer bloom in the flower border, and some have become acquainted with the more or less evergreen varieties which can well be used as groundcovers. These grow equally well in sun or shade, have no pests, and stand drought in all kinds of soils. The showy blossoms come during the long summer months according to variety in tones of yellow, orange, maroon, red, and pink. Set about 2 feet apart, they are most effective in large, mass planting of either single or mixed varieties in drifts; an area of as much as an acre in extent planted in them makes a memorable display. For more solid effect, plantings may be set as close as 12 inches apart but at some sacrifice of bloom quality. New introductions are appearing each year, and so the following suggestions for evergreen varieties preferred for groundcovering cannot be complete by any means. Yellow: Amaryllis, Aureole, Cressida, Florham, J. A. Crawford, Patricia, Soudan. Orange: Emily Hume, Gypsy, George Kelso, Ophir, Queen of Gonzales, Vesta. Copper: Chengtu, Painted Lady. Red: Baronet, Blanche Hooker, Garnet Red, Indianola, Kanapaha. Pink: Pink Charm. Bicolor: Athlone, Caballero, Cinnabar, Granada, Mikado (a good variety possibly not quite evergreen), Rajah. Most nurseries are carrying a selection of Daylilies now, and the gardener will do well to visit one of these to select varieties which are successful locally. They can be effective the year around and can add summer color to many a garden which looks dead after the spring Azalea season has passed. The major qualifications limiting their general planting are (1) they are somewhat untidy, especially when covered with stalks of past blooms, and they are thus preferable for large-scale designs of coarse character, (2) in cooler sections very few if any varieties are truly evergreen, and the foliage is thin in winter in all areas, and (3) the flowers usually fade at the end of the day when, during the evening hours, outdoor living areas generally enjoy their greatest use. Untidiness can only be overcome with care or through planting where it is not a problem. Roadside plantings of Daylilies are handsome and their coarseness is not objectionable. Winter thinness of foliage effect can be countered in most of the Southeast by interplanting with Spider Lilies, *Lycoris radiata*. Also hybridizers are now producing strains which flower during the evening. A list of some 30 varieties of this type has been published by the American Horticultural Society (*Gardeners' Forum*, September 1960).

*Hesperaloe parviflora*, Red Hesperaloe. This is a native of Texas which is successful in dry sunny sites in the Coastal Plain and the Piedmont. It forms clumps of leaves about a foot long, similar to, but smaller in scale than those of the common Spanish Bayonet. Rose-red flowers appear in summer on graceful slender spikes about 4 feet high. This may be used as a specimen effectively on account of its bold texture and its flowers. Its habit of spreading by means of underground suckers is desirable in a groundcover, but the process is almost too slow to make this a practical material for covering extensive areas.

*Hypericum calycinum*, Aaronsbeard St. Johnswort. This probably is one of the superior groundcovers for large areas of coarse character in all parts of the Southeast. It is characterized by a matted root system made up of numberless underground stems which, in light or heavy soils, form rapidly a thick sod which should be particularly valuable in protecting sandy banks from erosion. The stems rise in a graceful arch about a foot above the ground, bearing the grayish green leaves in opposite pairs and the scattered deep yellow flowers, which look something like enlarged buttercups, in sporadic succession through the summer. The foliage is medium in texture, semi-evergreen, and usually keeps its attractive, somewhat unusual color until early spring unless the winter is severe. It may prefer lighter soils although it does well in the clays of the Piedmont. It grows with aggressive vigor in either sunny or slightly shaded locations although it will not bloom in shade. There seem to be no insects or diseases to bother it. For tidy locations it may be improved by a spring shearing. There are other Hypericums which might be worth trying, particularly *H. moserianum*, the Gold-Flower, which is notable for its large blossoms in midsummer. This is a hybrid of the above, but it does not retain the parent's spreading habit, and consequently it is somewhat inferior for the purpose of groundcovering. *H. buckleyi*, the Blueridge St. Johnswort, a deciduous form from the mountains of the Upper South, would be a likely candidate for a trial in this section.

*Jasminum parkeri*, Parker Jasmine. This looks like a miniature of the common Flowering Jasmine, hardly exceeding a foot in height. It is rare in the region, but it is possible that it may become well-liked at least in the Coastal Plain for its dainty habit and its fine-textured evergreen foliage. It does need further testing, however, before it can be recommended widely. The Jasmines have the habit of rooting wherever their branch tips touch the ground, which makes them valuable as groundcovers. On this account the taller *J. floridum*, *J. mesnyi*, and *J. nudiflorum* are employed successfully for this purpose in larger scale. All like sunny exposures, and they are hardy, easy to grow, and free from troubles for the warmer parts of the Southeast.

*Juniperus chinensis* varieties, Chinese Juniper varieties. *Juniperus horizontalis* varieties, Creeping Juniper varieties. These are among the best of materials for dry, poor, acid or alkaline soils in full sun and exposure to wind and cold. Indeed, they may be said to decline with shelter. Generally speaking, they are recommended for the Upper South and cooler parts of the Piedmont, but they will grow quite well into the Coastal Plain on open sites. They vary in height from a few inches to a foot and all spread in time to cover sizable areas, the stems rooting where they rest on the ground. This latter characteristic makes them difficult to cultivate and to dig in nurseries; therefore planting stock is not grown in quantity and large plants are rarely procurable. The foliage of all forms is evergreen, often of a positive color in winter, fine in texture. The junipers are somewhat subject to a disease which acts like fireblight on apples, killing back an occasional branch, but this is rarely serious. Spider mites often cause a browning of the foliage of plants grown in sheltered or shaded spots. These mites are not usually serious in open sites, and, in any event, can be controlled easily by spraying.

The species Creeping J. is not the best, being rather open in habit and turning somewhat rusty in winter. It is a native of the northern U. S. and southern Canada, and it is important as the parent of several choice varieties. Among these, the Waukegan Juniper, *J. h. douglasi*, is a handsome compact variety with positive horizontal branching habit and bluish gray foliage, a fairly rapid grower for generous areas. More dwarf and slower-growing are one or more other varieties, the names of which are usually mixed and indeterminate, likely to be listed as "Bar Harbor," *procumbens*, or *alpina*. These are quite choice and well worth the trouble of seeking out. The Andorra Juniper, *J. h. plumosa*, is a widely grown vigorous species with a light-green summer color turning purplish in winter. It is taller (to 1 foot), more open, and not so desirable except where exposure will keep it compact and trim.

Mention should be made here of two other groundcovering species. *J. chinensis sargenti*, the Sargent Chinese Juniper, is very much like the above in habit of growth, with a blue-gray color. *J. conferta*, the Shore Juniper, is seen fairly commonly in the South, making a good cover on exposed hilltops about Birmingham, Alabama, and on the sandy Coastal Plain soils of North Carolina. For poor, thin, dry soils and severe exposures it is very good, but it will be disappointing under favorable growing conditions.

*Lantana sellowiana*, Trailing Lantana. This might be included among the best groundcovers for a restricted section of the Coastal Plain, for it tolerates sun, wind, and poor sandy soils where few other materials succeed. With this plant, such barren areas can be covered and protected and transformed with a minimum of care into mounds and billows of blossom and foliage. It must be admitted, however, that the Lantana is not a first-rate choice for much of the region. It is rather tender and will freeze back some years, although it makes a speedy recovery from the root. The habit of growth is a little untidy, and the foliage may look poor at winter's end. Still, in warmer sections in the sun there are places where it has no challenger. Through the long summer and autumn it produces an unbelievable succession of rosy lilac flowers. It is kept neater in appearance if it is sheared occasionally; and, if the plants are set from 2 to 3 feet apart, the stems will root where they touch the soil to make a solid cover. The new hybrid, *L. callowiana*, Gold Rush, originated in California, is being tried here with some promise of success. It is said to be a smaller plant than the above, neater in habit of growth, and equally at home in sun, heat, and drought.

*Liriope muscari*, Bigblue Liriope. *Liriope spicata*, Creeping Liriope. The Bigblue Liriope is characterized by a clumpy habit of growth, strap-like dark evergreen leaves about 10 inches long, and rather attractive spikes of violet flowers in late summer which are succeeded by black berry-like fruits. It is commonly planted as an edging for walks or shrubbery beds, but it is also handsome in larger masses as a groundcover. There is also in rather common use a variegated type having cream-colored leaves. Few plants can be more satisfactory than this one, which is almost pest free, at home in any soil or exposure, perfectly hardy, and requires no care. Since it develops rapidly from the seeds which are produced freely, and, in addition, the clumps can be divided frequently, Liriope can be used generously. It is larger in scale than the species below with which it can be combined to give accent at important points and to provide variety in texture. This is highly recommended throughout the Coastal Plain and the Piedmont. In the Upper South it may be set out with more caution although it will grow as far north as Cleveland, Ohio.

In discussing the Creeping Liriope one runs into the serious confusion of names involving this and the Dwarf Lilyturf, *Mondo japonicum* or *Ophiopogon japonica*. The use of these plants is identical and their range is similar although the Liriope is said to be the more hardy of the two. For details of planting, reference is made to the section on *Mondo* below.

*Lonicera japonica halliana*, Hall's Japanese Honeysuckle. Because it has become such a nuisance in many sections, this will not be suggested for the Coastal Plain nor the Piedmont, but in cooler parts of the Upper South it will have some use for covering extensive areas and protecting them from erosion as long as the site boundaries are sufficiently well-defined to keep the plant from escaping into nearby woodlands. It is to be recommended only because it is cheap, easily obtained, quick to cover, effective in its protection of large areas, and strong enough to smother competition. Sites which otherwise seem quite hopeless can be made attractive with this plant and they will remain so through many years without cutting or any care whatsoever. Its effect is coarse, but it is practical and economical material for many park, highway, and industrial projects.

*Lycopodium complanatum*, Groundcedar. This is a member of a primitive family of plants called the Club Mosses of which several species are to be found in parts of the Upper South. This rather common woodland native will likely be the most useful—it is a most attractive material—often completely clothing quite extensive areas with its fern-like, fine-textured, light green foliage. In autumn it bears candelabra-like spore cases which also are decorative. This is likely to prove difficult to transplant and to establish, but this species is tolerant as to soils and likes simply a well-drained spot in shade with moisture.

*Mahonia repens*, Creeping Mahonia. This will have limited use almost entirely in the Upper South and largely on limestone soils in sunny to lightly shaded exposures. It reaches a height of almost 1 foot, spreading by underground stems to make a good cover, bearing attractive, deciduous, holly-like foliage of dull sheen and coarse texture. It has no important pests except for the lacewing fly in certain sections. But it is not easily established, and there are usually other materials which can be employed more effectively.

*Mitchella repens*, Partridgeberry. A native of cool, deep woodlands of the Upper South, this miniature comes into the Piedmont along the shaded banks of the stream valleys. Where it can be given a well-drained but moist spot of acid soil similar to its native habitat, this plant can be effective in small areas for a close mat-like cover of fine evergreen foliage ornamented in spring by shy white flowers and in fall by bright red berries. Usually this is better on banks than on flat places because it smothers if accumulations of leaves cover it for long.

*Mondo japonicum*, Dwarf Lilyturf. Reference has been made to this plant under Liriope above. It is listed often as *Ophiopogon japonica*, and it goes under a wide assortment of common names. It is unfortunate that this confusion exists and that the resolution depends on minute details of flower structure which are not readily determined, for this involves one of the finest of groundcovers for both the Coastal Plain and the Piedmont, which may be planted also in the Upper South when caution in the matter of exposure is exercised.

Growing to a height of about 4 inches, this forms broad, dark evergreen expanses of uniformly fine-textured quality, untouched by summer's drought, winter's cold, or by infestations of pests. Its habit of increasing by means of creeping underground shoots makes well-established plantings a sod-like mat which is excellent for protecting soil against erosion. The plants produce small white flowers in May, but these are inconspicuous because the tiny spikes usually are covered by the leaves. For the same reason the beautiful blue berries of late summer also are overlooked. The Lilyturf is recommended chiefly for shaded places and always for well-drained soils. It grows in the sun as well as shade, but invasions of Bermuda grass, which usually occur sooner or later in open sites, may make the upkeep here an almost impossible undertaking. Good soil preparation, including the incorporation of plenty of humus, is most beneficial in establishing new plantings. Old clumps may be divided into single crowns which, set about 6 inches apart, should form a new sod within two years. After this, watering or fertilizing or mowing will not be necessary. Rabbits sometimes eat the foliage in winter when other forage is scarce.

Both the Creeping Liriope and the Dwarf Lilyturf are fine groundcover materials separated apparently by botanical differences which are very subtle. The Liriope is said to be the more hardy of the two. One should request samples when he wants to make a planting of one or the other in order to see that he will get what he wants. There is also a large species of *Mondo*. This is *M. jaburan* or White Lilyturf, with leaves as long as 3 feet, having variegated as well as dark green foliage color. No doubt this too is in cultivation in this area, possibly often confused with the Bigblue Liriope.

*Neomarica gracilis*, Slender Falseflag. This is fairly common in gardens of warmer parts of the Coastal Plain and is valued for its interesting foliage and flowers, both of which resemble those of the closely related Iris. To a limited extent this makes a good groundcover, spreading by virtue of rooting and forming new plants wherever the leaf tips touch the soil. This is not reliably hardy north of Charleston, S. C., and it is inferior to other materials listed for general use.

*Pachysandra terminalis*, Japanese Pachysandra. For cool, shaded areas, either large or restricted, this is among the best of groundcovers for the Upper South and the coolest parts of the Piedmont—to Memphis, Atlanta, and Richmond. Its evergreen leaves of olive green color are arranged in whorls around the numerous, upright, 6-inch stems, giving this a rich and rather coarse textured effect. The plant is stoloniferous in habit, forming a mat of uniform consistency, tolerant of acid or alkaline soils, demanding little if any attention. Almost its only requirement is shade, for the foliage turns yellowish and may die back on overexposure to sun and wind especially in warmer locales. Greenish flowers are produced in spring, but these have no ornamental value. The plant is easily established if older sods or clumps can be procured and separated into individual stems, each with a few rootlets, and set out 6 inches apart in early spring in well-prepared, humus-rich soil. This plant needs to be watched for attacks of scale insects which are not often serious but which, if they are not arrested in the early stages, can spread to become difficult to eliminate and thus destroy the effectiveness of the plantings.

Another species is *P. procumbens*, the Allegheny Pachysandra, which is a native of the mountain regions from Virginia south and along cool stream valleys to Florida and Louisiana. As a groundcover it is inferior because it is deciduous and clumpy in habit. It is interesting, however, for cool moist woodlands.

*Phlox subulata*, Moss Phlox. For small banks in full sun the Phlox is a good choice, seemingly equally at home in all but the warmest parts of the Coastal Plain. This is a well-known creeping plant, about 2 inches high, with fine, moss-like evergreen leaves and a spectacular blaze of early spring flowers which makes a solid sheet of color. The color usually seen is a harsh rose which is very difficult to harmonize with other tones; but varieties with flowers of white, lilac, etc., are available, and these are more attractive. Strong clumps of the plant may be set as much as a foot apart and the creeping stems, which will root along their length, will fill in the intervals. They should be located only in sunny spots in well-drained soils, but they will do well in either light or clay soils. They do not require high fertility nor do they need watering or other care after they are once established.

*Pleioblastus pygmaeus*, Dwarf Bamboo. This dwarf Bamboo grows to a height of about 6 inches, making a rather good dense cover, just as free of troubles as most of the other Bamboos. However, it shares with others of its genus a rampant, hard-to-control spreading habit of growth which makes widespread use very questionable. This does not seem to be available in nurseries although a few slightly larger types of great beauty, growing to about 2 feet and listed under the name of *Sasa*, are to be found. These too may be employed as groundcovers of larger scale or as accents in beds of other materials. Apparently Bamboos of this size group still are not sufficiently known or tried to be placed accurately in landscape usage, but they deserve attention for exotic texture interest and for ability to endure hard growing conditions. They probably will be most useful in the Coastal Plain and the Piedmont, but some types will come also into the Upper South.

*Rosa rugosa* Max Graf, Max Graf Rose. *Rosa wichuraiana*, Wichura Rose. Two Roses coming within this size class will be rarely useful in the Upper South, less so in the Piedmont. Both need large areas in which to spread, but for sunny rocky banks under severe soil and exposure conditions, they are occasionally excellent. The Wichura Rose has dainty semi-evergreen leaves, small white flowers in May, and red fruits in autumn. The Max Graf Rose is more coarse in foliage and habit, bearing showy fragrant single pink flowers. Occasionally some of the old-fashioned Rambler Roses are effective also as bank covers. All of these should find their service in housing projects and parks where it may be absolutely essential to fend off intruders on banks liable to serious erosion. Plantings of these roses often become difficult to maintain because they do not form a sufficiently heavy cover to prevent intrusion of tree seedlings such as Locust and Elm.

*Serenoa repens,* Saw Palmetto. This is so common in its extensive native stands in the Coastal Plain and so coarse in habit that it is likely not to be used widely in landscape work. Still it is an excellent, practical, large-scale groundcover in this section for certain difficult areas, and it should not be neglected entirely. Occasionally it makes a good specimen, effective for foliage contrast. The creeping stems usually stay at or under the ground surface, but they do sometimes ascend to some height. This material should be excellent for park work and highway protection, especially effective in barriers or beds to prevent pedestrians from trespassing.

*Trachelospermum jasminoides nana,* Dwarf Starjasmine. This is a relatively new introduction about which not too much is known, but which may become a favorite ground cover in the future. The characteristics of the common vine form are discussed in the chapter on Vines and are not repeated here. This plant will be useful chiefly for lightly shaded areas where good soil and moisture are available, but it is reported to grow poorly in deep shade. Scale insects may bother it occasionally, but its beautiful dark waxy evergreen foliage will make it a desirable material for foundation plantings and such choice spots, largely in the Coastal Plain but also in warmer parts of the Piedmont.

*Vinca major,* Bigleaf Periwinkle. *Vinca minor,* Common Periwinkle. The Bigleaf Periwinkle, although not so refined and choice as the smaller Common Periwinkle, is the only one of these that can be recommended for the Coastal Plain and the lower Piedmont. The latter may succeed here in cooler situations in the shade of the north side of a building, but generally the summers are too long for it to be happy. The former does grow very well in partial to deep shade, and its foot-high stems bear a good evergreen foliage of medium texture and of a bright fresh color. There is also a form called *variegata* in which the leaves are edged with creamy white. New shoots in the early spring bear the attractive flowers of lilac blue. This is one of the very rapidly spreading groundcovers. Complete coverage may be achieved within a few months from plants set as much as 18 inches apart in fairly good soils. The Bigleaf Periwinkle will endure drought fairly well, but it needs moisture to keep it looking fresh. It does not require spraying or other upkeep except possibly restraining from over-running other plantings, for it is an active spreader.

The Common Periwinkle is possibly the most valuable single groundcover for the Upper South for either large or small areas in sun or shade. In the Piedmont it is also choice but it should be used with caution and planted in cooler shade where moisture is adequate. It is tolerant of most soils, resistant to diseases and to insect attacks. Its glossy, dark, evergreen foliage is medium and unobtrusive in effect, and flowers are produced in early spring. These are violet-blue in the usual variety, but a white and a red-purple are not uncommon, and forms with double blossoms and variegated leaves are known. The Bowles variety has larger blooms of lilac color, and is said to be more hardy although winterkill will not usually be a consideration in this region. The plant spreads by means of horizontal stems which root along their length to make a thick mat of uniform texture about 6 inches high. Old clumps can be divided easily into individual crowns and reset about 6 inches apart in early spring for new plantings. Where one is launching a new planting, he should take particular pains to remove all old weed and grass roots from the soil, because these are impossible to eradicate later in established plantings unless the whole is torn up. The weed problem is likely to be troublesome where there is more sunlight.

*Xanthorhiza simplicissima*, Yellowroot. Although it is somewhat tall for a groundcover and unfortunately has deciduous leaves, this still will be desirable occasionally in broad sweeps or drifts for natural gardens. A native of the Eastern U. S., this plant spreads by means of underground shoots to cover sizable areas, sending up its woody stems to a height of about 2 feet. The foliage is compound and lacy in effect. There are tiny purplish flowers in spring, but these are rarely showy. The plant grows in woodsy well-watered soils in sun or shade with very little attention, making a pleasant ornament.

*Yucca filamentosa*, Adamsneedle Yucca. This hardly grows in solid mat form in true groundcover fashion, but it does form clumps often of some size. In small areas or mixed with other materials, it provides an effective contrast. With its bold spiky evergreen foliage about 1 foot high, it appears exotic as if it belongs with the cacti of the Southwest. But it is native to this region from North Carolina to Florida and Mississippi, culturally well adapted to all parts of the Southeast, thriving without any care wherever it has a sunny to lightly shaded and well-drained site, enduring the poorest and driest of soils. In early summer it produces handsome bold spikes of bell-shaped white flowers to a height of 5 feet. The landscape effect is very coarse, and old bloom stems and dead foliage must be removed at times to maintain a neat appearance.

*Zamia integrifolia*, Coontie. This is of questionable hardiness in colder portions of the Coastal Plain, but is a plant of most distinctive appearance that must be included with the best in its range. It is classed with the Palms, to which it is related, although it grows to only 1 or 2 feet in height. The foliage is heavy, rather like that of a very coarse fern, dark in color, and exotic in appearance. This suggests that it may well be used in smaller accent clumps rather than in extensive areas. Indeed, this practice is recommended also by its slow-growing habit, which makes it expensive to buy. There are no flowers of consequence, but seeds are produced occasionally by female specimens in ornamental furry brown growths bedded in the center of the plant. The Coontie is a native of the swamps of middle and southern Florida, but it does well in any sandy soil of average quality in sun or partial shade and asks for little attention. It is the source of starchy arrowroot and is of some economic importance in its native area.

*Zephyranthes candida*, Autumn Zephyrlily. This comes from South America. It retains its foliage in winter to make it occasionally useful as a groundcover in small areas. The leaves are like those of a coarse grass in texture, and the flowers are white, quite showy in late summer and autumn when they spring up almost overnight following a heavy rain. This is a plant valuable for moist places where many others will not thrive, and in milder sections it grows vigorously and naturalizes in large clumps. The Atamasco Lily, *Z. atamasco*, is native to damp sites in this region and is widely planted in gardens for its bold displays of white flowers about 8 inches high in March and April. It is inferior as a groundcover because its foliage is temporary.

Butchersbroom

# 3

# LESSER

# SHRUBS

GROUP III - DWARF
GROUP IV - SMALL

THE many shrubs which can be grown in the Southeast are divided into two large classes, Lesser and Major, by the height of the eye level which is taken to be, roughly, 6 feet. This is a simple and obvious point from the standpoint of use because, since it is possible to see over the Lesser Shrubs, they are capable of blocking and directing circulation but not vision, and the Major Shrubs are effective for screening.

Two minor classifications of the Lesser Shrubs are recognized: Dwarf (Group III - heights 1 to 4 feet) and Small (Group IV - heights 4 to 6 feet). The former includes materials which some designers will use as groundcovers (Group II). For this purpose they are not ideally suited because either (1) they remain individual in character, not matting to make a continuous surface, or (2) they grow a little taller than a groundcover should. These are small points, however, and on occasion Dwarf Shrubs can be very effective as bank covers of a larger scale (the Jasmines); they can be planted in beds to guide circulation and to prevent pedestrians from cutting corners (the Barberries, Ruscus); or they can be introduced into beds of other groundcovers to give pattern and variety in texture, height, and color (Ardisia, Sarcococca, Skimmia).

In general, since these plants are dwarf in habit, it is only natural that they should be slow growing. The buyer should expect to find that they are relatively expensive in the nursery for their bulk in comparison to other things. They are costly in time and care to produce, but, if they are well located, often prove to be good investments, repaying handsomely their cost in quality of appearance and ease of upkeep.

Because of the relatively high cost common among these materials, one is often tempted to substitute shrubs from one of the larger growing classes, expecting to keep them within prescribed bounds by shearing. In some cases, this reasoning is practical and sound. Some projects are built for temporary effect. Shrubs set in the plant boxes and beds of motels, restaurants, shopping centers, and roof gardens are often replaced every third or fourth year (if they live that long) because of poor growing conditions and because an ever-fresh appearance is vital. Whether any one plant ever reaches maturity is of little importance since the cost of constant replacement is negligible in comparison with the value returned. Except for such unusual circumstances, however, it is better practice, and generally more economical and satisfactory, to select a species from the Lesser Shrub lists when one wants something in this range. Substitutes from the lists of larger growing materials should be made only after careful review of the special conditions involved and at some risk of future disappointment.

Constantly the plantsmen call for more good dwarf shrubs that will remain dwarf. Unfortunately these are comparatively rare, and it is difficult to make up a list of a dozen species which can be relied upon for dependable performance under the wide range of growing conditions prevailing in the Southeast. Still, it is not impossible to assemble a representative list of species, and new dwarf sports of standard varieties are being introduced to cultivation annually.

Shrubs in this size group are in great demand chiefly for two purposes: (1) to "face down" plantings of larger materials, and (2) to furnish foundation plant material for the modern, low-lying house. However, a serious consideration of both these cases may show that this demand need not, and possibly should not, be so insistent. In many instances a planting plan which calls for many of these small scale plants in variety may need simplification. A planting composed of many little things runs the risk of looking spotty, lacking the unity given by a dominant mass.

There is nothing wrong with seeing the stems of a plant, and "facing down" is not a practice deserving universal praise. In fact, these trunks are really rather beautiful in their place. However, if certain varieties become too "leggy" for any particular spot, then some other choice should have been made in the beginning. In other words, if one cannot endure a leggy shrub in the border planting, he should never have set it out at all, but should have chosen originally some species which retains its lower branches. The old practice of widening shrub borders to include several rows of plants, each one lower toward the front to hide the base of the taller ones behind, has proved to be wasteful of plants and wasteful of the space which cannot often be spared on today's small lot. It also makes maintenance exceedingly difficult.

The practice of "facing down" has little place in today's planting design. When it comes to foundation plantings for small houses, one might well stop to inquire whether he tends to use too many kinds of plants. The "standard design" seems to repeat on a facade 20 to 30 feet long the same number of varieties one would choose for another 50 to 60 feet long, but with everything scaled down accordingly. Too often this kind of design tends to appear trivial; these tiny shrubs simply emphasize the general effect of smallness, because all the dimensions of doors and windows, which are also part of the architectural composition, will remain normal in size. Perhaps the tiny house might be slipped into its place in the landscape more gracefully through the use near it of a single small tree or one or two normal-sized shrubs of choice variety, combined with some groundcovers, bulbs, and/or flowers. Contemporary landscape design aims for simplicity, restraint, and continuity, avoiding over-elaboration, stuffiness, and spotty complication.

All this is not to say that there is no need for small shrubs, but only that there is apparently more demand for them than need be. Plants of this size are often necessary for accents of detail interest near steps, gates, doorways, and on terraces. For these locations it is important to select materials which remain in scale with their surroundings without restraint rather than to set out plants which one knows can be kept in bounds only with clipping. For such uses it may be desirable to select something of a rather stiff, solid, formal character (dwarf Holly, Viburnum), but in others a more loose informal habit may be preferable (Sarcococca, Cotoneaster). A few are highly desirable to give continuity of effect in mass or foliage in flower borders when the herbaceous plants are dormant. In these lists are many splendid plants for using in low hedges which will need little or no shearing. The older practice of planting rows of one Privet or another or Japanese Barberry and then shearing to any desired height is not good planting design today, when there is at hand a wealth of materials naturally tailored to suit such a variety of conditions.

## III. Dwarf Shrubs for the SOUTHERN COASTAL PLAIN

| *Botanical Name* | *Common Name* |
|---|---|
| RECOMMENDED FOR GENERAL USE | |
| Ardisia crispa | Coral Ardisia |

| Botanical Name | Common Name |
|---|---|
| Aucuba japonica nana | Dwarf Japanese Aucuba |
| Buxus harlandi | Harland's Box |
| Gardenia jasminoides radicans | Dwarf Gardenia |
| Ilex cornuta rotunda | Dwarf Chinese Holly |
| Ilex vomitoria nana | Dwarf Yaupon Holly |
| Jasminum floridum | Flowering Jasmine |
| Jasminum nudiflorum | Winter Jasmine |
| Punica granatum nana | Dwarf Pomegranate |
| Raphiolepis indica | India Raphiolepis |
| Rhododendron macrantha hybrid | Macrantha Azalea |
| Ruscus aculeatus | Butchersbroom |
| Serissa foetida | Serissa |

### RECOMMENDED FOR RESTRICTED USE

| | |
|---|---|
| Berberis julianae nana | Dwarf Wintergreen Barberry |
| Berberis verruculosa | Warty Barberry |
| Buxus sempervirens suffruticosa | Truedwarf Common Box |
| Chaenomeles japonica | Japanese Floweringquince |
| Cotoneaster horizontalis | Rock Cotoneaster |
| Cotoneaster microphylla | Rockspray Cotoneaster |
| Danae racemosa | Alexandrialaurel |
| Daphne odora | Winter Daphne |
| Heteropteris argentea | Heteropteris |
| Hypericum kalmianum | Kalm St. Johnswort |
| Hypericum moserianum | Goldflower St. Johnswort |
| Hypericum patulum henryi | Henry St. Johnswort |
| Iberis sempervirens | Evergreen Candytuft |
| Ilex crenata helleri | Heller Japanese Holly |
| Juniperus sabina tamariscifolia | Tamarix Savin Juniper |
| Malpighia coccigera | Holly Malpighia |
| Myrica pumila | Dwarf Waxmyrtle |
| Myrtus communis compacta | Compact True Myrtle |
| Prunus glandulosa | Flowering Almond |
| Rhododendron atlanticum | Coast Azalea |
| Rhododendron chapmani | Chapman Rhododendron |
| Rosa floribunda | Floribunda Rose |
| Salvia greggi | Autumn Sage |
| Sarcococca hookeriana humilis | Small Himalaya Sarcococca |
| Skimmia japonica | Japanese Skimmia |
| Skimmia reevesiana | Reeves Skimmia |
| Spiraea bumalda Anthony Waterer | Anthony Waterer Spiraea |
| Vaccinium crassifolium | Creeping Blueberry |
| Vaccinium myrsinites | Ground Blueberry |

III. Dwarf Shrubs for the SOUTHERN PIEDMONT

*Botanical Name*                                    *Common Name*

RECOMMENDED FOR GENERAL USE

| | |
|---|---|
| Aucuba japonica nana | Dwarf Japanese Aucuba |
| Buxus sempervirens suffruticosa | Truedwarf Common Box |
| Hypericum kalmianum | Kalm St. Johnswort |
| Ilex cornuta rotunda | Dwarf Chinese Holly |
| Ilex crenata helleri | Heller Japanese Holly |
| Ilex vomitoria nana | Dwarf Yaupon Holly |
| Jasminum floridum | Flowering Jasmine |
| Jasminum nudiflorum | Winter Jasmine |
| Juniperus sabina tamariscifolia | Tamarix Savin Juniper |
| Rhododendron macrantha hybrid | Macrantha Azalea |
| Ruscus aculeatus | Butchersbroom |
| Sarcococca hookeriana humilis | Small Himalaya Sarcococca |
| Skimmia japonica | Japanese Skimmia |

RECOMMENDED FOR RESTRICTED USE

| | |
|---|---|
| Aronia melanocarpa | Black Chokeberry |
| Artemisia abrotanum | Oldman Wormwood |
| Berberis julianae nana | Dwarf Wintergreen Barberry |
| Berberis verruculosa | Warty Barberry |
| Buxus microphylla koreana | Korean Littleleaf Box |
| Calluna vulgaris | Scotch Heather |
| Caryopteris clandonensis | Bluebeard |
| Chaenomeles japonica | Japanese Floweringquince |
| Cotoneaster horizontalis | Rock Cotoneaster |
| Cotoneaster microphylla | Rockspray Cotoneaster |
| Danae racemosa | Alexandrialaurel |
| Daphne odora | Winter Daphne |
| Gardenia jasminoides radicans | Dwarf Gardenia |
| Heteropteris argentea | Heteropteris |
| Hypericum moserianum | Goldflower St. Johnswort |
| Hypericum patulum henryi | Henry St. Johnswort |
| Iberis sempervirens | Evergreen Candytuft |
| Lavandula officinalis | True Lavender |
| Myrica pumila | Dwarf Waxmyrtle |
| Myrtus communis compacta | Compact True Myrtle |
| Physocarpus monogynus | Mountain Ninebark |
| Prunus glandulosa | Flowering Almond |
| Punica granatum nana | Dwarf Pomegranate |
| Raphiolepis indica | India Raphiolepis |

| *Botanical Name* | *Common Name* |
|---|---|
| Rhododendron atlanticum | Coast Azalea |
| Rhododendron chapmani | Chapman Rhododendron |
| Rosa floribunda | Floribunda Rose |
| Salvia greggi | Autumn Sage |
| Santolina chamaecyparissus | Cypress Lavendercotton |
| Serissa foetida | Serissa |
| Skimmia reevesiana | Reeves Skimmia |
| Spiraea bumalda Anthony Waterer | Anthony Waterer Spiraea |
| Symphoricarpos chenaulti | Chenault Coralberry |
| Taxus baccata repanda | Spreading English Yew |
| Teucrium chamaedrys | Germander |
| Vaccinium crassifolium | Creeping Blueberry |
| Vaccinium myrsinites | Ground Blueberry |
| Viburnum opulus nanum | Dwarf European Cranberrybush ✓ |

## III. Dwarf Shrubs for the UPPER SOUTH

### RECOMMENDED FOR GENERAL USE

| | |
|---|---|
| Berberis verruculosa | Warty Barberry |
| Buxus microphylla koreana | Korean Littleleaf Box |
| Buxus sempervirens suffruticosa | Truedwarf Common Box |
| Cotoneaster horizontalis | Rock Cotoneaster |
| Hypericum kalmianum | Kalm St. Johnswort |
| Ilex cornuta rotunda | Dwarf Chinese Holly |
| Ilex crenata helleri | Heller Japanese Holly |
| Juniperus sabina tamariscifolia | Tamarix Savin Juniper |
| Rosa floribunda | Floribunda Rose |
| Taxus baccata repanda | Spreading English Yew |
| Taxus cuspidata nana | Dwarf Japanese Yew |
| Viburnum opulus nanum | Dwarf European Cranberrybush |

### RECOMMENDED FOR RESTRICTED USE

| | |
|---|---|
| Aronia melanocarpa | Black Chokeberry |
| Artemisia abrotanum | Oldman Wormwood |
| Aucuba japonica nana | Dwarf Japanese Aucuba |
| Berberis julianae nana | Dwarf Wintergreen Barberry |
| Calluna vulgaris | Scotch Heather |
| Caryopteris clandonensis | Bluebeard |
| Ceanothus americanus | Jerseytea Ceanothus |
| Chaenomeles japonica | Japanese Floweringquince |
| Cotoneaster microphylla | Rockspray Cotoneaster |
| Daphne cneorum | Rose Daphne |

| *Botanical Name* | *Common Name* |
|---|---|
| Daphne odora | Winter Daphne |
| Hypericum moserianum | Goldflower St. Johnswort |
| Hypericum patulum henryi | Henry St. Johnswort |
| Iberis sempervirens | Evergreen Candytuft |
| Ilex vomitoria nana | Dwarf Yaupon Holly |
| Jasminum floridum | Flowering Jasmine |
| Jasminum nudiflorum | Winter Jasmine |
| Lavandula officinalis | True Lavender |
| Pachistima canbyi | Canby Pachistima |
| Physocarpus monogynus | Mountain Ninebark |
| Potentilla fruticosa | Shrubby Cinquefoil |
| Prunus glandulosa | Flowering Almond |
| Rhododendron macrantha hybrid | Macrantha Azalea |
| Santolina chamaecyparissus | Cypress Lavendercotton |
| Sarcococca hookeriana humilis | Small Himalaya Sarcococca |
| Skimmia japonica | Japanese Skimmia |
| Skimmia reevesiana | Reeves Skimmia |
| Spiraea bumalda Anthony Waterer | Anthony Waterer Spiraea |
| Symphoricarpos chenaulti | Chenault Coralberry |
| Taxus canadensis | Canada Yew |
| Teucrium chamaedrys | Germander |

Only two of the Dwarf Shrubs on the following chart are natives of the region: *Hypericum* and the dwarf variety of the Coastal Plain *Ilex vomitoria* species. None seems to be quite reliable throughout the Southeast although the *Aucuba*, the three *Ilex*, and *Jasminum nudiflorum* are almost so. *Ilex helleri* is locally successful throughout the Coastal Plain, but it is hardly at its best in the heat and in sandy soils. The *Ardisia*, *Gardenia*, and *Serissa* are rather limited to warmer sections, while the *Taxus* is confined largely to cooler settings. The *Gardenia*, *Rhododendron*, and *Skimmia* prefer acid soils, but the other materials are rather tolerant. The *Berberis*, *Buxus*, and *Cotoneaster* may be slightly better in alkaline soils.

*Ardisia crispa*, Coral Ardisia. One (or possibly more) species of Ardisia is commonly grown in the Coastal Plain in its warmer sections. This is probably *A. crispa* which may be listed also as *A. crenulata*. However, more work should be done on this genus to determine the possibilities of such other species as one listed by a certain nursery as *A. japonica* which is said to be hardy to Philadelphia. This is of some importance because the inclusion of the Ardisias among the "best" of this size class may be challenged on account of hardiness. On the basis of present knowledge, this plant can be rated as safe in the coastal strip as far north as Charleston, S. C. It has

## RANGE CHART FOR GROUP III. DWARF SHRUBS

### Ardisia crispa

| | Coastal Plain | | Piedmont | | Upper South | |
|---|---|---|---|---|---|---|
| Ardisia crispa | x x x | x x x | - - - | | | |
| Aucuba japonica nana | x x x | x x x | x x x | x x x | - - - | - - - |
| Berberis verruculosa | | - - - | - - - | x x x | x x x | x x x |
| Buxus harlandi | x x x | x x x | - - - | | | |
| Buxus microphylla koreana | | | | - - - | x x x | x x x |
| Buxus sempervirens suffruticosa | | - - - | x x x | x x x | x x x | x x x |
| Cotoneaster horizontalis | | - - - | - - - | x x x | x x x | x x x |
| Gardenia jasminoides radicans | x x x | x x x | - - - | - - - | | |
| Hypericum kalmianum | | - - - | x x x | x x x | x x x | x x x |
| Ilex cornuta rotunda | x x x | x x x | x x x | x x x | x x x | - - - |
| Ilex crenata helleri | - - - | x x x | x x x | x x x | x x x | x x x |
| Ilex vomitoria nana | x x x | x x x | x x x | x x x | - - - | |
| Jasminum floridum | x x x | x x x | x x x | x x x | - - - | |
| Jasminum nudiflorum | x x x | x x x | x x x | x x x | x x x | - - - |
| Juniperus sabina tamariscofolia | | - - - | x x x | x x x | x x x | x x x |
| Punica granatum nana | x x x | x x x | x x x | - - - | | |
| Raphiolepis indica | x x x | x x x | x x x | - - - | | |
| Rhododendron macrantha hybrid | x x x | x x x | x x x | x x x | - - - | |
| Rosa floribunda | | - - - | - - - | x x x | x x x | x x x |
| Ruscus aculeatus | x x x | x x x | x x x | x x x | - - - | |
| Sarcococca hookeriana humilis | | - - - | x x x | x x x | - - - | |
| Serissa foetida | x x x | x x x | - - - | - - - | | |
| Skimmia japonica | | - - - | x x x | x x x | - - - | |
| Taxus baccata repanda | | | | - - - | x x x | x x x |
| Taxus cuspidata nana | | | | - - - | x x x | x x x |
| Viburnum opulus nanum | | | | - - - | x x x | x x x |

been grown successfully through middle Georgia to Norfolk, Va., but the exceptional winter of 1951-52 wiped out most of these more northerly plantings. The Ardisia grows to a height of 18 to 24 inches in a rather loose upright form with coarse-textured, evergreen leaves about 3 inches long. It produces loose terminal heads of small white flowers in spring, followed in autumn by clusters of exceptionally colorful bright red fruits. This makes a good plant for shaded areas (it will not endure sun) both for color and for foliage contrast. It seeds itself readily, forming in time sizable clumps which, because of the loose form, are more attractive than single specimens. The Ardisia is commonly recommended for pot culture, making an effective ornament for porch, terrace, or patio garden.

*Aronia melanocarpa*, Black Chokeberry. This is a rather straggling open shrub up to 4 feet in height, sometimes spreading into large clump formations. The foliage is fairly thin, deciduous, of medium texture; there are white flowers in May followed by small black, cherry-like fruits in late summer. Although it will not be widely planted, this native of the eastern United States will have occasional use mostly in the Upper South for its free and graceful habit in naturalizing.

*Artemisia abrotanum,* Oldman Wormwood. This is a semi-evergreen with foliage of very fine feathery texture and gray-green color. The leaves are strongly scented, and the plant is one of the several Artemisias which have been grown in herb gardens for centuries. It is an excellent material for including in the sunny border or dooryard garden to provide mass, accent, and a foliage foil for flowers. It may be inferior to the Rosemary for this purpose but it is more hardy. This plant has no flowering effect and requires watchful pruning to maintain its shape and to prevent it from becoming leggy. It grows well in all soils in full sun exposure throughout the Upper South and the cooler Piedmont; it is not subject to insect and disease damage. It is an interesting and decorative plant for limited use.

*Aucuba japonica nana,* Dwarf Japanese Aucuba. The dwarf form of the Aucuba is one of the most reliable and best of this group for coarse foliage effect. Growing to a height of almost 4 feet, it acquires, with some pruning, a broadly oval, compact form which is admirable. The rather narrow, sharp pointed leaves are about 4 inches long, dull olive green in color. The well-known variegated "Gold Dust" foliage form of the larger Aucuba is also available in this size. The Dwarf Aucuba bears the inconspicuous purplish flowers and the showy scarlet berries characteristic of the species; but, in order to secure a display of these fruits, one must set both male and female plants in fairly close proximity for cross-pollination. The Aucuba is reliably hardy throughout the Coastal Plain and the Piedmont and is safe, with a protected location, in warmer parts of the Upper South to Knoxville and Richmond. It likes good soils, preferring clay subsoil, but endures drought, smoke, and neglect. It has no insect enemies. Since the evergreen foliage will scorch easily in sun, the plant must be located in shade. It should be pruned occasionally to maintain compact form.

*Berberis julianae nana,* Dwarf Wintergreen Barberry. *Berberis verruculosa,* Warty Barberry. The Barberries of this size class include several species of considerable value, none of which is very common in the region. Possibly the rarity is due to their thorny nature which makes them disagreeable to handle, but this characteristic adds to their favor for public projects of all kinds. One of the best of this group is the Warty Barberry which grows into a compact ball form of nearly 4 feet in height with small, fine-textured, glossy evergreen leaves, showy yellow flowers in May, and black fruits in autumn. The silver-white undersides of the leaves and of the older stems provide added ornamental value. Like others of the genus this grows best in full sun, in light, well-drained soils with adequate moisture. It is a good choice for alkaline soils. It is fine as a specimen or in either the clipped or unclipped hedge, calling for little care. It is well adapted to the Upper South and the Piedmont, and may be good in the upper Coastal Plain.

There is listed a dwarf form of the Wintergreen Barberry, *B. julianae nana,* which appears to be rare in the Southeast. The standard species is one of the most dependable evergreens of its size group for all parts of this section, suggesting that the variety, where available, might be an exceedingly valuable addition to the Dwarf Shrub class. Other Barberries which should be mentioned here are the Paleleaf Barberry, *B. candidula,* and the Dainty Barberry, *B. concinna,* both evergreen or nearly so. These are rare and should be tried further. There are also in this size class two dwarf varieties of the common Japanese Barberry, the deciduous species which is often used for hedges, valued for hardiness under all conditions. These are the Box Barberry, *B. thunbergi minor,* and the Dwarf Barberry, *B. t. compacta.*

*Buxus harlandi,* Harland's Box. *Buxus microphylla koreana,* Korean Box. *Buxus sempervirens suffruticosa,* Truedwarf Common Box. The Harland's Box is widely grown in the Coastal Plain as a clipped edging, and it is probably the best available material for this use here. Left to itself, it forms a dense, usually rather top-heavy, mound which may rarely slightly exceed the 4-feet limit of this class. It is tender but is sufficiently hardy and reliable for all but the coldest areas of the Coastal Plain, and may be grown with some winterburn as far north as Memphis. The leaf, of glossy bright green color, is easily differentiated from those of other Boxwoods by its larger size (about ¼ inch) and by its obovate, spatula-like shape. This is a material of refined character, requiring feeding, watering, trimming, and an occasional spraying to maintain it at its best. With care it is fast growing and is adaptable to both sunny and shaded areas.

The Korean Box is best known as the most hardy of the Boxwoods. It is also reliably dwarf, slow growing, remaining under 3 feet in height, taking on a rather loose and open rounded form. The evergreen leaves are very small, fine in texture, and glossy. Unlike most of this genus, Korean Box does not improve materially with clipping, and it is more attractive in its natural informal state employed as a specimen, in clumps, or in combination with other shrubs. It tolerates all well-drained good soils, sunny or partly shaded exposures, and requires little care. In the Upper South it will be one of the best of its class, but in the Piedmont and the Coastal Plain, its hardiness, paradoxically, is questionable. A sharp cold spell after a long warm autumn, catching it off balance, destroys it. A variety called *compacta* is said to remain under one foot in height.

Placing the Truedwarf, or as it is commonly called, the English Box, in this size class is arbitrary because it will grow in time somewhat over the limit of 4 feet. However, the growth is usually so slow that plants of this size may be half a century or more old. This is planted often as an edging material for flower gardens, remaining under a foot in height for many years. Larger specimens have innumerable uses as accents in foundation plantings, in flower gardens, and in other refined settings. The boxwood parterre, or pattern garden, was an inseparable part of the Southern residence in the 18th and early 19th centuries, carrying out the formal lines of the architecture and reflecting the aristocratic ideals of the period, while, at the same time, providing a carpet of year-round green before the house in a country where turf was not permanent. With an honorable tradition to support it, in addition to its intrinsic beauty, the Box is unchallenged in its first rank position in the Upper South and the Piedmont. However, it is not always easy to establish in the lower Piedmont and is not happy in the Coastal Plain. It will not endure excessive heat and drought nor the glare of summer sun, and it is likely to scald in winter where there is too much exposure to southern sun or to blasts of wind. Infestations of the cottony cushion scale are increasingly menacing, especially inasmuch as the cure depends upon the rather capricious behavior of the Vedalia beetles which must be imported, or on sprays of Parathion which are dangerous to handle. In some areas attacks of leaf miners and mites are only slightly less troublesome. When all these troubles are taken into account, however, one will still want to grow and to pamper his Boxwoods, and the chances are that they will do fairly well over a long time provided they are given a favorable location. They are tolerant of nearly all kinds of soils and do not require high fertility, but they must have good drainage. They like sun for at least part of the day through the summer, but in winter they should have protection from at least the morning sun and from severe exposure to wind. Their roots are shallow and so will not endure cultivation. They enjoy a mulch. Feeding should be done frugally and only with slow-acting organic materials in spring and early summer. Watering through long hot spells may be necessary, especially syringing, but this should not continue into fall when new growth should be hardening off. It is said that cleaning out accumulations of dead leaves and branchlets in the centers of old plants is beneficial. Where the preceding conditions can be met, these plants can be counted on to perform with even less care than might be expected, giving a permanence and an elegance of effect unmatched in any other material.

*Calluna vulgaris,* Scotch Heather. Occasionally one encounters in gardens and nurseries of this region one or another of the heathers or heaths (*Erica*) of which there are many varieties. These are useful chiefly as specimens or in clumps in rock gardens although, in places where they grow really well, they make excellent ground-covers. Unfortunately growing conditions here are not generally favorable for them since they like high humidity combined with sharp drainage, moderate temperatures, and full exposure to sunlight which the extremes of this climate do not provide. Generally they need pruning after flowering and some light shade in winter. With care, however, they can be grown successfully in parts of the Piedmont and the Upper South on acid soils of low fertility. Their fine textured needle-like evergreen foliage, their scrambling habit of growth, and their interesting summer flowers of rose or white make them highly desirable for rare occasions. A collection of these interesting plants is growing fairly well in the National Arboretum in Washington, D. C. It is said that approximately 30 varieties of *Calluna* and 10 varieties of *Erica* are available in American nurseries. Conditions for growing them should be good in the mountains of the Upper South where they would make an interesting and instructive collection for the hobbyist.

*Caryopteris clandonensis*, Bluebeard. This is a rather weedy looking shrub which is planted mostly in flower gardens for its grayish foliage and its deep blue flowers in small flat clusters which appear over a rather long period in late summer. The plant may reach to 4 feet, but it is better restrained to less than this by cutting it back each spring almost to the ground. It has little substance, but it is nice for cutting and is a good trouble-free grower in hot dry seasons.

*Ceanothus americanus*, Jerseytea Ceanothus. A native shrub of dry, sunny hillsides, this is commonly called the Jersey Tea because its leaves were substituted for tea in colonial times. This low, 3-foot, rather straggling shrub has light green deciduous foliage, medium in texture, and attractive white flower clusters in midsummer. It is a good material for naturalizing, tolerant of poor growing conditions, but it is not an outstanding ornamental for usual garden conditions. Its range is confined to the Upper South and cooler parts of the Piedmont.

*Chaenomeles japonica*, Japanese Floweringquince. Most of the Flowering Quinces so common in gardens belong to a larger size class, but this species grows not over 3 feet in height. It is attractive for its light orange flowers in early spring, and for its apple-like yellow fruits of autumn. However, its very open and irregular-spreading growth habit and its deciduous foliage which is likely to shed in late summer make it of slight value. It stands poor soils, drought, and exposure throughout all of the Southeast except the lower Coastal Plain.

*Cotoneaster horizontalis,* Rock Cotoneaster. *Cotoneaster microphylla,* Rockspray Cotoneaster. The Cotoneaster genus is represented in this size class by its most widely known species, the Rock Cotoneaster. This has long been a favorite because of its positive horizontal branching habit reaching a height of 2 to 3 feet, draping and rambling over rockeries and rough ground in a unique and graceful manner. The tiny glossy, close-ranked leaves are deciduous, although sometimes fairly persistent, with a fine texture effect. There are small pinkish flowers in spring and showy red berries in fall to increase its interest. The Cotoneasters can suffer from fire blight and from the foliage-marring depredations of red spider mites and lacewing flies. Much as this species is planted, however, these troubles do not seem too difficult, and the plant makes an excellent specimen where its rangy character suits. With some shearing it can be a fairly good groundcover. It likes sunny exposures, is tolerant as to soils, endures starvation, drought, and wind, and can be suggested for all of the Upper South as well as for the cooler parts of the Piedmont.

The Rockspray Cotoneaster is a somewhat more tender evergreen species growing to 3 feet in height with a broad spread, very small glossy leaves, white flowers, and red fruits. This needs further trial, but it may be successful for covering rough ground in the Piedmont and parts of the Upper South.

*Danae racemosa,* Alexandrialaurel. This is an unusual member of the Lily Family which is quite rare in the region but certainly worth a serious trial. It is an old plant of the Mediterranean world, said to have been used by the Greeks for crowning their poets. It was introduced into this country in colonial times. The foliage is evergreen, of fine to medium texture, on gracefully arching unbranched stems arising directly from the ground to a height of about 3 feet. For a brief time in autumn it bears orange-red fruits about the size of a cherry; the flowers are not showy. This plant requires good soils, humus, moisture, and a shaded location. It should be well suited to the Coastal Plain and the Piedmont, valuable in small city gardens and in shaded borders. It is not available in many of the local nurseries, a strong point against its wider use.

*Daphne cneorum,* Rose Daphne. *Daphne odora,* Winter Daphne. The Winter Daphne is a great favorite in the Deep South for its exquisitely fragrant flowers of February and March. It is also an appealing shrub, growing very slowly to a height of about 4 feet in a broadly oval, somewhat loose form. The leaves are narrow, oval in shape, from 2 to 3 inches long, giving a medium to coarse texture effect. They are normally dark green in color, but there is a common variegated form in which the leaves are edged in white. The flowers, coming in early spring, occur in clusters on the ends of the twigs;

they are colored white or rosy purple, not particularly showy, but are valued highly for their powerful perfume. This plant is adaptable throughout the Coastal Plain and the Piedmont, and it will go into warmer parts of the Upper South as far as Asheville. It is a lover of shade and needs adequate moisture with good drainage, but it does not respond to feeding or cultivation. It is probably suited to either acid or alkaline conditions. Despite its charm, this is not recommended for general use because it is difficult to establish, apparently no amount of pampering being of any help, and the experience of many good gardeners has failed to reveal a formula for successful culture.

Gardeners of the Upper South may take pleasure in the charming dwarf Rose Daphne, *D. cneorum*, a shy evergreen with fine foliage growing to a height of almost a foot with delightfully fragrant pink flowers in late spring. This, however, is also an unpredictable grower. It likes sun, good drainage, adequate moisture, and does not seem to mind exposure and poor soils. It is said to like lime, but lime does not appear to be essential to success. If one can find a spot which it likes, it will live on without care for years; but often as not, no amount of care suffices to habituate the plant to a new environment.

*Erica* species, Heath (see *Calluna*).

*Gardenia jasminoides radicans*, Dwarf Gardenia. For generations the Gardenias or Capejasmines have been popular and in general favorites in Southern gardens; but in recent years they have fallen into second place because of liability to nematode attacks and difficulty in controlling infestations of the white fly and the sooty mold which together disfigure the foliage and sap the vitality of the plants. However, the Dwarf Gardenia is still one of the best of the dwarf shrubs for the Coastal Plain, and it is a fine subject for pot culture in other sections. Growing to a height of 1 to 3 feet, it has an interesting, picturesque, horizontal branching habit, and occasionally strong lateral branches will droop to the ground and root of themselves. The foliage is dark green and glossy on healthy plants, fine in texture value. The small white flowers, known everywhere for their typical fragrance, are borne intermittently through the summer after a good June show. This dwarf form of the Gardenia is not as hardy as the standard bush form, but it is dependable through the Coastal Plain. As suggested above, the chief handicap in growing this plant is its attractiveness to the white fly which, after sucking the juices of the foliage, leaves a sweet excrement that makes a good growing medium for the sooty mold which may completely cover the leaves, choking the breathing pores and killing them. Infestations of the insect are particularly hard to control in congested city areas.

Therefore this shrub is recommended chiefly for open spaces. It likes sun, but it does well under the high light shade of Pines, well removed from other plants such as the Privets, which also attract the white fly. Of course, one can grow Gardenias almost anywhere if one is willing to pay the price of spraying. This variety, at least, is almost worth the trouble since materials of this size are scarce. Another dwarf form of the Gardenia, called *G. stricta nana*, is said to be more hardy than the above, and it may be worth a trial in both the Coastal Plain and the Piedmont.

*Heteropteris argentea*, Heteropteris (Red Wing). This is a comparatively new shrub in much of the Coastal Plain, but it could have wider use here and in the Piedmont. It is somewhat vine-like in habit, low and sprawling, with deciduous foliage and winged seeds, both of which are tinged with red. The plant is hardy for these regions. It likes a sunny or only lightly shaded site. Were it evergreen, it might make a good groundcover. As it is, it will be useful chiefly as a cutting material or as a spot of colored foliage interest in borders and foundation plantings.

*Hypericum kalmianum*, Kalm St. Johnswort. *Hypericum moserianum*, Goldflower St. Johnswort. *Hypericum patulum henryi*, Henry St. Johnswort. Several of the St. Johnsworts are either native to or well suited to this region, and they are, as a genus, valuable because of their showy yellow flowers of midsummer which are effective in masses and with Hemerocallis. As a group they like sun, stand drought, exposure, and less fertile soils, and are free of pests. The only care which they require is an annual pruning to thin out old wood. They are well suited to the Upper South and the Piedmont but are not recommended for warmer sections of the Coastal Plain.

Of these, the Kalm St. Johnswort is possibly the choice one. This is a native of the Northeastern U. S., growing to a height of 3 feet in a loose, rounded form, with attractive gray-green, fine-textured deciduous foliage. The flowers are not large, but they are numerous and showy in late summer. The Golden St. Johnswort, *H. frondosum*, a native of the Southern Piedmont, is similar to this in character with excellent flowering effect and might well be selected in preference to the above except that it is not available in the nurseries of the area.

The Henry St. Johnswort is a good form, often praised for its larger, 2-inch flowers of June and its coarser, almost evergreen foliage. This bush does not have quite the character of the above and is not as hardy, although it renews itself quickly even if it is frozen to the ground. This might be called a more gardenesque form; with it would be classed the Goldflower St. Johnswort, a hybrid, which is distinguished by its very large buttercup-like flowers produced in a long succession throughout the summer. An improved form of the latter is called "Hidcote Beauty." This is dwarf, squatty in habit, adaptable to use as a groundcover. For this purpose it is, however, inferior to the Aaronsbeard mentioned in Group II since it remains clumpy and does not make a solid cover.

*Iberis sempervirens*, Evergreen Candytuft. This is a favorite material for the flower garden for its brilliant display of white flowers in early spring and its fine-textured evergreen foliage good throughout the year for edging and as a foil for other flowers. Growing to a height of 6 inches and spreading into clumps, Candytuft might be used as a groundcover. However, it is not well suited for this purpose because it is not entirely dependable, a plant dying here and there for no apparent reason, and it should have the care of a shearing each spring after blooming. It thrives in any good soils in sun in the Upper South and in the cooler Piedmont, but in warmer sections it is almost an annual and is replanted extensively each year in flower borders for its spring display. When once established, it becomes a rewarding long-lasting dwarf shrub requiring little attention.

*Ilex cornuta rotunda*, Dwarf Chinese Holly. *Ilex crenata helleri*, Heller Japanese Holly. *Ilex vomitoria nana*, Dwarf Yaupon Holly. The Dwarf Chinese Holly is a recent introduction but it is now widely planted, and it is known as one of the most dependable of this size class for the Coastal Plain, the Piedmont, and the warmest parts of the Upper South. Its evergreen foliage is rather coarse in texture, spiney, light green in color, and glossy. Its habit is compact and symmetrically rounded, making a small formal cushion without any pruning. It grows well in sun or light shade in any soil and without care, and so is a first-class selection in warm sections for accents, for foundation planting, for the clipped or unclipped hedge, or for any place its rather formal character may suit. It is questionable whether this form will produce fruits.

Many horticultural varieties of the Japanese Holly have become important in landscape work in recent years, and the Heller is one of the older ones in this size class growing to about 2 feet in height, spreading with age to twice that much. Like others of the species, Heller is not distinguished for its tiny white flowers which are borne along the stems in April, nor for its black berry-like fruits of fall and winter. Its small evergreen foliage and its dwarf, compact spreading form are, however, very good. The plant makes an excellent substitute for the Dwarf Box and is superior to the latter in its freedom from scale and leaf miners. Its use may be limited somewhat, however, because it is slow in its growth, difficult to transplant successfully, very brittle to handle, and is hardly more successful in the hot summers and sandy soils of the lower Coastal Plain than is the Box. Its use is advised for cooler sections of the Southeast in areas of any good soil (it requires fertility) and adequate moisture. Where it does well, this plant is something of a gem of its class for border edgings and accents.

More recently several dwarf Japanese Holly varieties have been introduced which are generally superior to the Heller in color and form. The Stokes Holly is a fine patented form (No. 887) originated near Pittsburgh, Pennsylvania. Still others are Green Cushion, Green Island, Kingsville, *microphylla*, and *nummularia*. Because seedlings are quite variable one may expect newer introductions to appear from time to time with varying qualifications. One of these is *I. c. procumbens*, a sort of weeping or spreading type, which is interesting for its informal scrambling growth although its habit of thinning out at the center is somewhat objectionable.

The Dwarf Yaupon, with the Dwarf Chinese Holly, will prove the best of this group for planting in the Coastal Plain and the warmer Piedmont. In contrast to the Dwarf Chinese, however, the Dwarf Yaupon has a fine texture together with its dense, rather formal and symmetrical habit of growth. The Yaupon is native to this section, free from pests, and thus can be used with some confidence in any soil or exposure, even along the seacoast. It probably can be planted in the Upper South as far north as Nashville, Tenn., and Lexington, Ky.

*Jasminum floridum*, Flowering Jasmine. *Jasminum nudiflorum*, Winter Jasmine. Both of these are tough, reliable Dwarf Shrubs for the Coastal Plain and the Piedmont, hardy in the Upper South as far as Knoxville. Their habit of growth can be described best as fountain-like and informal with many stems rising from the crown and arching back to touch the soil and root again. Normally they reach about 4 feet in height with a broad spread; the stems can be trained against walls or trellises, vine-like, in which case they can attain a height of 8 feet or so. The foliage is fine and delicate in texture, almost evergreen. The leaves fall in early spring, but even then the effect of greenness is prolonged by the color of the stems. The two are distinguished in their flowering. The Winter Jasmine blooms in January or early February, its solitary flowers coming out along the stems very much like those of the Forsythia. It makes a good show in the garden, and is excellent for forcing in the house. The Showy Jasmine blooms in May, with tiny fragrant yellow flowers appearing in clusters. Both of these are good as informal specimens, as vines, in unclipped hedges or borders, or in mass as large scale groundcovers for holding banks. They are free from pests, tolerant of almost any soil and of drought, and do well with very little care in almost any sunny exposure.

*Juniperus sabina tamariscifolia*, Tamarix Savin Juniper. This is an excellent selection for very exposed locations in the Upper South. Like the Junipers in the groundcover class, the poorer, drier, sunnier, and more windy the site, the more effective this hardy plant will be. It also is valuable for its adaptability to either limestone or acid soils. This Juniper grows to a height of 2 to 3 feet with a strong horizontal branching habit and a form which is irregular, informal, picturesque, and widespreading. The needle-like evergreen foliage is bluish green in color. This is a good material for rockeries, irregular ground, and informal arrangements either as a specimen or as a large groundcover. Like the other Junipers, this can be damaged badly by red spider mites, but these pests are not often serious when the plant is set in an exposed site.

*Lavandula officinalis*, True Lavender. One of the loveliest shrubs of this size group, True Lavender is adapted to the Upper South and to cooler parts of the Piedmont where it can be given a neutral to alkaline soil, sunshine, and good drainage. It has a somewhat irregular but compact growth, rarely reaching 3 feet, gray, evergreen, fragrant fine-textured foliage, and midsummer spikes of fragrant flowers. Having been grown for perfume since early times, the plant has many associations. Its quality does not lend itself well to common use, but it is choice in gardenesque surroundings for bordering or as a specimen, and it is essential in the herb garden. Plants set a foot apart and clipped in early spring and again after flowering make an excellent low hedge. Where conditions are to its liking, this plant requires very little care.

*Malpighia coccigera*, Holly Malpighia. This is widely grown in warmer sections of the Coastal Plain as a dwarf shrub, 2 to 3 feet in height. Its evergreen leaves, rather like those of the American Holly in miniature, scattered over a delicate twig structure give this plant an unusually dainty appeal for detail interest. In spring lacy pinkish flowers are also scattered and, later, red fruits appear. The plant apparently likes moisture and partial shade; because it is quite tender, it is perhaps best used in the small patio which provides a sheltered location. The plant is sometimes confused in some offerings with *M. glabra*, the Barbados Cherry, which grows to 10 feet in height and has entire leaves.

*Myrica pumila*, Dwarf Waxmyrtle. The Dwarf Waxmyrtle, about 3 feet in height, is said to be native to the Pine barrens of north Florida. This plant does not appear to be grown in either the nurseries or the gardens of this region. It is mentioned here because, considering the valuable qualities of the common Southern Waxmyrtle (*M. cerifera*) for landscape work, it seems quite possible that the gardening world is missing a very good thing in neglecting this smaller form. Should it become available, it might well be ranked with the very best evergreens of this size class for naturalizing, ground covering, and for borders in the Coastal Plain and the lower Piedmont.

*Myrtus communis compacta*, Compact True Myrtle. The dwarf form of the True Myrtle is about the most handsome available plant for edgings and small specimen use in hot, dry, exposed sites on the Coastal Plain and mild sections of the Piedmont. But it is also considered difficult to maintain and rather unreliable here. Growing to a height of about 3 feet, this plant has a compact rounded habit of growth and takes shearing well. The closely-spaced, tiny, glossy evergreen leaves are attractive to look at and are aromatic. The small white flowers and the black berry-like fruits are not particularly ornamental. The Myrtle is a native of the Mediterranean area, and it is somewhat tender. As it also resents transplanting, the person buying new plants should try to secure them in cans or pots. This shrub seems to enjoy exposure to the full heat of the sun, and perhaps it likes a more alkaline soil than one usually finds in this region.

*Pachistima canbyi*, Canby Pachistima. This comes from the mountains of Virginia and West Virginia, and this range gives a clue to its area of usefulness. It is better in cool sections farther north than it is in most of the Southeast. It is a desirable shrub of low growth (1 foot), beautiful evergreen foliage of medium texture, and a dense, spreading habit of growth. For acid soils in partial shade, it is useful in informal clumps and, occasionally, as a groundcover in situations in which it grows well.

*Physocarpus monogynus*, Mountain Ninebark. The Ninebarks are natives of stream banks of the north central states. This species is quite a dependable deciduous shrub of about 4 feet in height with foliage of medium to fine texture and small flat heads of white flowers in early summer. This is a plant of no character, and one would use it only where nothing else more interesting could be used. Yet it is a dependable, pest-free, easily grown material for a temporary filler, for "facing down" borders, and for massing in partially shaded areas.

*Potentilla fruticosa*, Shrubby Cinquefoil. Although this plant is found often in native stands in swamps of the north central states, it also succeeds in high, dry sites. It is probably better grown in the most sunny and exposed positions in poor soils in cooler parts of the Upper South. Not a material of wide usefulness, this shrub is interesting, however, for its often picturesque branch forms, its small five-parted leaves, and its yellow or white flowers appearing in almost continuous succession from spring to fall. The Cinquefoil has been employed extensively in hybridizing in England where it is very popular, but it is not widely available in the nursery trade in this country.

*Prunus glandulosa,* Flowering Almond. For spring effect in combination with early bulbs and Wistarias, the Flowering Almond has a proper place in the flower or cutting garden. At this season the 3- to 4-foot plants, still bare of leaves, are clothed in bright, double, white or pink flowers which make a lovely show. Except for this one season, however, the shrub has little to offer. It is hardy, equally adaptable from the lower Coastal Plain throughout the Upper South, and easily grown in any sunny spot. On the other hand, it is often damaged by borers, and its deciduous foliage and rather shapeless habit are undistinguished.

*Punica granatum nana,* Dwarf Pomegranate. Pomegranates have been familiar subjects in the gardens and literature and art of Mediterranean and Near Eastern countries for centuries. They probably were introduced into America in early colonial times. The dwarf form makes a valuable addition to this size group because it enables anyone, even though his garden may be the tiniest, to grow this celebrated plant. It makes a low, mounded, rather formal and compact growth to about 3 feet, with narrow, oval, deciduous leaves of medium texture. It is distinguished by its flaming orange-red flowers of summer and by its decorative, many-seeded fruits maturing in the fall and winter. The Pomegranate also is a most dependable, pest-free plant, tolerant of either sand or clay, acid or alkaline soil, sea salt, and full exposure to sun throughout the Coastal Plain and warmer parts of the Piedmont. It is a good suggestion for the low unclipped hedge and would make a fine specimen in the small herb garden, or even in the flower border, if the color could be harmonized with that of other materials.

*Raphiolepis indica,* India Raphiolepis. This is a broad-spreading, slow-growing shrub which does not often exceed 4 feet in height and which may be treated as one of the dwarf shrubs. Foliage, habit of growth, and flowers all are fine qualities in this plant. The evergreen leaves are thick and leathery, dark in color but taking on a purplish cast in winter in open sites. The texture is medium to coarse. The stems of the plant are likely to be few, becoming with age rather like trunks of a miniature tree which twist, turn, spread, and recline back to the ground in a picturesque way. Clusters of attractive white or pink flowers appear in April, and these are succeeded in autumn by black fruits. The Raphiolepis is fairly common in gardens along the seacoast where it seems to be ideally suited to take exposure to sun, wind, and salt spray in poor sandy soils. There is no reason why it cannot be planted more generally in other portions of this region. It is sufficiently hardy, having stood normal winters as far north as Atlanta, and it seems to adapt itself to dry sunny places, tolerating partial shade. It should be placed always with consideration for its natural character which is rugged, irregular, and somewhat dramatic and open. In the wrong setting, old specimens of the plant may appear simply shaggy, worn out, and a little forlorn. The pink form, *R. i. rosea*, is recommended for a somewhat more compact habit of growth, smaller foliage, and more intense flower color. It is said to be also more vigorous and generally more attractive, possibly reaching slightly over the 4-foot limit of this size class. The Raphiolepis are subject to root knot nematodes and can suffer from scales and, occasionally, from blight.

*Rhododendron atlanticum*, Coast Azalea. *Rhododendron chapmani*, Chapman Rhododendron. *Rhododendron* species "macrantha hybrids," Macrantha Azalea. The first two representatives of this group are natives which may have been neglected to an unfortunate degree. The haunts of the Coast Azalea are described as the coastal area from Delaware to South Carolina, but it does not seem to be grown in either the gardens or the nurseries of the region. The plant is open, more or less prostrate and stoloniferous in habit, reaching about 2 feet in height. The foliage is deciduous, and the fragrant white to pinkish flowers appear in spring before the new leaves. Most of the native Azaleas are very beautiful and graceful in flower, but, during much of the remainder of the year, they are not sufficiently appealing to demand widespread propagation. Still, they do have a place, and this little species should be no exception. Even though it may reach slightly over 4 feet in height, the Chapman Rhododendron, a true Rhododendron with evergreen foliage found in Pine woodlands of the upper Coastal Plain and the Piedmont, also should be mentioned. It bears in April rather attractive rose-colored flowers. This plant can hardly rival in color the effect of other members of this genus, but it could be an interesting subject for naturalizing if means can be found to collect it from native stands, for it is not commercially available.

The so-called "Macrantha hybrid" Azaleas are relative newcomers in this favorite genus, and they represent an appealing addition with their dwarf, compact, and picturesque habit of growth. The flowers are not outstanding. They come late in the season and are sparse in number as a general rule. Paradoxically, the plant may be said to be almost more attractive without bloom. In spite of this disappointment, this hybrid appears to be one of the best materials of its size class for general landscape use because of its foliage and form, which are as good as those of the Dwarf Japanese Hollies, for example. The growth is very slow, probably not reaching much over 2 feet in height, with a broad spread. The evergreen leaves are small and dense on the rather ruggedly horizontal branches, and retain their greenness through the winter better than most Azaleas. This plant is reliably hardy throughout the Coastal Plain, the Piedmont, and into warmer parts of the Upper South. Like others of its genus, it likes light soils, humus, acid plant food, and a lightly shaded situation. It may need some spraying. This is an attractive little subject for massing, for foundation plantings, and for a diminutive spot of interest in a terrace garden.

*Rosa floribunda*, Floribunda Rose. Most discussions of trees and shrubs do not include mention of the Floribunda Rose. There seems to be little reason for this omission except the tradition that Roses should always be grown in separate Rose Gardens. However, this tradition has been largely broken in recent years since the emphasis on the Floribundas has shown how excellent they may be, treated as color accents among other shrubs in foundation plantings, in borders, and in many other places where Roses have not been used heretofore. Most of these plants grow to a height of 3 to 4 feet, but there are several more vigorous varieties, such as Betty Prior, which may reach 5 feet or so quite easily. The habit of growth tends to be rather open and the foliage is likely to be sparse where there is blackspot disease—which is almost everywhere. The leaves generally fall some-time during the winter, although in the lower South many varieties retain them until quite late. Like all Roses, the Floribundas do require good soil preparation, pruning, feeding, and fairly steady spraying to do their best, but thousands of gardeners feel that these extra pains are worthwhile in terms of the continued summer floral display. Several members of this class have been among the All-America Rose Selections in recent years: "Jiminy Cricket" (1955) tangerine; "Lili-bet" (1954) dawn pink; "Ma Perkins" (1953) varicolored; "Vogue" (1952) cherry red; "Fashion" (1950) coral pink; and "World's Fair" (1940) red. "Floradora," with orange-pink blossoms, is recommended because the flowers look fresh in the heat of the sun longer than those of most other varieties; but the color is somewhat difficult to harmonize with others. These could serve as a starting collection to which many other tried varieties might be added. In general, roses belong in areas of gardenesque character, and the care they need will limit their usefulness. In the Coastal Plain they will perform more satisfactorily if they receive light shade such as that from high Pines or from buildings, but they should not be located where air circulation is poor. In the cooler parts of the Upper South they are at their best in open sunny exposures.

*Ruscus aculeatus*, Butchersbroom. Sprays of dried Butchersbroom, dyed bright red or green, used to be common in the florists' shops at Christmas time, but the plant is not as well known in southern gardens as it should be. It belongs, curiously enough, to the Lily Family, and it grows somewhat in the manner of the closely-related Asparagus, sending up its shoots directly from the ground in gradually expanding clumps. In height it reaches 3 or 4 feet. The leaves, which are not true leaves but are called "cladodes" by the botanists, are evergreen, dull olive in color, small, and sharp-pointed. The total landscape effect of the plant is rugged, bristly, and rather coarse. Inconspicuous flowers are followed by red berries which are effective, but the setting of fruit is rather unreliable even when one secures both the male and female plants. Although the *Ruscus* is a litttle forbidding and spiney for close quarters, it is hard to understand why it is so rare in southern nurseries. The plant has been known for a long time; it is perfectly hardy throughout the Coastal Plain and well into the Piedmont; it is easy to grow, pest-free, and tolerant of a wide variety of soils, drought, and neglect in shade or sun. It is fine for city gardens, needing no care but a spring thinning of older shoots. It should make an excellent material for borders or unclipped hedges and for massing in areas of rugged character.

*Salvia greggi*, Autumn Sage. A native of Texas, Autumn Sage is valued for its autumnal spikes of red flowers and its ability to stand up in the heat, drought, and intense sunshine of the southern summer. It forms a somewhat leggy, insubstantial plant with grayish, medium-textured, deciduous foliage. It is easy to grow and free of problems except the minor one of an occasional pruning. While it cannot be considered absolutely first-rate, it has occasional use in the flower garden as a color note for the Coastal Plain and the Piedmont.

*Santolina chamaecyparissus*, Cypress Lavendercotton. This too has long been cultivated in gardens of the South as a dwarf subject for the herb or flower garden, edging, or rockery. Reaching to just over a foot in height, the plant makes a clumpy spreading growth with aromatic, fine-textured, silver-gray foliage that is evergreen, effective throughout the year. It bears showy clusters of button-like, yellow flowers in midsummer. A green foliage form, *S. c. virens*, is also available. In the Piedmont, the upper Coastal Plain, and the warmer Upper South as far as Knoxville these plants are excellent for well-drained, dry, sun-drenched sites in poor soils as edgings and in masses. They are sometimes suggested as groundcovers, but this is a doubtful practice since they are not permanent, are somewhat un-reliable, and do need shearing to keep them in good condition.

*Sarcococca hookeriana humilis*, Small Himalaya Sarcococca. This has not been planted widely in southern gardens and so its range of usefulness is not fully defined. Tests show that it is excellent in the Piedmont, and it is successful in Washington, D. C. It should be equally useful in most of the Coastal Plain, but it has not been deter-mined how far into the Upper South it would be hardy. Probably it would go easily to Knoxville, and it is said to be hardy to Connecticut. The plant is attractive for its rich dark evergreen foliage of medium texture and its loose informal habit of growth to about 2 feet in height. It requires a well-shaded site and a soil which may be either acid or alkaline but rich in humus. The small white flowers and the black fruits are of no consequence. This is effective in clumps as a foil for other plants, and it could make a good informal border or a fair groundcover.

*Serissa foetida*, Serissa. This is a low-growing shrub with tiny evergreen foliage and delicate habit of growth which is handsome in masses in sunny places in the warmer sections of this region. The small white flowers are borne over a long period in fall and early winter, making a good show, for instance, in combination with white Sasanqua Camellias. The species has green leaves, but there is also an attractive variegated type with leaves edged in yellow. The plant is probably hardy as far north as Asheville with shelter, but it is better used on the Coastal Plain and in the lower Piedmont. It apparently likes the sandy coastal soils, but is tolerant and has few pests. It should be sheared once or twice a year for best appearance. Planted 12 to 18 inches apart and clipped, it makes a satisfactory groundcover.

*Skimmia japonica*, Japanese Skimmia. *Skimmia reevesiana*, Reeves Skimmia. The Japanese Skimmia is a desirable evergreen, growing to almost 4 feet with a loose habit and coarse-textured rich foliage. It produces attractive white flowers in clusters at the ends of the branches in late spring, and these are followed by red berries in autumn. The sexes are separate in this species, and both males and females must be acquired to insure fruiting. The plant is quite hardy through the Piedmont to Washington, and Wyman rates it as safe to Knoxville. Its performance in warmer parts of the Coastal Plain should be tested. The plant likes shade, moisture, and humus, but it does not seem to have strong soil reaction preference or to be molested by pests. It is said to adapt well to small city gardens.

The Reeves Skimmia, lower growing and finer in texture, is said to be more desirable than the above because both male and female flowers are borne on the same plant, and so a showing of the bright fruits is always assured. This species is sometimes available as a pot specimen at Christmas time from florists' shops, making a colorful ornament. Neither of these species is widely grown or available in the nurseries of the area, and both, although apparently well adapted to the soils and climate of the Piedmont, need further testing here. In the Upper South they probably reach the limit of their cold resistance.

*Spiraea bumalda Anthony Waterer*, Anthony Waterer Spiraea. This is mentioned here because it is a popular deciduous shrub of this size category, easily grown and pest-free in almost any soil or exposure throughout the Southeast, producing showy heads of magenta blooms over a long period in midsummer. The plant has no character, however, and its flower color is disagreeable for all but very few places. It should be planted rarely and only with caution.

*Symphoricarpos chenaulti,* Chenault Coralberry. The native species of Coralberry, *S. orbiculatus,* has been employed in areas of alkaline soils in the Upper South as a bank cover, but it is quite weedy and can become a nuisance. The better form is the Chenault hybrid which is usually of rather open habit, spreading by suckers to make clumps of some size, about 3 feet in height, with deciduous foliage of fine texture, rather inconspicuous flowers, and showy coral-red fruits in late summer. This plant is occasionally very good for massing and for bank covering, enduring all kinds of soils in sun or partial shade, requiring no care except for occasional removal of old wood to keep it in neat condition.

*Taxus baccata repanda,* Spreading English Yew. *Taxus canadensis,* Canada Yew. *Taxus cuspidata nana,* Dwarf Japanese Yew. In cooler parts of the Southeast two Yews at least are among the first rank of materials in this class for use as specimens, hedges or borders, or in mass plantings. The Spreading English Yew may be somewhat the less hardy of the two, but it should prove entirely reliable throughout the Upper South except for its higher exposed sites; and when it has shade, it is the better for warmer sections and the Piedmont as far south as Washington, Atlanta, and Memphis. Of dark green color and compact habit, this plant makes a fine clipped edging or trimmed specimen. Left to itself, it shows a somewhat weeping habit, and it spreads outward in an irregular mounding picturesque form, attractive in informal clumps and masses.

Of the Japanese Yew there are several dwarf varieties which may have mixed names in the nurseries. These include the Dwarf variety listed above, the Cushion Japanese Yew, *T. c. densa,* the Pygmy Yew, *T. c. minima,* or the now discarded name, *T. c. brevifolia.* These are generally fine for the same design functions as the above. They have excellent dark evergreen color. The natural form is compact with a more upright branching character and a clumpy effect rather like that of the Dwarf Box. Being very slow growing, these plants are expensive to buy, but they are among the best for long-term beauty, well suited to both heavy and light soils of acid or alkaline character in sun or shade in cool climates. In most of the Upper South they must be planted in cool, partial shade. They are quite drought and smoke tolerant. They may be said to have no pests as a general rule, but occasionally old plants are attacked by an insect called the Black Vine Weevil which eats at the roots. A DDT spray on the soil about the plants is said to be effective for control, or Chlordane or Dieldrin may be dusted on the soil and watered in.

Mention should also be made of the Canada Yew. This is a native of woodlands from Canada to Virginia and Iowa. This hardy species prefers cool shade, ample moisture, and a rooting medium rich in humus although it is found frequently in rocky places where soil is very thin. It is open, sometimes straggling in form, graceful and informal, with a broad-spreading, creeping habit of growth. Excellent for natural woodsy plantings, the Canada Yew is attractive also for its bright red fruits borne on female plants in fall. This plant can reach to 6 feet in height but it is usually more like a groundcover; there is a dwarf variety called *T. c. stricta* remaining under 2 feet.

*Teucrium chamaedrys*, Germander. This dwarf, not exceeding a foot in height, is often seen in herb gardens. The evergreen foliage is grayish in color, of fine texture, and dense; in midsummer showy spikes of rose-purple flowers are displayed over a period of several weeks. Hardy and thriving in the Upper South and the cooler Piedmont in full sun on well-drained neutral soils, Germander forms irregular spreading clumps and submits to clipping in a dwarf edging very nicely. It could possibly be employed for groundcovering — it should be sheared annually after flowering — but it is not entirely dependable for this purpose.

*Vaccinium crassifolium*, Creeping Blueberry. *Vaccinium myrsinites*, Ground Blueberry. These occur in sandy woodlands of the Coastal Plain, and they sometimes form groundcovers of considerable beauty. However, these wildlings do not seem to adapt easily to cultivation. Therefore they can be of little importance, in all probability, until the secret of growing them is more widely known and they become generally available to gardeners. Where one wants naturalistic effects, it is possible that the Blueberries can be collected, but this is often slow and only partially satisfactory in results.

*Viburnum opulus nanum*, Dwarf European Cranberrybush. This is a good material for its rounded, compact, definite form which makes it useful as a specimen or in an edging, hardly over 2 feet in height or spread. The foliage is fairly coarse for a diminutive plant, deciduous, yellow-green in color, turning red in autumn. There are rarely, if at all, any flowers or fruits. This plant is hardy through the Upper South, but it is not very vigorous in the Piedmont and warmer regions. It is adaptable to all soils, endures harsh exposures, and prefers sunny or lightly shaded sites. Since it has no insect or disease pests and requires no care, it is adaptable to many uses.

# IV. Small Shrubs for the SOUTHERN COASTAL PLAIN

*Botanical Name*                                    *Common Name*

### RECOMMENDED FOR GENERAL USE

| Botanical Name | Common Name |
| --- | --- |
| Berberis julianae | Wintergreen Barberry |
| Buxus microphylla japonica | Japanese Littleleaf Box |
| Cycas revoluta | Sago Cycas |
| Fatshedera lizei | Fatshedera |
| Jasminum mesnyi | Primrose Jasmine |
| Mahonia bealei | Leatherleaf Mahonia |
| Raphiolepis umbellata | Yeddo Raphiolepis |
| Rhododendron obtusum japonicum | Kurume Azalea |
| Rosa chinensis Louis Philippe | Louis Philippe Rose |
| Viburnum japonicum | Japanese Viburnum |
| Viburnum suspensum | Sandankwa Viburnum |
| Yucca gloriosa | Moundlily Yucca |

### RECOMMENDED FOR RESTRICTED USE

| Botanical Name | Common Name |
| --- | --- |
| Buxus sempervirens | Common Box |
| Deutzia gracilis | Slender Deutzia |
| Fatsia japonica | Japan Fatsia |
| Fortunella japonica | Marumi Kumquat |
| Hydrangea macrophylla | Bigleaf Hydrangea |
| Ilex crenata convexa | Convexleaf Japanese Holly |
| Leucothoe axillaris | Coast Leucothoe |
| Lonicera nitida | Box Honeysuckle |
| Mahonia fortunei | Chinese Mahonia |
| Malvaviscus arboreus | South American Waxmallow |
| Osmanthus delavayi | Delavay Osmanthus |
| Rhus aromatica | Fragrant Sumac |
| Rosa odorata | Tea Rose |
| Rosmarinus officinalis | Rosemary |
| Sabal minor | Dwarf Palmetto |
| Sarcococca ruscifolia | Fragrant Sarcococca |
| Serenoa repens | Saw Palmetto |
| Severinia buxifolia | Chinese Boxorange |
| Spiraea cantoniensis | Reeves Spiraea |
| Spiraea thunbergi | Thunberg Spiraea |
| Syringa persica laciniata | Cutleaf Persian Lilac |

# IV. Small Shrubs for the SOUTHERN PIEDMONT

### RECOMMENDED FOR GENERAL USE

| Botanical Name | Common Name |
| --- | --- |
| Berberis julianae | Wintergreen Barberry |

| Botanical Name | Common Name |
|---|---|
| Buxus sempervirens | Common Box |
| Deutzia gracilis | Slender Deutzia |
| Euonymus alatus compactus | Dwarf Winged Euonymus |
| Fatshedera lizei | Fatshedera |
| Ilex crenata convexa | Convexleaf Japanese Holly |
| Mahonia bealei | Leatherleaf Mahonia |
| Rhododendron mucronatum | Snow Azalea |
| Rhododendron obtusum japonicum | Kurume Azalea |
| Rhodotypos scandens | Black Jetbead |
| Rosa chinensis Louis Philippe | Louis Philippe Rose |
| Spiraea cantoniensis | Reeves Spiraea |

### RECOMMENDED FOR RESTRICTED USE

| | |
|---|---|
| Berberis thunbergi | Japanese Barberry |
| Callicarpa dichotoma | Purple Beautyberry |
| Comptonia peregrina | Sweetfern |
| Cytisus scoparius | Scotch Broom |
| Diervilla sessilifolia | Southern Bush Honeysuckle |
| Fatsia japonica | Japan Fatsia |
| Fothergilla gardeni | Dwarf Fothergilla |
| Fothergilla monticola | Alabama Fothergilla |
| Hydrangea macrophylla | Bigleaf Hydrangea |
| Jasminum mesnyi | Primrose Jasmine |
| Juniperus virginiana globosa | Globe Redcedar |
| Kerria japonica | Japanese Kerria |
| Leucothoe catesbaei | Drooping Leucothoe |
| Lonicera nitida | Box Honeysuckle |
| Mahonia aquifolium | Oregongrape |
| Mahonia fortunei | Chinese Mahonia |
| Osmanthus delavayi | Delavay Osmanthus |
| Paeonia suffruticosa | Tree Peony |
| Pieris floribunda | Mountain Pieris |
| Raphiolepis umbellata | Yeddo Raphiolepis |
| Rhododendron carolinianum | Carolina Rhododendron |
| Rhododendron molle | Chinese Azalea |
| Rhus aromatica | Fragrant Sumac |
| Rosa hugonis | Father Hugo Rose |
| Rosa odorata | Tea Rose |
| Rosa rubrifolia | Redleaf Rose |
| Rosmarinus officinalis | Rosemary |
| Sarcococca ruscifolia | Fragrant Sarcococca |
| Spiraea thunbergi | Thunberg Spirea |

*Botanical Name*                    *Common Name*

| | |
|---|---|
| Syringa persica laciniata | Cutleaf Persian Lilac |
| Viburnum acerifolium | Mapleleaf Viburnum |
| Viburnum carlesi | Koreanspice Viburnum |
| Viburnum japonicum | Japanese Viburnum |
| Viburnum suspensum | Sandankwa Viburnum |
| Yucca gloriosa | Moundlily Yucca |

## IV. Small Shrubs for the UPPER SOUTH

### RECOMMENDED FOR GENERAL USE

| | |
|---|---|
| Berberis julianae | Wintergreen Barberry |
| Buxus sempervirens | Common Box |
| Deutzia gracilis | Slender Deutzia |
| Euonymus alatus compactus | Dwarf Winged Euonymus |
| Ilex crenata convexa | Convexleaf Japanese Holly |
| Leucothoe catesbaei | Drooping Leucothoe |
| Mahonia aquifolium | Oregongrape |
| Pieris floribunda | Mountain Pieris |
| Rhododendron carolinianum | Carolina Rhododendron |
| Rhododendron mucronatum | Snow Azalea |
| Rhododendron obtusum japonicum | Kurume Azalea |
| Rhodotypos scandens | Black Jetbead |

### RECOMMENDED FOR RESTRICTED USE

| | |
|---|---|
| Berberis thunbergi | Japanese Barberry |
| Callicarpa dichotoma | Purple Beautyberry |
| Comptonia peregrina | Sweetfern |
| Cytisus scoparius | Scotch Broom |
| Diervilla sessilifolia | Southern Bush Honeysuckle |
| Fatshedera lizei | Fatshedera |
| Fothergilla gardeni | Dwarf Fothergilla |
| Fothergilla monticola | Alabama Fothergilla |
| Hydrangea arborescens grandiflora | Snowhill Hydrangea |
| Hydrangea macrophylla | Bigleaf Hydrangea |
| Juniperus virginiana globosa | Globe Redcedar |
| Kerria japonica | Japanese Kerria |
| Lonicera nitida | Box Honeysuckle |
| Mahonia bealei | Leatherleaf Mahonia |
| Paeonia suffruticosa | Tree Peony |
| Picea abies varieties | Dwarf Norway Spruce |
| Pinus mugo mughus | Mugho Pine |
| Rhododendron molle | Chinese Azalea |

| *Botanical Name* | *Common Name* |
|---|---|
| Rhus aromatica | Fragrant Sumac |
| Ribes alpinum | Alpine Currant |
| Rosa hugonis | Father Hugo Rose |
| Rosa rubrifolia | Redleaf Rose |
| Rosa rugosa | Rugosa Rose |
| Rosmarinus officinalis | Rosemary |
| Sarcococca ruscifolia | Fragrant Sarcococca |
| Spiraea cantoniensis | Reeves Spiraea |
| Spiraea thunbergi | Thunberg Spiraea |
| Syringa persica laciniata | Cutleaf Persian Lilac |
| Thuja occidentalis varieties | Dwarf Eastern Arborvitae |
| Viburnum acerifolium | Mapleleaf Viburnum |
| Viburnum carlesi | Koreanspice Viburnum |

### RANGE CHART FOR GROUP IV. SMALL SHRUBS

| | *Coastal Plain* | | *Piedmont* | | *Upper South* | |
|---|---|---|---|---|---|---|
| Berberis julianae | x x x | x x x | x x x | x x x | x x x | x x x |
| Buxus microphylla japonica | x x x | x x x | - - - | | | |
| Buxus sempervirens | - - - | | x x x | x x x | x x x | x x x |
| Cycas revoluta | x x x | x x x | - - - | | | |
| Deutzia gracilis | - - - | | x x x | x x x | x x x | x x x |
| Euonymus alatus compactus | - - - | | x x x | x x x | x x x | x x x |
| Fatshedera lizei | x x x | x x x | x x x | x x x | - - - | |
| Ilex crenata convexa | - - - | | x x x | x x x | x x x | x x x |
| Jasminum mesnyi | x x x | x x x | - - - | | | |
| Leucothoe catesbaei | - - - | | - - - | | x x x | x x x |
| Mahonia aquifolium | | | - - - | | x x x | x x x |
| Mahonia bealei | x x x | x x x | x x x | x x x | - - - | |
| Pieris floribunda | | | - - - | | x x x | x x x |
| Raphiolepis umbellata | x x x | x x x | - - - | | | |
| Rhododendron carolinianum | | | - - - | | x x x | x x x |
| Rhododendron mucronatum | - - - | | x x x | x x x | x x x | x x x |
| Rhododendron obtusum japonicum | x x x | x x x | x x x | x x x | x x x | x x x |
| Rhodotypos scandens | - - - | | x x x | x x x | x x x | x x x |
| Rosa chinensis Louis Philippe | x x x | x x x | x x x | x x x | - - - | |
| Spiraea cantoniensis | - - - | | x x x | x x x | x x x | - - - |
| Viburnum japonicum | x x x | x x x | - - - | | | |
| Viburnum suspensum | x x x | x x x | - - - | | | |
| Yucca gloriosa | x x x | x x x | x x x | - - - | | |

Only two of the Small Shrubs, both broad-leaved evergreens, are recommended, and with qualifications, for all zones. The *Berberis* is good everywhere, but the Kurume Azaleas (*Rhododendron o. j.*) are restricted by acid soil requirements and by the degree of hardiness shown by certain varieties (such as *amoenum* and *hinodegiri*) in comparison to others which may hardly go beyond the Piedmont. The *Ilex*, like many other Japanese Holly varieties, seems to lack vigor in the warmest zones although it will do well with care. *Rhododendron mucronatum* grows well in the Coastal Plain as do the Indica Azaleas with which it is sometimes grouped. In this Zone it is an inferior white, however, whereas in cooler sections, where the Indicas are not hardy, it is the best of the semi-evergreen white Azaleas. The *Leucothoe, Pieris,* and *Rhododendrons* need acid soils. The other species are tolerant, but the *Berberis, Buxus,* and *Mahonia aquifolium* may be somewhat better in limestone sections. *Leucothoe, Pieris, Rhododendron carolinianum,* and *Yucca* are natives of the Southeast, and *Mahonia aquifolium* comes from the West Coast.

*Berberis julianae,* Wintergreen Barberry. *Berberis thunbergi,* Japanese Barberry. Although the Wintergreen Barberry is fairly common, other evergreen Barberries as a group apparently are not popular in the Southeast, possibly because of their forbidding spines. Some nurserymen do not grow them because the genus (though not all species) fosters the black stem blister rust disease of wheat. However, the propagation of susceptible species is generally controlled by state laws. This particular species seems to be the one most generally available in this size group, and it is possibly the best. It grows somewhat rugged and upright to a height of about 6 feet. The foliage has an excellent dark green, glossy appearance. The texture effect is rather coarse because of the irregular habit of growth. Attractive and showy flowers are produced in small clusters along the stems in mid-spring, and these are followed by inconspicuous black fruits in fall. To gain the best effect from this plant one should place it in full sun in cooler sections of the Upper South and the Piedmont, in light shade in the Coastal Plain. It likes good soil and a fair supply of moisture and is a good choice for alkaline soils. Given a good start, it thrives without care and under severe conditions of exposure, smoke and dust, or salt spray. Although this certainly is not one of the choicest plants in this group, it is an excellent low-upkeep material for hedges and borders in parks and housing developments, and it makes a happy foliage contrast in combination with other shrubs. It should be planted with allowance for its full size since its beauty, except in hedges, is ruined by shearing. The botanical literature lists a dwarf variety called *nana* which, if it can be located, could be an excellent addition to Group III. *B. sargentiana* is a closely related species probably often confused with this in landscape work. The latter probably is not as hardy as the former. *B. gagnepaini* and *B. triacanthophora* are other evergreen species to be found occasionally in this region, but they seem to have little to offer in beauty or usefulness which the Wintergreen Barberry does not equal or surpass.

The Japanese is the best known of the deciduous Barberries. Indeed, it is too much planted. But it is an excellent hardy plant for the Upper South, thriving in poor and exposed sites on all soils, making a good, thorny hedge or a fair specimen. Its fall color is attractive, and its red fruits make a brilliant show until they are finally devoured by the birds. In sheltered areas the Japanese Barberry is sometimes hard to prune satisfactorily to prevent legginess and to clean out old wood, and the shrub is more dense and attractive on sunny sites. The variety, *B. t. atropurpurea*, is one of the best red-leaved shrubs. The Truehedge Columnberry, *B. t. erecta*, is a patented variety (#110) which is useful for hedges up to 4 feet in very narrow spaces. A hybrid of the Japanese and Wintergreen Barberries is the Mentor variety, *B. mentorensis* (#99), which has the habit of the Japanese but with semi-evergreen leaves. It is said to tolerate extremes of heat, cold, and drought very well. The Korean Barberry, *B. koreana*, is said to be proving a good substitute for the Japanese, having colorful clustered flowers in spring, red fruits in winter, and red foliage in fall. These plants are not choice or refined in character, but they have many possibilities in tough conditions.

*Buxus microphylla japonica*, Japanese Littleleaf Box. *Buxus sempervirens*, Common Box. The Japanese Box is the one which would be recommended for this size class for the Coastal Plain. It makes a good specimen. Its growth is rather open, but with a little shearing it will form a handsome globe up to about 6 feet in height. The leaves are larger than those of most Boxwoods, dark rich green in color, and medium in texture. In shaded places this variety does well as far south as middle Florida and is hardy for the Coastal Plain, although it probably should not be counted on north of this zone. All the Boxwoods have shallow roots, and, at least until they are well established, they should be mulched and watered during periods of severe drought. They are attacked occasionally by leaf miners and scale insects, and need to be watched for the first signs of trouble. Boxwoods have a certain refined grace and beauty suited to garden and architectural settings, and for such places they are well worth the care they demand.

The Common Box develops into an elegant specimen of this size class in the Upper South and in cooler sections of the Piedmont. Perhaps the greatest difficulty in obtaining Common Box is in the possibility of confusing this with the Tree Box variety, *B. s. arborescens*, a larger growing, more vigorous type which is often sheared in order to secure sizable specimens in shorter time. The buyer should see the parent stock in order to avoid disappointment, for there are many forms of this species which has been long in cultivation. The Tree Box usually can be identified by its rather linear, bluntly round-pointed leaves. This variety should be sheared annually to promote compact growth. Further remarks on care will be found under the discussion of the Truedwarf Box in Chapter III.

*Callicarpa dichotoma*, Purple Beautyberry. This is useful in the cutting garden for its colorful purple fruits borne in clusters in the axils of the leaves along the stems during the fall season. Otherwise the plant is undistinguished, formless, rather weedy, with deciduous foliage, requiring a severe pruning each spring. This practice will restrict the plant to just over 4 feet in height. Similar to this is *C. japonica*, the Japanese Beautyberry, which bears its purple fruits at the ends of the stems. This is not so common as the above, and it is no more desirable. Both are easily grown throughout the Southeast under average garden conditions and are suitable for the cutting garden.

*Comptonia peregrina*, Sweetfern. A member of the Bayberry Family, the Sweetfern is interesting for its aromatic, fine-textured, fernlike deciduous foliage, and for its spreading, suckering, informal habit of growth. Native to parts of the Upper South, it likes cool sites and a sunny exposure and it does well in poor, acid, sandy, or gravelly soils. It has been planted sometimes as a groundcover to protect road cuts. It is fine for naturalizing, but is somewhat ragged and coarse for tidy settings.

The Sweetfern is listed often as *C. asplenifolia*. This name should refer to a variety of the above called the Littleleaf Sweetfern. Its habitat is the pine woodlands of the Coastal Plain. Both of these plants are said to be very difficult to transplant, and they are probably to be secured only by collecting from native stands.

*Cycas revoluta*, Sago Cycas. This is usually called Sago Palm, but it is not a Palm, being more closely related to the Yews and Pines and to the Ginkgo tree. Under favorable conditions this striking and distinctive plant may reach 10 feet in height; but in the Coastal Plain area it may be considered to have a maximum height of about 6 feet. Since the plant is slow in maturing, the height is usually less than that. The "Sago Palm" may grow from a single stem, like a miniature palm, or it may form a clump with several stubby trunks each bearing its own crown of fronds. The latter form is often the more desirable in landscape work. The 2- to 3-foot-long leaves, dark and glossy green in color, are most attractive, giving a coarse, rich foliage effect. The sexes are separate in the Cycas; the female bears in alternate years orange-red fruits on interesting brown, woolly growths clustered in the crown. For all its tropical appearance, this plant is hardy, and old specimens may be seen in gardens as far north as Macon, Ga., and along the seacoast well above Charleston, all of which must have survived the severe winter trials of 1951-52. When it has become established, the Cycas requires a minimum of care, being perfectly at ease in poor soils, enduring drought, and proving resistant to pests. It seems to do well in either lightly shaded or open sites. It makes a good material for foundation plantings and for specimen use; its bold character is effective in combination with architectural features. Since it is a slow grower, perhaps a weighty drawback to its widespread use will be the cost of production.

*Cytisus scoparius*, Scotch Broom. This is valuable for poor soils and notable for enduring drought and sun. It comes from Europe, but was introduced in colonial times and has become naturalized in some sections. It is more a curious than a beautiful plant, interesting for its minute deciduous leaves and deep green twigs which keep their color all winter, and for its irregular and weeping habit of growth. The plant reaches a height of about 6 feet. It is fine as a soil builder, and is sometimes planted to hold sandy banks. The bright yellow, pea-like flowers make a vivid show in May. But Scotch Broom is not too reliable in the garden, where its character is hardly appropriate in most cases. It grows well in cooler sections of the Piedmont and throughout the Upper South, sometimes becoming almost a weed. There are many cultivated varieties of the Broom which could be interesting for trial if they were available.

*Deutzia gracilis*, Slender Deutzia. This is the best of its genus and is one of the finest flowering shrubs for the Upper South and the Piedmont, slightly less desirable in warmer parts of the Coastal Plain, where it lacks vigor. Growing to a height of just over 4 feet, the Slender Deutzia has a rounded form, and a neat and fairly compact habit. The deciduous foliage is linear, medium to fine in texture, and light green in color. The graceful, white, single flowers with yellow stamens appear early in May in short terminal racemes which almost entirely clothe the bush. They are effective in the garden and also in the house in arrangements. This plant likes some sunlight, but it succeeds in shade. It is also surprisingly tolerant of poor soils, drought, and general neglect, although it responds handsomely to better conditions and occasional thinning of older branches. It makes a beautiful material for mass and color in flower gardens. It is excellent also for low unclipped boundary plantings, for the foreground of shrub borders, and it might fit occasionally into foundation plantings of light scale.

*Diervilla sessilifolia*, Southern Bush Honeysuckle. This is a native of the southern Appalachians, suitable for the Upper South and cooler parts of the Piedmont, but it is not seen much in ornamental plantings. It is a coarse deciduous shrub, reaching a height of just over 4 feet, spreading and squatty in form, with branches inclined to droop. The simple elliptical leaves are fairly large and dark green in color. The flowers are small and tubular, scattered along the stems in the axils of the leaves, dull yellow in color and not showy. These appear in midsummer and are followed by inconspicuous brown seed pods. The chief merits of this plant lie in its hardiness and its ability to thrive under unfavorable circumstances. In any soil it will stand either the full glare of the sun or a dense shade. It is useful for planting as an understory, or at the front of a shrub border where it is difficult to find something which will grow. It is excellent also for massing on dry hot banks along roadsides because of its spreading, rooting underground shoots. It is perfectly free of diseases and requires no care except for an occasional pruning to remove old wood where neatness of appearance is important.

*Euonymus alatus compactus*, Dwarf Winged Euonymus. One of the excellent deciduous shrubs for the Piedmont and the Upper South, this plant is most notable for its rugged, horizontal growth character. The stems branch stiffly into strongly horizontal twigs bearing the striking bark ridges or "wings" which are especially prominent in winter and which give the plant its name. It bears no flowers of consequence, but the orange, bittersweet-like fruits of autumn are usually effective. The leaves are rather small, medium in texture, and scattered and light in density. In autumn they take on a vivid rose-purple tone which makes this one of the most colorful materials in the landscape at that time. The rose of the foliage makes a stirring combination with the orange of the fruits. This is an excellent hedge material, requiring little pruning to keep it shapely and within bounds. For general garden use the Dwarf Winged Euonymus is much more adaptable than the standard Winged Euonymus which, despite its strong and desirable character, is too large for most properties. It prefers a sunny location or one with only light shade; it is not particular as to soil; and it is generally a clean, pest-free material.

*Fatshedera lizei*, Fatshedera. This plant is the result of a cross between the evergreen shrub from Japan called Fatsia and the common vine, English Ivy, both members of the Aralia family. It is a sprawling, irregular, open, informal shrub which sends up its stems to just over 4 feet in height at which point they are likely to topple and spread outward to rise again. Consequently the plant can look ragged in the wrong place, and needs pruning if it is to be confined. The evergreen foliage is heavy, coarse in texture, of a starlike configuration, and exceptionally rich and decorative. The flowers, too, are attractive although not overly showy, appearing in spherical white heads about an inch in diameter, in autumn. The plant is resistant to pests and exceptionally well suited to urban surroundings in shade. For the Coastal Plain and the Piedmont it is probably among the very best materials as an informal shrub for foliage character or for an espalier. It succeeds in Washington, D. C., but in cooler parts of the Upper South it probably will not be hardy unless it is given the protection of buildings and shielding from winter as well as summer sun.

*Fatsia japonica*, Japan Fatsia. The Fatsia may be planted much as the Fatshedera for rich, coarse evergreen foliage effect mostly in deep shade in the Coastal Plain and the warmer Piedmont. It is probably somewhat more tender than the above, but it will stand outdoor exposure in protected spots to Atlanta and Memphis although it remains rather small, usually less than 4 feet. Normally it is said to reach 15 feet, but older stems probably ought to be cut out to keep it at about 6 feet unless it is espaliered against a wall, a use for it which is highly recommended. The ball-like heads of white flowers are decorative in autumn, but the plant is valued chiefly for the glossy leaves which may become a foot in diameter. Both the Fatsia and the Fatshedera will be useful chiefly in architectural settings, in plant boxes, in patios, and in small city gardens, where they stand confined conditions very well.

*Fortunella japonica*, Marumi (Round) Kumquat. For limited specimen use there could hardly be anything nicer than this. Growing in the form of a miniature tree, this plant is decorated in summer with small fragrant white flowers and in winter with the dwarf "oranges" which are good to eat. It is unfortunate that the ornamental possibilities of this particular citrus are not exploited more fully since it is hardy throughout at least half of the Coastal Plain, and it would make a good pot plant wherever it could be given the protection of a cool porch through the winter. The reason probably lies in the need for considerable spraying in order to control white fly and scale depredations. Hence the use of the Kumquat is not widespread, but it is worthy of consideration as an unusual decorative object for spots of highly cultivated character. It may grow somewhat over 6 feet in height in favorable environments and without some control pruning.

*Fothergilla gardeni*, Dwarf Fothergilla. *Fothergilla monticola*, Alabama Fothergilla. It is possible that the two Fothergillas listed, both natives of this region, belong in the first list for this size class for the Upper South and the Piedmont. They are most unusual and handsome in flower with their white, bottle-brush-like spikes in May, and their showy foliage color in autumn. They belong in the Witchhazel family and are somewhat similar in character, with

an individual, informal open habit of growth, interesting branching
patterns, and coarse foliage texture. The Dwarf Fothergilla possibly
belongs with the Dwarf Shrubs of Chapter III, as it hardly exceeds
4 feet in height. The Alabama Fothergilla grows to about 6 feet with
a broad spread. Both prefer cool well-watered sites with some shade
although they will take sun under good garden conditions. They are
especially effective in naturalizing and in combination with evergreen plants against which the flower and foliage colors can be
displayed with heightened results.

*Hydrangea arborescens grandiflora,* Snowhill Hydrangea. *Hydrangea macrophylla,* Bigleaf Hydrangea. The Snowhill Hydrangea is
a large-flowered sport of the species which is native to cool damp
woodlands of most of the eastern U. S. Its foliage is deciduous, yellow-
green in color, coarse in texture, and the growth habit is mounding
to about 5 feet in height, open, and suckering to form clumps of
some spread. The flowers of the parent species are white, appearing
in flat heads of little effect in summer. This plant may be employed
rarely in naturalizing in deep woods. The Snowhill variety is much
more showy, producing in early summer a fulsome display of great
rounded heads of white blossoms which may remain on the bush
for months, turning greenish after a time, but still making some
effect. The character of the Hydrangea calls for sympathetic handling. It has been much overplanted, but it is pleasing seen from a
distance in gardenesque surroundings. It takes shade well although
it blooms more spectacularly in sunny locations. It likes good soils
(acid or alkaline), feeding, and watering, and it is perfectly resistant to
pests, requiring no care except an annual cutting back in spring.

The Bigleaf Hydrangea is an old-fashioned favorite which has
fallen into disrepute in recent years. To be just, it may be well to
enumerate the faults of this plant before considering its merits. First,
the leaves are deciduous in winter; and, when they have fallen, a
stark and ungainly skeleton is exposed. The plant cannot well be
used, therefore, in places where a year-round effect is desired. Second,
it must be pruned with some skill at least once a year. Left to themselves, specimens might reach 10 feet or so in height, but in doing
so the flowers become ever smaller and the plants ragged. The annual
winter or spring pruning should be designed to restrain height to
about 3 to 5 feet, and to encourage the production of vigorous stems
which will in turn produce handsome flowers. Third, Hydrangeas
must have plenty of water and plant food through the summer. Feeding should be carefully balanced, too, since an alkaline soil reaction
tends to turn the flowers pink in color and acidity encourages blue
tones. It is apparent that these plants have their limitations for many
gardens. However, when they are well grown there is nothing finer

for a cool, rich floral display in midsummer than these gorgeous Hortensias, as they are sometimes called. For specimen use in tubs in patio gardens, one might choose one of the exotic French importations in one of the various tones of rosy purple or lilac. For massive clumps under trees on the lawn or in the shaded border, the more common blue or pink tones serve very well. Given shade, moisture, intelligent feeding, and proper pruning, nothing can give more satisfaction through the long southern summer than these. They are often excellent in city gardens, and they thrive along the seashore as far north as Long Island. They are quite hardy through the Coastal Plain and the Piedmont, but they may need some protection in parts of the Upper South.

*Ilex crenata convexa*, Convexleaf Japanese Holly. This appears to be one of the most useful of broad-leaved evergreens to come into general use in recent times. The shrub has glossy, small, closely-crowded leaves, oval in shape and curiously convex, almost like shallow inverted cups. They are light green at first, maturing to a dark tone, almost black. The habit is horizontal and somewhat squatty, becoming rounded, reaching with age to 10 feet in height, with an equal spread. Thus it may be properly in the class with the Medium Shrubs of Group V, but it is placed here because it is slow growing and easily restrained, and thus for practical purposes a member of this class. New branches tend to shoot out at odd angles on younger plants, causing a somewhat ragged appearance; these should be sheared in early summer to promote compactness of growth. This plant is successful as a substitute for the Box, which it resembles in many respects. While it does not have quite the elegance of the latter, it is superior in speed of growth, resistance to scale, and in greater tolerance of exposure, glare, winds, snow loads of winter, deep shade, drought, and average growing conditions. A neat deception may be found in a few gardens of the Memphis area where larger specimens are clipped close into clumpy, billowy forms which look very much like those taken on naturally by very old plants of the English Box. The Convexleaf Holly is suitable for foundation plantings and as an accent in formal schemes, but it is also fine in mass in informal borders and naturalistic settings. It makes a fine hedge, either sheared or unsheared. Since it has seemed to be so tolerant, the shrub is in danger of being overplanted, but it does have limitations. While it is ideally suited to the Upper South and cooler parts of the Piedmont, it takes some care in warmer sections where it probably ought to be planted in partial shade. It requires ample feeding with nitrogenous materials to prevent the foliage color from yellowing, and in close quarters it can be infested severely with red spider mites.

*Jasminum mesnyi*, Primrose Jasmine. This is one of the time-tested reliables for the Coastal Plain and is usually listed as *J. primulinum*. Like some of the others of the genus, this one is weeping in habit, forming in open sites a fountain-like mound about 6 feet high, sometimes more, with ultimately a very large spread. The plant may be trained as a vine over arbors, trellises, and fences. Sometimes when it is set near a low-branching tree it will scramble among the limbs by itself. In such cases it may reach a greater height. The evergreen foliage is light in color and fine in texture. In early spring a long succession of scattered double flowers, an inch or more in diameter, of a soft clear yellow color, make a pretty display. This Jasmine accommodates itself nicely to both sunny and shady locations, to drought, and to poor soils. It is reliable throughout the Coastal Plain and is hardy into the Piedmont with protection to Atlanta and to Norfolk. Unfortunately the poor pruning which it usually receives often ruins its natural grace and beauty. The tops should never be sheared back to form a stiff ball shape, but each year some of the older and less vigorous wood should be cut back as close to the ground as possible and pulled out. This practice will help to prevent its center from filling up with dead wood, and will also help to preserve the natural form. Primrose Jasmine is a good plant for holding banks and for draping over walls, and, as suggested above, for training on supports.

*Juniperus virginiana globosa*, Globe Redcedar. This is a low rounded form of the common native species which, when well grown, becomes quite a good specimen for year-round, dark green foliage of fine needle type. Occasionally this plant will be ornamented with the characteristic blue, berry-like fruits in autumn. It should be grown in full exposure to sun and wind in poor dry soils where it will be compact in habit, mounding and billowing in form, often picturesque and interesting in character for an unusual site. It likes alkaline soils and probably will be at its best in the Upper South or the cooler Piedmont. Usually free of pests, the Globe Redcedar can be attacked by bag worms and will host the Cedar-Apple Rust if planted near apple orchards. Red spider attacks will ruin it in shaded, sheltered sites.

*Kerria japonica*, Japanese Kerria. This is a neat slender shrub sometimes seen in old-fashioned gardens. Its roots tend to spread underground, often sending up a considerable clump of green stems to a height of just over 4 feet. The medium-sized deciduous foliage is deep green in color and trouble free. The variety commonly seen, *K. j. flore pleno*, has double, pompon-like flowers of bright orange appearing in late spring. The single flowering parent species is more graceful, however. This shrub naturalizes well and maintains itself for years without care in open woodlands and partially shaded places. This is the best setting for it since the growth is almost too insubstantial and the color almost too strong for the usual border or foundation planting. It can be trained easily as a vine against a wall or fence, and in this form it can be induced to grow canes 10 to 12 feet long. This will succeed in the Upper South and in cooler parts of the Piedmont.

*Leucothoe axillaris,* Coast Leucothoe. *Leucothoe catesbaei,* Drooping Leucothoe. Both of these are native to the Southeast, and it is likely that they are mixed in the nursery trade, being similar in habit of growth. The Drooping Leucothoe is more likely to be found in sheltered mountain valleys, and the Coast Leucothoe is common on stream banks of the Piedmont and into the Coastal Plain. The chief beauty of these plants is their dark and glossy evergreen foliage which is of rather coarse texture, sometimes turning purplish in autumn if plants are situated in exposed places. Determination of these two species is based on the length of leaf petiole, which is over ¼ inch in the former, less in the latter. Both grow to a height of 4 to 6 feet, spreading slowly by stems that root along the ground to make irregular clumps of gracefully arching, informal growth. Both flower in early spring with small white bell-form blossoms in attractive axillary drooping clusters which give the plants their often heard common name of "Lily-of-the-Valley Shrub." These shrubs are restricted to acid soils and to shaded sheltered locations of high humidity in the Upper South and, to a lesser degree, the Piedmont. They need a heavy mulch and cannot endure cultivation. Given a suitable spot, they need little care but will be more attractive if 2- and 3-year-old canes are cut out after blooming to stimulate new growth. The shrubs are beautiful in masses, making good groundcovers and fillers for mixing with Rhododendrons or with deciduous native shrubs. They are often good selections for small enclosed city gardens.

*Lonicera nitida,* Box Honeysuckle. This shrub is not widely planted in the Southeast, but it is becoming better known as a bank cover or as a specimen of informal character. It is sometimes recommended for the low clipped hedge. It is one of the few Bush Honeysuckles with evergreen leaves. The leaves are very small, fine in texture, and are closely spaced in opposite pairs along the stems to give the plant a distinct appearance. The habit of growth is sprawling, drooping, and irregular, growing usually to a height of about 4 feet although it is said to reach 6 feet. Small white fragrant flowers are produced in spring, followed by dark blue fruits in autumn. In good soils this plant grows rapidly and accumulates a quantity of dead wood. Usually, therefore, it is better located in poor soils and in full exposure to sun and wind. It is tolerant of limestone, and said to be a good choice for the seashore. Though the shrub is somewhat tender, it is safe in the Coastal Plain and the Piedmont, and is rated by Wyman as hardy as far north as Knoxville. A still smaller evergreen species, *L. yunnanensis*, the Yunnan Honeysuckle, may also be found rarely as a low rockery specimen or groundcover in this region. Like most of the Bush Honeysuckles, the Box and the Yunnan lack the substance to make them first-class materials although they are fine for quick and temporary effects.

*Mahonia aquifolium*, Oregongrape. *Mahonia bealei*, Leatherleaf Mahonia. *Mahonia fortunei*, Chinese Mahonia. The Mahonias include some of the most attractive foliage plants of this group. The Oregongrape has compound leaves of coarse texture, and each glossy dark green leaflet with its spiny teeth looks very much like a Holly leaf (hence another common name, Hollygrape). In general form the shrub is quite irregular and informal. It is inclined to be stoloniferous and spreading with age, forming a broad clump. Mature plants may attain a height of over 6 feet, but it is good practice to cut to the ground the older stems every few years in order to make way for more vigorous basal shoots. In late March the clusters of brilliant yellow flowers appear hugging the main stems. The blooms are showy, but the blue-black fruits, which mature through the summer, are not conspicuous. The winter color on plants exposed to sun is a pronounced red-purple. The Oregongrape is native to the rainy Pacific Northwest and, although somewhat unpredictable, is successful in the Upper South and cooler parts of the Piedmont. It seems to prefer alkaline soils, and will stand full exposure to sun and wind. In such places it forms low clumps to make a good groundcover. It is sometimes good in partial shade, but here it is often leggy. It is excellent for the foreground of a shrub border and for foundation plantings, where its strongly individual character is most effective. Through the limestone sections of Tennessee and Kentucky, the Oregongrape appears particularly happy although it is often planted inconsiderately against brick houses where its winter color does not show up well. It requires no care except an occasional pruning as noted above, but the foliage should be watched for lacewing fly.

The Leatherleaf Mahonia is the better choice in the Upper South below Knoxville and through the Piedmont and the Coastal Plain. It may be listed here as *M. japonica*. This variety also tends to be leggy, often forming a clump of from three to six or more stiff, unbranched stems up to 8 feet tall and topped with flat whorls of bold compound leaves. This growth habit results often in a rather awkward looking plant, and the awkwardness should be corrected by occasionally cutting back the older stems to the ground, forcing new growth to come from the crown and keeping the over-all height at 4 to 6 feet. The foliage is very coarse in texture, leathery to the touch, spiny, evergreen, and dull bluish-green in color. The plant is distinctive in form and in foliage, but it is also notable for its lovely flowers and fruits. The flowers open in earliest spring in nodding racemes clustered near the tips of the stems, making a pretty show of light lemon-yellow color. The small fruits mature slightly later, with a beautiful bluish bloom which is quite unusual. This Mahonia is perfectly hardy through this range, well adapted to its soils and its weather, free of insect enemies, but it does insist on a place in at least partial shade. It is likely to winterburn and to grow thin in sun. The unfortunate thing about it is that, since it is so obliging in nature, one sees a great deal of it here and there, often poorly grown. It makes a fine striking specimen for strong accent in architectural settings, and an extra supply of it for cutting is always welcome.

The Chinese Mahonia is not so common, and it is also more tender. Its range should probably be confined to the Coastal Plain and the milder parts of the Piedmont. Reaching about 4 feet in height, this plant grows in typical Mahonia fashion with many basal shoots, but it shows less tendency to become leggy. The slender evergreen leaflets give a fine texture effect. There are yellow flowers in early spring which are not very showy, and the fruits do not seem to mature here. When it is further tested, the Chinese Mahonia may be rated as one of the finest materials in this range.

*Malvaviscus arboreus*, South American Waxmallow. Commonly called the Turk's Cap, this shrub is seen very commonly in gardens along the southern edge of the Coastal Plain, where it is grown for its colorful orange-red flowers which bloom almost the entire year. The habit of growth and the foliage both are rank and coarse. The plant does well in sunny or partly shaded spots under the poorest conditions. It is tender and not generally recommended north of New Orleans and Jacksonville, although even in areas considerably farther north the roots will produce new growth quickly after the tops have been nipped by unusually cold weather. This plant is worth keeping in mind for difficult, hot sites where a garish show of color is a major consideration.

*Osmanthus delavayi*, Delavay Osmanthus. While there are three Osmanthus or Tea Olives of larger size classes commonly grown in the Deep South, there are also smaller forms which may be seen rarely and which ought to be better known. A fine one of these is the Delavay Osmanthus, often listed by the botanical name *Siphonosmanthus*. It develops slowly into a dense, compact mound, about 4 feet high or more, with fine-textured, glossy dark evergreen leaves like those of the American Holly in miniature. In late fall and again in early spring there are scattered, white fragrant flowers followed by black fruits. This plant is difficult to obtain, but it should make an excellent substitute for the Common Box in the Coastal Plain and the lower Piedmont as a refined garden specimen or in foundation plantings. It is said to like moist, humus-rich soils in shade, but it grows dense and compact in sun in the sandy earth of Southern Pines, N. C.

In discussing the smaller Osmanthus, three other forms should be mentioned even though they are quite rare and little tried. The Chinese Osmanthus, *O. armatus*, bears large bristled leaves of coarse texture and light green color. Two forms of the Holly Osmanthus, *O. ilicifolius rotundifolius* and *O. i. myrtifolius*, are small-leaved types which may be encountered. All of these need to be further tried and better known to determine their best use and their range.

*Paeonia suffruticosa*, Tree Peony. After many years of comparative neglect, the Tree Peony may well prove to be one of the favorite materials of this size class. The shrub form is not outstanding in character; it is rounded and somewhat irregular, growing very slowly to a height of a little over 4 feet, with deeply cut, deciduous, medium-textured foliage of a pleasant grayish green color. The flowers of May are, however, most outstanding in a great array of colors, from white through pinks to red, lavender, and purple, yellow, maroon, and almost black, in endless variations, both single and double. Hybrids have been produced over a long period of time in both the Orient and in Europe, so there are hundreds of varieties from which to choose. Once established these plants require no care except for an occasional pruning, but finding the right place for them and getting them started are matters which need more trial in this area. Their hardiness is proved by the outstanding collection in Rochester, N. Y.; but they also succeed in Washington, D. C., and are grown rather commonly in the Mediterranean area of Europe where, it is said, they stand the warm climate better than herbaceous sorts. In warmer areas at least, it is fairly certain that they should have partial shade. Plants freshly bought from the nursery are usually grafted on herbaceous peony roots which eventually die as the new plant develops its own roots. Consequently the union should be set 2 to 3 inches below the soil surface. This shrub is said to like an alkaline soil, good fertility, adequate watering, and shelter, but it is one which does not want to be disturbed after once being established. It should be a choice garden ornament for cooler parts of the Upper South and the mountains.

*Picea abies* varieties, Dwarf Norway Spruce. Several dwarf forms of the Norway Spruce belong in this class. They should be kept in mind since they make interesting, choice, and unusual specimens for colder localities, even if the occasion for their use may be rare where broad-leaved evergreens are available. Dwarf Norway Spruce varieties are easily grown in almost any soil of the Upper South provided plants are in the sun, and they can endure exposure and drought. A major drawback to their more common circulation is the cost of propagation, for their slowness in developing makes them somewhat precious and rare and thus, in some instances, even more desirable. In general they are resistant to plant pests. Their forms are often irregular and picturesque, sometimes making the shrubs outstanding garden features. The names of these varieties are likely to be confused, some of them being Barry (*clanbrasiliana*), Nest (*nidiformis*), Prostrate (*procumbens*), etc. The buyer takes a gamble on these in respect to ultimate size and form. Usually they remain quite low, but often they take on a wide spread.

*Pieris floribunda*, Mountain Pieris. Often called the Mountain Andromeda, this plant is a native of the mountains of this region. It is one of the finest broadleaved evergreens for the Upper South within those sections in which acid soil conditions can be provided. The habit of growth is informal, loose, stoloniferous, often forming clumps of sturdy upright stems to just over 4 feet in height. The leaves are rather coarse in texture and dark green in color. Flower buds are formed in upright racemes at the ends of the stems in the fall; after they have provided some ornament all winter, they open in the early spring to form small white bells which are quite effective. This plant likes light shade although it will take full sun exposure at higher elevations. It should have a mulch for the creeping roots, and, rarely, the older stems should be cut to the ground to encourage new growth. Insect pests do not seem to bother the Pieris, but it is neither easy to establish nor widely available. It is subject to leaf spotting, for control of which a dusting of sulfur is suggested. For naturalizing and for garden borders it is choice.

*Pinus mugo mughus*, Mugho Pine. There are several horticultural varieties of the Mugho Pine, usually cushion-like in form, ranging in height from only a few feet to 15 feet or more, depending on the variety and the growing conditions. These plants are often excellent for exposed sites in the Upper South although they are not entirely satisfactory in warmer sections. The pleasure to be derived from this plant depends, first of all, on the assurance of receiving from the nurseryman one of the true dwarf forms, some of the names of which are Shrubby (*pumilio*) and Globe (*compacta*). These are at their best facing full sun and wind in poor dry soils, making good specimens and beautiful billowing informal masses. In sheltered or shaded locations and in richer growing conditions Mugho Pines become leggy and require shearing.

*Raphiolepis umbellata*, Yeddo Raphiolepis. The India Raphiolepis has been discussed in Chapter III together with optimum growing conditions and other characteristics. Without repeating these data, one might add that the Yeddo Raphiolepis, although in a larger size class, is similar in flowering, which is effective in mid-spring, in fruiting, and in handsome, rather coarse foliage. The habit of growth, instead of being spreading, however, is upright and inclined to legginess. The plant is a fine evergreen for sunny locations in the Coastal Plain and milder parts of the Piedmont.

*Rhododendron carolinianum,* Carolina Rhododendron. *Rhododendron molle,* Chinese Azalea. *Rhododendron mucronatum,* Snow Azalea. *Rhododendron obtusum japonicum,* Kurume Azalea. *Rhododendron* hybrids, Gable and Glen Dale Azaleas. The one true Rhododendron of this size class is the Carolina, one of the characteristic native species of the southern Appalachians. This may easily reach a height of 6 feet, but often it is much lower, making a spreading 4-foot bush which is rugged, open, and picturesque in form. The leaves, smaller than those of many Rhododendrons, are medium in texture and have a somewhat rusty appearance due to their red-brown under surfaces. The foliage may be sparsely scattered on the bush, revealing the sturdy and interesting twig structure. The clear fresh pink flowers open in mid-May in clusters at the ends of the twigs. The general flowering effect is pleasing, but not so spectacular as that of some other Rhododendrons and Azaleas. At higher elevations of the Upper South this variety stands sun and wind exposure well. Of the native Rhododendrons, it will adapt best to warmer sections and into the Piedmont, but here it should have partial shade.

For many years the so-called Snow Azalea has been a popular mainstay in plantings of this shrub in cooler areas of the middle and upper Southeast as far north as Philadelphia and Long Island. It has been listed ordinarily under the botanical names of *Azalea ledifolia alba* or *A. indica alba,* and is not to be confused with the "Snow" variety of the Kurume Azalea (see below). This is a comparatively hardy and vigorous species growing to about 6 feet in height, rarely more, with a spread of 8 feet, a fine showing of white flowers in spring, and rather thin grayish green foliage which is evergreen. Like so many of the genus, this needs monthly spraying for mites and for lacewing fly through the summer, but it is probably the most dependable white flowering Azalea for the Piedmont and the Upper South, making a splendid show with Dogwoods in sun or light shade in acid soils.

The Chinese Azalea is a deciduous species with large, coarse-textured leaves and a leggy upright form. It is very popular for its flowers, large in size, yellow flushed with apricot in color, and exceedingly showy, opening before the leaves. Like other Azaleas, this requires acid soil, but it is tolerant of sunny exposures and drought and is very hardy through the Upper South. It is effective with its massive glowing heads of blossoms silhouetted against evergreen backgrounds and it probably deserves a trial here for its color. Otherwise, in form, foliage, and general character, it is not supreme.

Presumably because of their brilliant massive floral displays, everyone would place the Kurume Azaleas among the best of garden materials for this region. They have generally an attractive habit of growth which, with their evergreen foliage, makes them good landscape materials throughout the year. They are dense and twiggy in habit, with a horizontal branching character which gives them a somewhat rugged unsymmetrical form. Young plants, especially those well-fed and watered, may become leggy and awkward in shape, and this tendency should be restrained by shearing in early summer. The leaves are small and glossy, usually retaining a good color through the winter except where they are over-exposed to the sun. Foliage colors vary strongly with varieties, however, and this fact should be given some study as a basis for selection. Special care should be given to the placing and combinations of flower color. It has been said that there are no clashing colors in Nature, but only the quickest glance at some Azalea groupings show how untrue this statement can be. On the Coastal Plain these Azaleas adapt very well to the usual sandy acid soils; they can stand sun but have better flower colors in light shade; and they are especially good for the usual landscape jobs on the smaller property because they can be restrained easily to this size range through pruning. While their natural habit is attractive, the plants can also be clipped into formal mounds very readily. The Kurumes are equally valuable in the Piedmont and the Upper South for providing a color spectacle and for general landscape design. Here they are more hardy than the Indian Azaleas although they may not be entirely reliable at higher elevations and in colder spots. There is considerable variation in the hardiness of some such as "Snow" which is dependable only through the Piedmont, and "Hinodegiri," the crimson-purple which is reliable to the Ohio River and Connecticut. The local nurseryman should be consulted on this selection. The Kurumes can be planted in full sun or in light shade; they will be more dwarf in a shady area, not much over 4 feet until they are quite old. In any planting of Azaleas, pests must be taken into account. These are chiefly the Azalea mealy bug, lacewing fly, red spider mite, and petal blight disease. The first three can be fairly well controlled with several sprayings during the summer of oil and nicotine or of malathion. The petal blight is serious only in the Coastal Plain. Once it is established in any area, it requires for control as many as three sprays a week with dithane or parzate during the flowering season, as well as rigid sanitation. These pests all are serious enemies, but their control is not too difficult, at least in small home plantings.

In recent years much work has been done in hybridizing Azaleas, chiefly for the purpose of widening the color and the hardiness ranges of the evergreen types. Two of the leading strains of these are the Glen Dale and the Gable hybrids. The first was developed at the Glen Dale station of the U. S. Department of Agriculture, and it is well represented in the collection at the National Arboretum in Washington where it grows well. The parentage is mixed, but it is said to include a large proportion of the rather tender Indica Azalea strain. The flowers exhibit a wide range of color and form, but the plants may be no more hardy than the Kurumes and probably should be planted with caution in the Upper South, although they may be excellent through the Piedmont and the Coastal Plain. The Gable strain was developed in Pennsylvania, and it probably is more hardy, having in its make-up a basic representation of *R. yedoense poukhanense*, the Yodogawa Azalea. The Gable hybrid should be tested in the Upper South. Colors in this group are likely to show the magenta influence of the Yodogawa parent, but in form, foliage, and hardiness it is quite promising.

*Rhodotypos scandens*, Black Jetbead. This is not only an attractive deciduous shrub, but it is also an "iron clad" material useful for filling in difficult and dry shaded areas through the Upper South and the cooler Piedmont. The bright green foliage has medium to coarse texture and pale yellow autumn color. The white flowers, appearing in May, look very much like those of the Mockorange and are followed in late summer by the curious hard black seeds which give the plant its name. The Jetbead is resistant to insects and diseases of all kinds, and requires little pruning or other maintenance. It reaches a height of almost 6 feet in a spreading, gracefully horizontal form, facing down well. It fits in all shrub plantings and in the foreground of deep borders. It makes also a most attractive untrimmed hedge.

*Rhus aromatica*, Fragrant Sumac. This is an excellent pest-free shrub for borders and informal masses in the Upper South and the Piedmont, native from the Canadian border to the Gulf. It spreads by underground stems to make broad scrambling clumps of heights from 3 to 5 feet, depending on soil and exposure. In very dry open sites it may be lower, not much more than a groundcover. In moist shaded spots it loses its character, growing thin and open to over 6 feet. The medium- to coarse-textured leaves are three-parted, and they may be mistaken easily for those of the ubiquitous Poison Ivy, a sister species, except that they are woolly and aromatic. The rather inconspicuous flowers occur in catkins in early spring, and the fruits are clusters of red berries in late summer. This adaptable shrub requires no care, and it is a good choice for naturalizing on acid or alkaline soils in sunny places where there is plenty of space. It is outstanding for its orange to red fall color.

*Ribes alpinum*, Alpine Currant. For the Upper South this is a superior deciduous shrub of about 6 feet in height for shrub borders and for trimmed or untrimmed hedges. Chiefly valuable for its dense upright habit and its fine-textured foliage, this plant adapts to a wide variety of soils in sun or shade and requires no care. It should not, however, be planted in sections where the White Pine is common because it is an alternate host of the White Pine blister rust.

*Rosa chinensis* Louis Philippe, Louis Philippe Rose. *Rosa hugonis*, Father Hugo Rose. *Rosa odorata*, Tea Rose. *Rosa rubrifolia*, Redleaf Rose. *Rosa rugosa*, Rugosa Rose. The value of certain shrub roses in landscape design has long been recognized. These have been chiefly certain species such as the Hugo, Redleaf, and Rugosa Roses listed here which are good in cooler areas of the Upper South and farther north. In the Piedmont and the Coastal Plain more attention has been given to some of the old-fashioned roses of the region, some of generations of cultivation there, which are now called popularly "landscape roses" and which are being extensively employed in bedding and massing for long season color effect. One of the first to receive this name was the "Louis Philippe" Rose. Another is the Tea (*R. odorata*) variety, "Safrano," which is said to bloom throughout the year in warmer parts of the Coastal Plain. A nurseryman of this same section who has had wide experience with roses indicates that other Tea varieties are equally good, and he suggests for trial "Anna Olivier" (silver pink), "Duchesse de Brabant" (shell pink), "Marie van Houtte" (canary yellow), "Old Gold" (bicolor), and "Snowbird" (white).

It is probably desirable to establish the criteria by which a rose variety is qualified as a "landscape rose." For this purpose the old "Louis Philippe" may be taken as the standard for comparison since it is excellent in every respect save the color of its flower, a vivid purplish red, which is very difficult to harmonize with other colors. It is suggested that these plants should possess the following qualities: (1) Habit of growth: low (about 4 feet or slightly over), rounded and fairly uniform, bushy and not awkwardly unsymmetrical as in the case of many hybrid teas which put all their energies into three or four canes. (2) Foliage: highly resistant to blackspot disease, or at least sufficiently so that spraying is not necessary to maintain appearance; foliage texture fine to medium, of good color, and sufficiently dense to clothe the bush structure in a pleasing manner; leaves nearly evergreen. (3) Flowers: need not be up to exhibition standards, but should be borne in sufficient profusion to give some color effect; fragrance desirable but not important; long season of bloom. (4) General Culture: some pruning required, chiefly for removing old wood, but cutting off flower heads and the usual spraying, feeding, and watering chores should not be necessary; to be grown with no special care in combination with other shrubs in average soils usually in sunny situations.

These standards seem, in part at least, to be the goals of the breeders of the Floribunda Roses (discussed in Group III), but none of the latter will survive neglect and poor conditions in the lower South as well as some of the "old-fashioned" Teas and their relatives which have, in some cases, maintained themselves for fifty years on abandoned plantation sites and in cemeteries here.

The remaining three shrub roses are valuable chiefly in the Upper South and for restricted use. The Father Hugo Rose is listed as representative of a group of showy, yellow flowering bush types, some of them equally desirable, including the Scotch Rose (*R. spinossissima*), the Manchu Rose (*R. xanthina*), Harrison's Yellow Rose (*R. foetida harisoni*), etc. One or another of these is often seen as a specimen in old gardens, where they seem most appropriate. They require little care and make a blaze of color in spring, but for the remainder of the year their undistinguished forms and their fine-textured foliage are not outstanding.

The Redleaf Rose is notable for its colored foliage. The single pink flowers of spring are attractive but ephemeral and not very showy. In late summer the red fruits are effective. This plant is slender, graceful, open, and informal in habit to a height of 6 feet. It is disease resistant, hardy, and adaptable to all soils in sunny places. It is useful in combination with other shrubs for foliage color relief, or it can make a delicate ornament for constructions such as walls and fences in the Upper South and the cooler Piedmont.

The Rugosa Rose may be best in masses in the highest and most exposed sites in this section. It has beautiful dark green foliage of medium texture which is colorful in orange and red in autumn. Throughout the summer it produces a long succession of scattered single flowers in white, pink, rose, and red, and these are followed by persistent showy orange-red fruits. In sheltered spots the growth is sprawling and awkward to nearly 6 feet, but in the open it is lower, compact, and well covered with foliage. It is disease resistant, but borers occasionally will kill one of the older stems.

*Rosmarinus officinalis*, Rosemary. This is an old favorite of the herb garden, associated in legend with remembrance. The plant is valuable for its aromatic grayish evergreen foliage of fine texture and also for its shy but attractive spikes of blue flowers in late winter. For many situations its somewhat sprawling and open habit of growth will rule against its use. Mature plants may reach a height of just over 4 feet, spreading even more as some of the stems root where they droop and touch the soil. It is somewhat difficult to prescribe the culture of this unpredictable performer because it will die out occasionally under what seem to be ideal conditions and again may survive unaccountably in poor environments. Rosemary needs good drainage, stands drought well, and is better in poor rather than very fertile soils (where it becomes rank). It may benefit from some lime about its roots. Normally it is a lover of sun, but old specimens are seen occasionally in fairly shaded spots. After it has become established in a place to its liking, this plant will grow for years without any attention save some pruning, and eventually will develop twisted trunks and a fantastic shape. This is always at home in the herb or flower garden, where its foliage makes a good foil for the blooms of other plants. It is hardy in the Coastal Plain and the Piedmont, but it is questionable in the Upper South. A variety called Prostrate (*R. o. prostratus*) is said to be available to make a groundcover on dry, sunny sites.

*Sabal minor*, Dwarf Palmetto. *Serenoa repens*, Saw Palmetto. Two members of the Palm family, both common natives of the Coastal Plain, may be discussed together. The two may be confused, but they are distinguished easily by the tooth-edged leaf petiole characteristic of the latter as opposed to the smooth petiole extending through the leaf blade of the former. Both are broadly spreading plants, about 4 to 5 feet in height, occasionally higher, likely to be too rank and coarse for the average small plot. Still, they have striking decorative qualities, and they are so well adapted to this region's growing conditions that they should be given more serious consideration, especially in larger scale landscape projects such as parks and parkways. For such places these are of the best; their coarse textures make a rich display in masses or in specimen clumps. The Saw Palmetto has been mentioned previously as a groundcover. It exceeds the size limits of the groundcover group, but it grows in its native state in masses of considerable extent and appears to best advantage in such plantings. It is the more hardy species and may be used into the warmer parts of the Piedmont for exotic specimen effect. *Rhapidophyllum* (*Chamaerops*) *hystrix*, the Needlepalm or Blue Palmetto, is another low growing species, native to a small section of this area, which might be useful as an occasional specimen. These plants are rarely handled in nurseries and therefore must be collected.

*Sarcococca ruscifolia*, Fragrant Sarcococca. The Small Sarcococca has been discussed with the Dwarf Shrubs of Chapter III as an excellent member of its class, well adapted to southeastern growing conditions in the Piedmont and cooler Coastal Plain. The Fragrant Sarcococca is somewhat larger growing, and it might be usable here. However, it is not now available and has not been tried to determine its value. It is reported to be suited to well-watered, acid soils in partial to deep shade where it grows to 4 to 6 feet with handsome evergreen foliage and with red fruits which are showy in autumn.

*Severinia buxifolia,* Chinese Boxorange. Along the southern limits of the Coastal Plain this Shrub has been used rather extensively as a hedge plant and in foundation plantings. Upon further testing it may prove to be sufficiently hardy for most of this section. Its low, dense, spiny growth makes it ideal for these purposes, but it also wears a most attractive glossy, light green foliage of medium texture which is excellent for any landscape use. It bears small white flowers and black fruits; the latter are often effective through the winter. The Boxorange does well in full sun, and it seems to prefer open sites, standing up well under seacoast conditions. It may be subject to disease in close, shaded quarters. Apparently there are two or more strains of this plant on the market. Of these the so-called "weeping" or dwarf form may be preferred.

*Spiraea cantoniensis,* Reeves Spiraea. *Spiraea thunbergi,* Thunberg Spiraea. Two of the Spiraeas falling in this size group are common in this region, and they are somewhat useful for deciduous foliage and spring flower interest.

The Reeves Spiraea blooms in flat white clusters which make a bright showing in mid-spring. It grows to 6 feet in height with a spread of 8 feet or so, preferably in sun but also in partial shade, and adapts to any soils. The grayish foliage of fine texture persists through much of the fall, and it is almost evergreen in warmer sections. This species is rated by some authorities as among the best of the deciduous flowering shrubs for the hot Coastal Plain where plants of this class are often disappointing. It is superior to the Vanhoutte Spiraea because the old flower heads are deciduous and the form is not so leggy. It is pest free but does need steady and intelligent pruning. It will be useful chiefly for cutting and for relief in solid evergreen border plantings.

The Thunberg Spiraea grows to a height of 4 to 5 feet in a broadly rounded form and is distinguished by a dense, fine twiggy growth of irregular form, bearing fine-textured, slender leaves of yellow-green color that turn orange or yellow in fall. The flowers open very early in spring, usually starting in January, and make a lacy white effect which is very pretty, especially when the winter has been sufficiently cold to retard their opening. Adaptable to almost any soil or site, this plant is more compact and shapely when grown in the sun. It is resistant to disease, but it should be thinned occasionally to prevent accumulation of dead and nonproductive branches. It is not very vigorous in the Coastal Plain, but it is occasionally useful in cooler areas for cutting and for flower interest in sunny difficult sites.

*Syringa persica laciniata,* Cutleaf Persian Lilac. This is the only Lilac that can be recommended for the Coastal Plain, and it is one of the better deciduous flowering shrubs for all parts of the Southeast, fine for cutting gardens or in connection with flower borders. Growing to nearly 6 feet in height, the plant has an oval form, an open loose habit, and finely divided leaves which give it a fine texture effect. It prefers a sunny spot and rich soil and is easy to handle under these circumstances. Occasionally the Lilacs are infested with scale insects, but these are easily controlled with a dormant spray.

*Thuja occidentalis* varieties, Dwarf Eastern Arborvitae. Several dwarf forms of the Arborvitae belong either in this size class or with the previously listed Dwarf Shrubs. These include the small globe types with either green or the rather disagreeable yellow variegated foliage which one sees so often in foundation plantings. They are not fine materials, but they have their place largely in the Upper South. They stand severe cold, tolerate moisture and poor drainage, like sun, and are easily grown and hence relatively inexpensive. Almost their only enemy is the bag worm. In design they are excellent in hedges and free borders. They may be employed as specimens but are not very choice for such emphasis. Some of the varieties in this group are Tom Thumb (*globosa*), Hovey (*hoveyi*), Little Gem (*pumila*), Woodward (*woodwardi*), etc.

*Viburnum acerifolium,* Mapleleaf Viburnum. *Viburnum carlesi,* Koreanspice Viburnum. *Viburnum japonicum,* Japanese Viburnum. *Viburnum suspensum,* Sandankwa Viburnum. For naturalizing, an excellent choice is the common native Mapleleaf Viburnum which has a rambling suckering habit of growth, making loose irregular clumps about 5 feet or less in height. The deciduous leaves are rather coarse, shaped like those of the Maple, of dark green color turning a most unusual purple-rose in autumn. The white flowers of May and the blue-black fruits are pretty but not very showy. This plant does require at least some shade, but once established, it demands no care. It is adaptable to all soils of reasonable fertility and moisture supply, but it should have a mulch through which its shallow roots can ramify. It grows well in all but the warmest parts of the Southeast.

The Koreanspice Viburnum is choice for its snowball-like heads of pinkish to white fragrant flowers in early spring. It is suitable in the flower garden, in foundation plantings, and as an occasional specimen, but is too thin and open in habit for borders. The foliage is deciduous, coarse in texture, grayish green in color. The fruits are black in midsummer. This species is adaptable in the Upper South and the cooler Piedmont, doing well in any good soil, preferring sun. It is relatively free of pests, but is said to be subject to a graft blight disease.

The latter two Viburnums are evergreens valuable in the Coastal Plain. They are lusty growers which can reach just over 6 feet, and this fact should be kept in mind in placing. The Sandankwa Viburnum is a broadly spreading shrub with dull rounded leaves of rich coarse texture. There are attractive, pink-tinged white fragrant flowers in early summer which are followed in autumn by clusters of red fruits. The plant grows in a wide variety of soils and sites, but apparently prefers a light shade and a good supply of humus. It has no insect pests or diseases of note. This is an excellent material for foundation plantings and for shrub borders. It suits well both refined and informal surroundings. The Japanese Viburnum is said to be more hardy than the above. It is sold sometimes under the name of *V. macrophyllum*. This also has fragrant white flowers in spring and red fruits in late summer, but its chief beauty is in its slender dark green glossy leaves of heavy texture. The form is not so attractive, being rather narrow and upright and somewhat more leggy than the Sandankwa,

*Yucca gloriosa*, Moundlily Yucca. The Spanish Bayonet (*Yucca aloifolia*) is a familiar ornament of southern gardens, especially the small gardens of Charleston, Savannah, and Birmingham. Moundlily Yucca, which is often called the Spanish Dagger, is a superior plant in most instances. Both are natives of the Coastal Plain, but the latter is smaller, reaching about 6 feet in height, and has leaves of a brighter, almost blue-green tone. A form with striped leaves is also noted, but it is rarely seen and not available. The flowers, rising in large spikes with many white to cream bell-shaped blossoms, make a regal showing in midsummer. The Spanish Dagger grows well under all conditions where it has good drainage and sunlight; it is never bothered by heat, drought, or pests. Its stiff, rugged, coarse foliage makes a pronounced accent, used either in combination with other shrubs or with architectural features. Its distinctly exotic appearance and its sturdy undemanding constitution assure it a place in a variety of garden or architectural settings.

Pittosporum

# 4
# MAJOR
# SHRUBS

Group V - Medium
Group VI - Large

Since the materials of this division reach above eye level in height, they are generally useful for screening, for backgrounds and borders, and occasionally they will find a place in larger foundation plantings or as specimens. The class of Major Shrubs is further broken down into two parts, the Medium-sized and the Large Shrubs, at the height limit of approximately 10 feet.

The decision to place certain species in this division will almost certainly be questioned with respect to some which are now great favorites for foundation plantings where materials of smaller dimension may be assumed to have been desired. It may be worthwhile to examine in some detail several aspects of landscape usage bearing on this question. To illustrate, the handling of the Japanese Holly forms from Group V and the Burford Holly from Group VI may be cited as examples.

The Japanese Hollies (Bigleaf and Littleleaf varieties) are capable of reaching well over 10 feet in height, but they are frequently set in foundation plantings where perhaps 4 feet would be the maximum desirable size. Both varieties are vigorous growers, but they take shearing very well; this process does not materially impair their effectiveness since flowers and fruits are of no great value. It might even be said that these plants are improved by clipping, becoming more dense and shapely. They also have some character if allowed to take their natural forms, but this is a matter of choice; they can be maintained at relatively small stature for many years, only gradually coming into this size category.

The Burford Holly, a general favorite in this region, also can be clipped to almost any size for some time, but each shearing removes the new growth that produces the showy red fruits which, with the waxy new foliage, are the plant's principal decorative assets. In its normal climate range, this Holly will grow to over 10 feet in height, and yet it is often placed in foundation plantings and close to walls where it cannot develop fully. Here the real quality of the plant has no chance for expression, and to use it thus is clearly a poor design practice.

From this brief comparison of the characteristics of two related species, it will be seen again that the use of the materials is properly governed by a knowledge of their individual qualities. This knowledge comes from experience, and its application involves good judgment. In general, however, even with materials of large size which are relatively slow to develop and of refined habit, and which one may be tempted to restrain artificially, there is a question. As these plants begin to assume their true dimensions and character, one hesitates to cut them back severely because each bit of development represents time and care. It seems almost shameful to mutilate in any way the maturing specimen as it becomes a perfect thing of its kind. If a plant of this type is set originally in a place designed to accommodate its full stature, all is well and one may say that the plan was good. If the contrary is true, however, troubles arise. Shearing becomes more difficult and is needed more frequently as the plant becomes established and waxes in vigor. When shearing becomes ultimately impractical, there must be a transplanting, an operation which is always expensive, difficult, and hazardous, and becomes increasingly so with the age and size of the specimen.

One violates basic size limitations of many materials only with some risk. On the other hand, in treating certain others, some such practice is often advisable. The native Azaleas may be taken as an example. They are listed here with Group V although many of them will reach 15 feet in height (Group VI). Once they have attained maturity, however, many of these shrubs tend to lose their vigor and quality. Old wood may bear poor, thin growths of foliage and flowers, or some branches may die out altogether. Often the beauty of such plants is preserved by judicious use of the pruning shears to thin out older stems, and their vigor is prolonged by literally preventing maturity and by maintaining them somewhat under their normal height expectancy.

It becomes clear with this discussion that personal discretion is to be employed to some extent in the placing of each plant in its size class. Entire agreement on these placements could hardly be expected because different designers have their favorite methods of handling their favorite materials. The matter is further complicated by the varying behavior of any one species in different climatic zones and even in different exposures within one small locality.

Many of the Large Shrubs placed in Group VI are listed also among Small Trees in Chapter VII. The Crapemyrtle is an outstanding example of a plant with such a dual character; the Yaupon and Cassine Hollies also are equally at home in either class. Even the Sweet Osmanthus or Tea Olive finally attains tree stature in the Coastal Plain, with a height of fully 25 feet. One must have an accurate appreciation of the size and the growth habits of these shrubs in order to design with them most effectively. While several of these plants obviously fit in both categories appropriately, all of the plants listed here are shrubby in their early years at least, and they may be treated permanently as such when pruned regularly to prevent legginess. In most cases, those that eventually do become tree-like have several trunks.

Most of the materials in the Major Shrub division will have little use on the average home property if we except a few choice flowering specimens of Camellia, Rhododendron, or Lilac in strategic locations. Some, such as the Crapemyrtle, may find a place as small, many-trunked trees for shade on terraces, walks, or at gateways. The thin and leggy Yaupon is excellent backed up against a fence or wall to give extra height to screening. Several species make fine clipped hedges. In general, however, these are massive growers with a broad spread that occupy more space than one can usually devote to borders on the small place, and they are too outsize for most foundation plantings.

These plants are better suited to projects of large proportions. They can be employed most effectively in combination with trees in screen and border plantings for parks, housing developments, and large properties. Specimen plantings of Camellias, Lilacs, or Rhododendrons make interesting hobby collections where space is ample. Masses of Forsythia or Elaeagnus are effective in covering sunny banks along roads and parkways, and Rhododendrons are handsome in large drifts on wooded slopes. In designing with all of these materials one must be at least somewhat conscious of the habit of growth, whether they are normally "leggy" or whether they "face down" well. Included in the lists for each zone are some of the most attractive of all shrubs for flowering and fruiting, but one must take care to allow ample space when planting them.

## V. Medium Shrubs for the SOUTHERN COASTAL PLAIN

| *Botanical Name* | *Common Name* |
|---|---|
| RECOMMENDED FOR GENERAL USE | |
| Aucuba japonica | Japanese Aucuba |

| *Botanical Name* | *Common Name* |
|---|---|
| Ligustrum japonicum | Japanese Privet |
| Loropetalum chinense | Loropetalum |
| Nandina domestica | Nandina |
| Prunus laurocerasus schipkaensis | Schipka Laurelcherry |
| Prunus laurocerasus zabeliana | Zabel Laurelcherry |
| Pyracantha koidzumi | Formosa Firethorn |
| Rhododendron arborescens | Sweet Azalea |
| Rhododendron austrinum | Florida Azalea |
| Rhododendron canescens | Piedmont Azalea |
| Rhododendron indicum | Indica Azalea |
| Viburnum odoratissimum | Sweet Viburnum |
| Viburnum tinus | Laurestinus Viburnum |

### RECOMMENDED FOR RESTRICTED USE

| | |
|---|---|
| Abelia grandiflora | Glossy Abelia |
| Acacia farnesiana | Sweet Acacia |
| Aronia arbutifolia | Red Chokeberry |
| Callistemon lanceolatus | Lemon Bottlebrush |
| Calycanthus floridus | Common Sweetshrub |
| Chaenomeles lagenaria | Common Floweringquince |
| Chimonanthus praecox | Wintersweet |
| Clethra alnifolia | Summersweet Clethra |
| Corylus americana | American Filbert |
| Cotoneaster francheti | Franchet Cotoneaster |
| Cotoneaster pannosa | Silverleaf Cotoneaster |
| Euonymus japonicus | Evergreen Euonymus |
| Euonymus kiautschovicus | Spreading Euonymus |
| Eurya japonica | Japanese Eurya |
| Forsythia intermedia | Border Forsythia |
| Fortunella margarita | Nagami Kumquat |
| Fothergilla major | Large Fothergilla |
| Gardenia jasminoides | Capejasmine |
| Hamamelis vernalis | Vernal Witchhazel |
| Hydrangea quercifolia | Oakleaf Hydrangea |
| Ilex crenata latifolia | Bigleaf Japanese Holly |
| Ilex crenata microphylla | Littleleaf Japanese Holly |
| Ilex glabra | Inkberry |
| Ilex verticillata | Common Winterberry |
| Juniperus chinensis pfitzeriana | Pfitzer Juniper |
| Juniprus sabina | Savin Juniper |
| Kalmia latifolia | Mountainlaurel Kalmia |
| Lonicera fragrantissima | Winter Honeysuckle |

| *Botanical Name* | *Common Name* |
|---|---|
| Myrtus communis | True Myrtle |
| Pieris japonica | Japanese Pieris |
| Rhododendron prunifolium | Plumleaf Azalea |
| Rhododendron serrulatum | Hammocksweet Azalea |
| Spiraea prunifolia plena | Bridalwreath Spiraea |
| Spiraea vanhouttei | Vanhoutte Spiraea |
| Viburnum rhytidophyllum | Leatherleaf Viburnum |
| Vitex agnuscastus | Lilac Chastetree |

## V. Medium Shrubs for the SOUTHERN PIEDMONT

### RECOMMENDED FOR GENERAL USE

| | |
|---|---|
| Aucuba japonica | Japanese Aucuba |
| Ilex crenata latifolia | Bigleaf Japanese Holly |
| Ilex crenata microphylla | Littleleaf Japanese Holly |
| Ligustrum japonicum | Japanese Privet |
| Loropetalum chinense | Loropetalum |
| Nandina domestica | Nandina |
| Prunus laurocerasus schipkaensis | Schipka Laurelcherry |
| Prunus laurocerasus zabeliana | Zabel Laurelcherry |
| Pyracantha koidzumi | Formosa Firethorn |
| Rhododendron arborescens | Sweet Azalea |
| Rhododendron calendulaceum | Flame Azalea |
| Rhododendron canescens | Piedmont Azalea |
| Viburnum burkwoodi | Burkwood Viburnum |
| Viburnum dilatatum | Linden Viburnum |
| Viburnum rhytidophyllum | Leatherleaf Viburnum |
| Viburnum tomentosum | Doublefile Viburnum |

### RECOMMENDED FOR RESTRICTED USE

| | |
|---|---|
| Abelia grandiflora | Glossy Abelia |
| Aronia arbutifolia | Red Chokeberry |
| Buddleia davidi | Orangeye Butterflybush |
| Calycanthus floridus | Common Sweetshrub |
| Chaenomeles lagenaria | Common Floweringquince |
| Chimonanthus praecox | Wintersweet |
| Clethra alnifolia | Summersweet Clethra |
| Cornus alba sibirica | Siberian Dogwood |
| Cornus racemosa | Gray Dogwood |
| Corylus americana | American Filbert |
| Cotoneaster francheti | Franchet Cotoneaster |
| Cotoneaster pannosa | Silverleaf Cotoneaster |
| Enkianthus perulatus | White Enkianthus |

| *Botanical Name* | *Common Name* |
|---|---|
| Euonymus alatus | Winged Euonymus |
| Euonymus kiautschovicus | Spreading Euonymus |
| Eurya japonica | Japanese Eurya |
| Forsythia intermedia | Border Forsythia |
| Forsythia suspensa | Weeping Forsythia |
| Fothergilla major | Large Fothergilla |
| Gardenia jasminoides | Capejasmine |
| Hamamelis vernalis | Vernal Witchhazel |
| Hydrangea quercifolia | Oakleaf Hydrangea |
| Ilex glabra | Inkberry |
| Ilex verticillata | Common Winterberry |
| Juniperus chinensis pfitzeriana | Pfitzer Juniper |
| Juniperus sabina | Savin Juniper |
| Kalmia latifolia | Mountainlaurel Kalmia |
| Kolkwitzia amabilis | Beautybush |
| Ligustrum obtusifolium regelianum | Regel Privet |
| Lonicera fragrantissima | Winter Honeysuckle |
| Malus sargenti | Sargent Crabapple |
| Philadelphus coronarius | Sweet Mockorange |
| Pieris japonica | Japanese Pieris |
| Pyracantha coccinea | Scarlet Firethorn |
| Rhododendron austrinum | Florida Azalea |
| Rhododendron indicum | Indica Azalea |
| Rhododendron prunifolium | Plumleaf Azalea |
| Rhododendron serrulatum | Hammocksweet Azalea |
| Sorbaria aitchisoni | Kashmir Falsespiraea |
| Spiraea prunifolia plena | Bridalwreath Spiraea |
| Spiraea vanhouttei | Vanhoutte Spiraea |
| Taxus cuspidata | Japanese Yew |
| Taxus media | Anglojap Yew |
| Viburnum tinus | Laurestinus Viburnum |
| Vitex agnuscastus | Lilac Chastetree |
| Weigela florida | Oldfashioned Weigela |

## V. Medium Shrubs for the UPPER SOUTH

### RECOMMENDED FOR GENERAL USE

| | |
|---|---|
| Abelia grandiflora | Glossy Abelia |
| Forsythia intermedia | Border Forsythia |
| Ilex crenata latifolia | Bigleaf Japanese Holly |
| Ilex crenata microphylla | Littleleaf Japanese Holly |
| Ilex glabra | Inkberry |
| Kalmia latifolia | Mountainlaurel Kalmia |

| Botanical Name | Common Name |
|---|---|
| Ligustrum obtusifolium regelianum | Regel Privet |
| Pieris japonica | Japanese Pieris |
| Prunus laurocerasus schipkaensis | Schipka Laurelcherry |
| Prunus laurocerasus zabeliana | Zabel Laurelcherry |
| Pyracantha coccinea | Scarlet Firethorn |
| Rhododendron calendulaceum | Flame Azalea |
| Rhododendron catawbiense | Catawba Rhododendron |
| Rhododendron nudiflorum | Pinxterbloom Azalea |
| Taxus cuspidata | Japanese Yew |
| Taxus media | Anglojap Yew |
| Viburnum burkwoodi | Burkwood Viburnum |
| Viburnum dilatatum | Linden Viburnum |
| Viburnum rhytidophyllum | Leatherleaf Viburnum |
| Viburnum tomentosum | Doublefile Viburnum |

## RECOMMENDED FOR RESTRICTED USE

| | |
|---|---|
| Acanthopanax sieboldianus | Fiveleaf Acanthopanax |
| Aronia arbutifolia | Red Chokeberry |
| Aucuba japonica | Japanese Aucuba |
| Buddleia davidi | Orangeye Butterflybush |
| Calycanthus floridus | Common Sweetshrub |
| Chaenomeles lagenaria | Common Floweringquince |
| Chimonanthus praecox | Wintersweet |
| Clethra alnifolia | Summersweet Clethra |
| Cornus alba sibirica | Siberian Dogwood |
| Cornus racemosa | Gray Dogwood |
| Corylus americana | American Filbert |
| Cotoneaster francheti | Franchet Cotoneaster |
| Cotoneaster pannosa | Silverleaf Cotoneaster |
| Enkianthus perulatus | White Enkianthus |
| Euonymus alatus | Winged Euonymus |
| Euonymus kiautschovicus | Spreading Euonymus |
| Forsythia suspensa | Weeping Forsythia |
| Fothergilla major | Large Fothergilla |
| Hamamelis vernalis | Vernal Witchhazel |
| Hydrangea quercifolia | Oakleaf Hydrangea |
| Ilex verticillata | Common Winterberry |
| Juniperus chinensis pfitzeriana | Pfitzer Juniper |
| Juniperus sabina | Savin Juniper |
| Kolkwitzia amabilis | Beautybush |
| Ligustrum japonicum | Japanese Privet |
| Lonicera fragrantissima | Winter Honeysuckle |
| Loropetalum chinense | Loropetalum |

| Botanical Name | Common Name |
|---|---|
| Malus sargenti | Sargent Crabapple |
| Myrica pennsylvanica | Northern Bayberry |
| Nandina domestica | Nandina |
| Philadelphus coronarius | Sweet Mockorange |
| Rhododendron arborescens | Sweet Azalea |
| Rhododendron canescens | Piedmont Azalea |
| Sorbaria aitchisoni | Kashmir Falsespiraea |
| Spiraea prunifolia plena | Bridalwreath Spiraea |
| Spiraea vanhouttei | Vanhoutte Spiraea |
| Vitex agnuscastus | Lilac Chastetree |
| Weigela florida | Oldfashioned Weigela |

RANGE CHART FOR GROUP V. MEDIUM SHRUBS

| | Coastal Plain | | Piedmont | | Upper South | |
|---|---|---|---|---|---|---|
| Abelia grandiflora | - - - | - - - | - - - | x x x | x x x | x x x |
| Aucuba japonica | x x x | x x x | x x x | x x x | x x x | - - - |
| Forsythia intermedia | | | - - - | x x x | x x x | x x x |
| Ilex crenata latifolia | - - - | x x x | x x x | x x x | x x x | x x x |
| Ilex crenata microphylla | - - - | x x x | x x x | x x x | x x x | x x x |
| Ilex glabra | - - - | - - - | - - - | x x x | x x x | x x x |
| Kalmia latifolia | - - - | - - - | - - - | x x x | x x x | x x x |
| Ligustrum japonicum | x x x | x x x | x x x | x x x | x x x | - - - |
| Ligustrum obtusifolium regelianum | | | - - - | x x x | x x x | x x x |
| Loropetalum chinense | x x x | x x x | x x x | x x x | - - - | |
| Nandina domestica | x x x | x x x | x x x | x x x | - - - | - - - |
| Pieris japonica | | | - - - | x x x | x x x | x x x |
| Prunus laurocerasus schipkaensis | x x x | x x x | x x x | x x x | x x x | x x x |
| Prunus laurocerasus zabeliana | x x x | x x x | x x x | x x x | x x x | x x x |
| Pyracantha coccinea | | | - - - | x x x | x x x | x x x |
| Pyracantha koidzumi | x x x | x x x | x x x | x x x | - - - | |
| Rhododendron arborescens | x x x | x x x | x x x | x x x | - - - | |
| Rhododendron austrinum | x x x | x x x | x x x | - - - | | |
| Rhododendron calendulaceum | | | - - - | x x x | x x x | x x x | x x x |
| Rhododendron canescens | | | | - - - | x x x | x x x |
| Rhododendron catawbiense | x x x | x x x | x x x | x x x | - - - | |
| Rhododendron indicum | x x x | x x x | x x x | - - - | | |
| Rhododendron nudiflorum | | | | - - - | x x x | x x x |
| Taxus cuspidata | | | | - - - | x x x | x x x |
| Taxus media | | | | - - - | x x x | x x x |
| Viburnum burkwoodi | | - - - | x x x | x x x | x x x | x x x |
| Viburnum dilatatum | | - - - | x x x | x x x | x x x | x x x |
| Viburnum odoratissimum | x x x | x x x | - - - | | | |
| Viburnum rhytidophyllum | | - - - | x x x | x x x | x x x | x x x |
| Viburnum tinus | x x x | x x x | x x x | - - - | | |
| Viburnum tomentosum | | - - - | x x x | x x x | x x x | x x x |

Few materials of this size group appear to be equally adaptable to all parts of the Southeast with the possible exception of the two *Prunus* varieties which are more hardy than the species and do quite well from the Coastal Plain to the Ohio Valley. The *Abelia* meets this range, but it is inferior in warmer sections in comparison with other available materials. *Ilex glabra* is hardy everywhere, but it is little valued in its native Coastal Plain. The other two *Ilex* are fair to locally good in the Coastal Plain, but they are often leggy and weak in the hot sandy soils. The *Kalmia* is native in all zones but in restricted spots, and it can hardly be generally recommended for landscape design in warmer areas. The *Nandina* is fairly hardy everywhere, but its fruiting is often destroyed in the Upper South. Special soil requirements must be met for *Kalmia*, *Pieris*, and all *Rhododendron* species.

*Abelia grandiflora*, Glossy Abelia. This fine reliable plant is abundant through this region. It commonly grows to about 8 feet in height in the milder parts of the Southeast, but it is set often in places where, obviously, it was never intended to reach this size. More often than not, it is seen with its top unfeelingly hacked off, and so has an awkward appearance. The foliage is fine in texture, of clean glossy green color, and semi-evergreen. Throughout a long season from early summer to autumn, the Abelia produces an almost continuous succession of white to pinkish flowers. It makes a good plant for borders although it is a little thin for screens; it is excellent for low clipped hedges from 2 to 4 feet high. It thrives in sun and also grows in open shade. It suffers from no pests, but does require intelligent pruning to keep it in good shape, for it tends to become leggy and to accumulate dead wood. It is really an excellent plant, and it is most unfortunate that it should be used with so little regard for its size, texture, and care. Although the Abelia grows very well everywhere in this region, it is more restrained in size in cooler sections and for this reason is rated higher in the Upper South than in the Piedmont and the Coastal Plain. In the coldest parts of the Upper South, this shrub may not prove entirely hardy although it will recover quickly after having been frozen back. An annual cutting back to ground level is sometimes recommended. The Abelia variety "Edward Goucher" is more compact in form, probably scarcely reaching 6 feet in height, with flowers of a deeper rosy purple color, hardly as attractive as the above. A still more dwarf variety, called "Sherwood," reaches to 3 feet.

*Acacia farnesiana*, Sweet Acacia. The only Acacia used at all in this region is the Sweet Acacia, often called Opopanax, which is seen occasionally in the warmer sections. Ordinarily this grows to a height of about 10 feet, sometimes a little more, with very delicate, finely divided foliage which never conceals entirely its rugged, thorny branch and twig structure. This habit gives the Opopanax particular interest as a specimen, especially for an architectural setting, or trained against a smooth-textured wall. It is a sun lover, tolerant of drought and poor alkaline soils, and free of pests. With its attractive small yellow powder-puff-like blossoms in early spring, this plant is an interesting material for limited use in protected sites. It needs pruning to keep it clear of accumulations of dead twigs.

*Acanthopanax sieboldianus*, Fiveleaf Acanthopanax. This is a practically foolproof shrub for poor soils, enduring drought, tolerating shade, and showing perfect resistance to ordinary diseases and insects. The poor features of this plant are its lack of flower or fruit interest and its usually rather sprawling habit of growth, reaching a height of 7 to 8 feet. The deciduous foliage, persisting into late autumn, is rich in effect, palmately compound, of medium texture and light green color; this is foiled to advantage by smooth masonry and other fine building surfaces. It might very well be pleached against walls in those too frequent narrow spaces beside walks where normal sun, air, and moisture requirements cannot be easily met. Possibly the plant will survive under the widespread eaves which are becoming more common with modern architecture, to the discomfort of most plants. The thorny stems provide a good barrier, but the shrub does not make a highly satisfactory clipped hedge. For exceptionally difficult spots this shrub is a fair solution for the Upper South and the Piedmont.

*Aronia arbutifolia*, Red Chokeberry. This occurs as a native in all parts of the eastern United States and is a good material for naturalizing, spreading by underground stems to make large clumps. It is rather thin, open, upright, and graceful in habit to a height of 10 feet in shaded places, somewhat less in exposed sites. As a rule it is more compact, lower, and more attractive grown in the open and given some pruning. The deciduous foliage of medium texture turns red in autumn. There are small white flowers in effective clusters in spring, and the red fruits of late summer and fall are decorative. This plant does well in most ordinary soils, and, except for thinning out occasional stems to ground level, it needs little care.

*Aucuba japonica*, Japanese Aucuba. This is well known and widely planted throughout the Southeast. It is a favorite for its rich, coarse-textured, evergreen olive-colored foliage and its colorful red fruits of mid-winter. In habit of growth, the Aucuba is likely to be rather rangy, upright, and spindly, rarely reaching more than 10 feet in height. But this is a plant on which occasional use of the pruning shears is advised to keep it lower and more compact. In early spring clusters of small brownish flowers, not at all conspicuous, are borne where the buds of the previous year's growth unfold; the cherry-like red fruits mature through the autumn to form colorful ornaments for Christmas. The sexes are separate; so in order to insure fruiting, it is necessary to include a male plant for every dozen or so females within reasonable proximity in the planting arrangement. The Aucubas require shade because the foliage is likely to be burned by the sun, especially in winter. They are excellent for dark corners near the north side of a house where they grow well with a minimum of care. They are fine as specimens or in groups and are grown occasionally in pots and plant boxes. The gold-spotted foliage form, called the Gold Dust Tree, *A. j. maculata*, is also excellent as a tub specimen, and it is much used for cutting and flower arrangements. Aucubas have no pests, but since they prefer a heavy soil they sometimes fail in excessively sandy locations in the lower portions of the Coastal Plain. They are somewhat tender for the Upper South, but, with protection from buildings and other plantings, they will grow to 6 feet or more as far north as Charleston, W. Va.

*Buddleia davidi*, Orangeye Butterflybush. About the only use for the Butterflybush will be in cutting gardens of the Upper South and the Piedmont where it will supply a long succession of spike form flowers in midsummer. Weedy and coarse in habit and growing rapidly in any soil in sun, this shrub is best cut nearly to the ground each spring and treated almost as a perennial. Colors in the named varieties are white, pink, lilac, and red-purple.

*Callistemon lanceolatus*, Bottlebrush. This is a tender shrub for the Coastal Plain which is effective planted near or against a wall where its thin and open habit and fine-textured evergreen foliage appear to best advantage. The brilliant flowers, so well described in the plant's name, are most decorative. The Bottlebrush likes sun, it endures drought and poor soils well, and it is free of pests. Shade, good fertilizing, and watering are its worst enemies for these make it grow overly rank and accentuate its weedy form. It is worth a try in sunny sites anywhere in the Coastal Plain; it is especially good on the exposed seashore. It should be purchased in cans to insure successful transplanting.

*Calycanthus floridus*, Common Sweetshrub. The Sweetshrub is a native of the Southeast from Virginia to Florida. It has been grown in flower gardens since colonial times for its brownish red or greenish yellow flowers of spring which have such a delicious aroma after they have been warmed in one's hand or pocket. The scattered brown urn-like seed pods of autumn are scarcely less interesting for their structure. This shrub adapts to almost any soil in sun or shade, spreads with suckering stems into a dense rounded mass to about 8 feet in height, and is heavily clothed in rich, dark, coarse-textured foliage which also is fragrant and which turns yellow in autumn. Although the Sweetshrub has no outstanding quality, its general adaptability, freedom from care, and solid satisfying beauty may well make it a first-rate shrub for any and all parts of this region. It is especially good for poorly drained sites. For unclipped borders or hedges it could be excellent.

*Chaenomeles lagenaria,* Common Floweringquince. This deciduous shrub is one of the best for cutting in cooler sections of this region. Its spreading habit produces in time a growth of large girth about 8 feet in height, dense, twiggy, and thorny. Most of the flowering shrubs require a good bit of pruning to maintain them in a vigorous state, but this is not so true of the Quince. The foliage is medium in texture, rather poor in quality, usually falling early in autumn. The apple-blossom-like flowers, appearing before the leaves, are beautiful in colors ranging from white through pink to red, both single and double. Much work has been done to produce finer flowering types, and these are worth investigating before planting. In autumn the fruits, yellow balls of 2 to 4 inches in diameter, are often decorative, and they may be cooked for jellies. The fruits have a spicy fragrance which, after picking, they retain for several months while the fruit dries, shrivels, and finally turns hard and brown. The shrub thrives in spite of neglect in any heavy soil in sun or light shade. It is attacked by aphids but these do not seem to injure it to any extent. It can be used as a hedge, and it is attractive when trimmed flat against a wall. Unfortunately the flowering is scattered and not too showy in areas of very warm winters; its effect is best in cooler sections.

*Chimonanthus praecox,* Wintersweet. This is a deciduous Chinese introduction which has long been a valued ornament in Southern gardens because of its January blossoms, which open on any warm day at this season, when flowers are scarce. For indoor arrangements the blossoms are especially desirable with their straw-yellow petals marked with deep maroon, their rich and spicy perfume, and their irregular and picturesque branch forms. In summer, too, the shrub has a satisfying appearance. The foliage is coarse in texture, and the bush is mantelled heavily in rich green. The form of the shrub is dense and rounded, reaching a height of about 10 feet with a spread of equal or greater dimension expanded by the slowly suckering stems. It grows well in full sun or in light shade, possibly even in fairly dense shade. Although it prefers fertile, moist soils, it readily adapts to average conditions and to general neglect. It does not require spraying, but occasional light prunings to remove old wood are desirable. The Wintersweet should be included in all cutting gardens where space is available, in warmer parts of the Southeast as far north as Memphis, Knoxville, and Washington, D. C. It fits well with shrub screens and borders. There is a more showy flowering form which is offered by some nurseries under the name of *C. p. grandiflorus.*

*Clethra alnifolia,* Summersweet Clethra. The Summersweet has been planted chiefly because its small spikes of fragrant white flowers appear in midsummer when there is little other shrub bloom. Native to the eastern states from Maine to Florida, this plant is adaptable to a wide variety of sites. However, it is probably only rarely useful for naturalizing along the seacoast or in wet places, and occasionally one may include it in the cutting garden. The bloom is not outstanding, nor is the deciduous foliage or upright bushy form—growing 6 feet or more in height. The persistent brown seed pods are disfiguring. There is a pink flowering variation, *C. a. rosea,* and other species, but none of these seems much superior to the above.

*Cornus alba sibirica,* Siberian Dogwood. *Cornus racemosa,* Gray Dogwood. The Gray Dogwood, often listed as *C. paniculata,* is almost certainly the finest of the many bush Dogwoods, and, being native from Maine to Florida and the Mississippi Valley, it is widely adaptable in the Southeast from swamp to hilltop. In very exposed sites on poor soils it may hardly reach 6 feet, but in fertile, moist, and sheltered spots it has quite a different character, possibly exceeding 10 feet. Sprouting and suckering from the root, this is a many-stemmed shrub, excellent in large clumps, with attractive gray branches and medium-textured deciduous foliage which turns deep red in autumn. The flat heads of white flowers in June are not very showy; these are followed in late summer by white berries on decorative reddish stemlets. Generally the fruits are quickly eaten by birds. With little care and no pest troubles except for possible invasions by scales which should be watched for, standing drought, exposure, poor soils, and urban surroundings, the Gray Dogwood is an excellent shrub for all soils in sun or shade, making a good border and handsome informal masses in areas of naturalistic character such as parks and roadsides. Plants set 2 feet apart form a good hedge. For smaller places it is somewhat coarse and aggressive in habit. Although this plant will probably adapt to all parts of the Southeast, it is little seen in warmer sections and is likely to be more useful in the Upper South.

In addition to the Gray, there are several other shrub Dogwoods which, although they are more rank and coarse in character, do have some value, chiefly for the color effect of their stems in the winter landscape. The Siberian Dogwood is the one chosen as representative of this group because it is considered to be the most brilliant with its branches of bright coral red. Similar to others of the group, this plant has coarse deciduous foliage, white flowers in spring, and clusters of white berries in autumn. The habit is stoloniferous and rank, making massive mounds to almost 10 feet in height. To encourage the production of new vigorous basal shoots which are brighter in color most gardeners make a practice of cutting older canes regularly in early spring, and thus keep the height to approximately 6 feet. This plant is somewhat inviting to scale insects. It tolerates most soils and situations although it is better in the sun in moist or poorly drained sites. Similar to the Siberian Dogwood and almost as desirable is the Redosier Dogwood, *C. stolonifera,* generally native to the eastern states, which has red or, in the variety *C. s. flaviramea,* yellow stems. There are unscrupulous mail-order dealers who list a "Red Dogwood" at a very low price, and then send one of the above to the buyer, who often expects, to his chagrin, to receive the Red Flowering Dogwood which is quite a different plant. The Silky Dogwood, *C. amomum,* also a native similar to the Redosier in character, has deep blue fruits. All of these will rarely be useful on the average small property. They are often desirable, however, for larger scale designs, particularly on poor soils in the cooler parts of the Upper South, and for naturalizing along streams. They also make fine informal, unclipped hedges.

*Corylus americana,* American Filbert. This is commonly called the Hazelnut and may be found in almost any part of this region, usually growing in thickets in sunny, open valleys near streams or runs. Forming dense and billowing masses of coarse deciduous foliage, this plant is not of great ornamental value and is often not available in nurseries, but it might be useful rarely for naturalizing and for borders. The male flowers are interesting in early spring with their clusters of hanging catkins, and in late summer curious leafy sheaths envelop the edible nuts. Some of the European Filberts are cultivated for their nuts and colored foliage forms. These are larger growing plants, however, litttle superior to the American form for normal ornamental use. The nuts are difficult to produce, chiefly because of pollination problems. The Curly European Filbert, *C. avellana contorta,* is a curious freak of interest for picturesque form.

*Cotoneaster francheti,* Franchet Cotoneaster. *Cotoneaster pannosa,* Silverleaf Cotoneaster. There are two semi-evergreen Cotoneasters of this size group which are good in warmer parts of this region, but they may not be quite hardy in all parts of the Upper South. The two resemble each other closely, and they are probably mixed in use. They have an upright, fountain-like growth form to a height of about 8 feet, fine-textured leaves of gray-green with silver undersides, small white flowers in spring, and in autumn showy red to orange fruits. If a gray foliage effect for a sunny site is desired, these plants offer a graceful, colorful, and elegant solution in the range from cooler parts of the Coastal Plain to Memphis, Knoxville, and Washington. Cotoneasters seem especially useful on alkaline soils. Set 2 feet apart, they are effective in hedges. One must recall, however, that the Cotoneasters are subject to blight, to attacks of scales, mites, and lacewing flies, and that they do need pruning.

In addition to these varieties, there is also an array of hardier deciduous Cotoneasters in this size class, most of them with good, fine-textured foliage, flowers, and attractive fruits. These will be in little demand in this area, however, where such a large variety of troublefree materials is readily available. These include C. *dielsiana*, C. *huphensis*, C. *foveolata*, and C. *lucida*.

*Enkianthus perulatus*, White Enkianthus. This will be interesting on occasion in combination with Rhododendrons, Azaleas, and other lovers of acid soils, which this too must have. It has a strong upright habit of growth to somewhat over 6 feet, attractive bell-like flowers in clusters in late spring, and a brilliant red autumn foliage color. While it is not widely applicable, the White Enkianthus as well as the larger growing Redvein Enkianthus, *E. campanulatus*, may be worth a trial to give contrast and lightness to somber masses of evergreens, in the Upper South and the Piedmont.

*Euonymus alatus*, Winged Euonymus. *Euonymus japonicus*, Evergreen Euonymus. *Euonymus kiautschovicus*, Spreading Euonymus. The most outstanding single feature of the Winged Euonymus is its habit of growth, which is strikingly horizontal with a heavy twig structure. In winter especially the prominent barky ridges along the stems accentuate this growth pattern. The rather thin, medium-textured, deciduous leaves are dark green in summer, becoming in fall a brilliant purple-red which is flamboyant even in regions of high autumn coloration. Contrasting with the leaves, the orange fruits, rather like those of the Bittersweet, add to the show and prolong the color effect into winter. With so many strong characteristics, this shrub should be planted with discrimination. It is too large and rank for average properties; but in designs large enough to hold it, it will do well in any fair to good soils in sun or light shade, without care, to make a brave effect, in the Upper South or the Piedmont. Its large size and rugged character will almost confine it to parks and industrial or institutional sites, where it is excellent.

The Evergreen Euonymus is simply mentioned here because it is frequently seen in the Coastal Plain and the lower Piedmont, where it is grown in hedges and in borders for its bright and glossy evergreen foliage. It is, however, a plant which should be avoided in landscape work, for it is very subject to scale infestations that are impossible to control.

The Spreading Euonymus, often listed as *E. patens*, is more useful because it is almost free of scale attacks; however, it should be watched for the first signs of trouble. Growing normally to a height of about 8 feet with a broad spread and an open informal character, this shrub has evergreen or, in colder climates, semi-evergreen foliage of medium to coarse texture. It produces inconspicuous greenish flowers in late summer, and by fall these mature into orange fruits which are often colorful where frost does not come too early to stop their development. The Spreading Euonymus is a rapid grower in all soils in sunny or shaded sites and, except for treating for scale, requires little care. In the Coastal Plain and the Piedmont, where there are many more choice broad-leaved evergreens, this plant will have little demand. In the Upper South, however, it is much used in the alkaline soil sections for hedges and borders, screens, and foundation plantings. The plant is half vining in habit, thus lending itself well to training on a wall or fence.

*Eurya japonica*, Japanese Eurya. This is a fairly rare shrub in this region, but its inclusion among the best in this size group might be justified in the future for its distinctive habit of growth. It is also possible that this belongs with the Large Shrubs group since it is said to grow as high as 20 feet, but further local testing will be required to determine this. The Eurya has an open, irregularly horizontal form which is picturesque and gives a rugged character to plantings. Its dense, dark, evergreen foliage of medium texture also is effective. It bears small flowers and black fruits, but these have little ornamental value although they are interesting in detail. The plant grows well in sun or light shade in average good soils, and it seems to require little care or spraying. It should be well adapted throughout the Coastal Plain, the Piedmont, and possibly a little farther north. The Eurya seems destined to become, when it is better known, one of the very useful materials of the region.

*Forsythia intermedia*, Border Forsythia. *Forsythia suspensa*, Weeping Forsythia. It is possible that there are no finer deciduous shrubs for flower and foliage for general planting needs through the Upper South and the cooler Piedmont than the Forsythias, even if they have become almost too common in recent years. Throughout this region, in any soil or exposure, they are fine for screens and borders, for weeping over walls and rough ground, as specimens, as large scale bank and ground covers, for small homes, estates, or parks. As they are so obliging in nature, they are overplanted, often in places too small for their natural growth. Then they are lopped off without feeling, making a sad sight and reminding one again that knowledge of the basic character of a plant's growth is fundamental to successful planting design. There are several Forsythia species of importance, differing mostly in habit of growth, but all bearing the showy yellow flowers in early spring. In this discussion, it is likely that only two species need be mentioned. The first of these is the Border Forsythia, which is rather upright in habit, reaching almost 10 feet, not quite so pronounced in the weeping form of its branches, and probably the most floriferous of all, especially in its variety, *F. i. spectabilis*. Another variety worth noting for its paler lemon yellow flower color is the Primrose Forsythia, *F. i. primulina*. For covering banks and draping over or training against walls, the species with a more pronounced weeping form is the Weeping Forsythia which normally reaches about 6 feet in height but which may produce cascading stems to 10 feet or more. There is a variety said to be a particularly good groundcover called *F. s. sieboldi*. Another, called Arnold Dwarf, originated recently at the Arnold Arboretum, is reported to be quite small, not over 2 feet high, but it does not flower. Still another form called "Beatrix Farrand" produces very large individual florets, but it probably is not more showy in the landscape than some of the above. All of the Forsythias should be planted with occasional pruning in mind. This should consist of removal of older canes to ground level after the spring blooming.

*Fortunella margarita*, Nagami (Oval) Kumquat. This grows in the shape of a small tree to about 10 feet, and in warmer sections of the Coastal Plain is of ornamental value for its fragrant white flowers, bright orange edible fruits, and good evergreen foliage of coarse texture. It requires good soil, moisture, a place in the sun or open shade, and spraying to control the many pests common to the citrus plants. It is said to be most satisfactory in country districts, away from sources of white fly infestations so common in urban areas, and near bodies of water which modify severe temperature drops. This species is quite tender and has limited usefulness, but where it is well grown it is very decorative.

*Fothergilla major*, Large Fothergilla. Two of the Fothergilla species have been discussed with the Small Shrubs of Chapter IV. The species discussed here is slightly larger, growing to almost 10 feet in a broadly rounded form of open informal habit, with the characteristic showy bottlebrush-like flowers of spring and the coarse deciduous foliage which has a good fall color. It is unfortunate that these are not easily available, for they are possibly among the very best of the deciduous flowering shrubs for this region. They are adaptable to all parts from the cooler Coastal Plain through the Upper South. They probably ought to be considered for use in well-watered, acid soils of good humus content in partially shaded sites.

*Gardenia jasminoides*, Capejasmine. For generations the bush of

Capejasmine was a traditional ornament in almost every garden of the Piedmont and the Coastal Plain, and its handsome waxy fragrant flowers of the early summer spiced all festive occasions of the season. Heavy infestations of the white fly, which rob the plants of their vigor and are responsible for the repulsive accumulations of sooty mold on the foliage, are now so common that this old favorite has dropped to second place. The pest damage is not so severe in open rural districts, removed from concentrations of other ornamentals; Gardenias may still be recommended here and in such other places where there is a gardener willing and able to give the plants the steady spraying of nicotine sulphate and summer oil which they require. Generally, the sites recommended for this plant are those which are protected by an open shade as that from high Pines or buildings, but one sees them occasionally in fully exposed places. They like good soils and a steady moisture supply, and they resent transplanting. Under certain conditions gardeners will still want to try the Capejasmine, and, where it is well grown, it is beautiful in form, foliage, and flower—a prize for cutting. This plant should be grafted on nematode resistant understock. While large old specimens used to be common throughout the Piedmont, the plant is somewhat tender here, and it should be planted with some protection at hand.

*Hamamelis vernalis*, Vernal Witchhazel. The Vernal Witchhazel is native to the Mississippi Valley, and it is well suited to cooler parts of the Coastal Plain, the Piedmont, and the Upper South. The shrub is noteworthy because of the rather inconspicuous but interesting flowers—small, spidery, yellow to reddish brown, and fragrant—which begin to open as early as February. The growth habit is fairly dense, depending on whether grown in sun or shade, with a rather horizontal irregular habit of some character, reaching just over 6 feet in height. The coarse-textured deciduous foliage turns a good yellow in the fall. This is a pest-free undemanding material, excellent for naturalizing in open woods or for sunny borders. It is possibly one of the best deciduous plants of this size class for borders and low screens.

*Hydrangea quercifolia*, Oakleaf Hydrangea. This is another native of the Southeast which is a fine reliable deciduous shrub for all parts of the region. Reaching ultimately a height of about 8 feet, it forms an enormous rounded mass of growth, richly covered with coarse-textured leaves and, in late spring, with tall clusters of white flowers sometimes a foot high. This bold plant, better suited to the scale of a park or large estate than to the average place, is a good one for specimen use and for cuttting, both for foliage and for flowers. It likes high, light shade and space, but it grows very well on any fertile, well-watered heavy soil with little or no care. Were it not for the fact that it is rather unsightly in winter and that it is out of scale with most other plants, the Oakleaf Hydrangea would be ranked with the most useful of this group.

*Ilex crenata latifolia*, Bigleaf Japanese Holly. *Ilex crenata microphylla*, Littleleaf Japanese Holly. *Ilex glabra*, Inkberry. *Ilex verticillata*, Common Winterberry. Both of the Japanese Hollies listed here grow rather rapidly for plants of refined character, easily reaching 6 feet or more with some spread. Both are likely to be somewhat open and a little ragged in form if left to themselves in ideal growing conditions, and both benefit from some shearing in late winter and again in June to promote compact growth and good form where a formal effect is desired. However, the Littleleaf variety can be left to itself to become an open informal and often picturesque form which is individual and interesting. The difference between the two lies in the foliage, which in the case of the Littleleaf variety is small, rather linear, and pointed, while that of the Bigleaf variety is larger (½ to ¾ inch long) and rounded. The foliage effect of the two is quite different in texture quality although the color is identical, a dark rich evergreen. These shrubs are fine materials for hedges, taking clipping very well, and as specimens in places where one might ordinarily choose Boxwood. Both stand heat better than the Box and possibly better than other Japanese Holly varieties, but in the Coastal Plain they should be planted in light shade and should have adequate feeding and watering. In the Piedmont and the Upper South they are perfectly hardy, adapting to either sunny or shady locations in all soils. Except for occasional attacks of spider mites, these varieties are remarkably free from insect and disease pests.

The Inkberry is a common native of swampy areas in the Coastal Plain, where it is usually called the Gallberry. In this location it is almost a weed which is a natural for poorly drained sites in either sun or shade, but it is not much planted in gardens. In the Piedmont, where there are so many other good broad-leaved evergreens to use, it probably will be no more popular than it is farther south. But this hardy plant, which will easily weather the winters as far north as Cleveland, Ohio, is one of the best evergreens of the size class for colder parts of the Upper South. The foliage is disease free, of a bright green in summer but turning almost black with cold. There are dainty white flowers in late spring and rather inconspicuous black fruits in late summer. Left to itself this plant grows in an open, informal, graceful habit to over 6 feet in height, making a fine material for naturalizing or for the border. It also takes clipping well to become a good substitute as a specimen, for the Box in severe exposures. For this purpose, however, the Inkberry probably is not as desirable as one of the Japanese Holly varieties.

The Winterberry is a deciduous Holly which makes a fine show of red berries in fall and early winter. It is a native of wet lands in most of the eastern U. S., but it grows well and sets fruit in most garden soils in sunny or lightly shaded places if one is careful to secure both male and female plants for cross pollination. The character of the plant, with its rather stiff upright growth to nearly 10 feet and its foliage of medium texture, is ordinary, but the fall and winter show is often quite worthwhile. This plant, again, is most useful in natural settings, particularly in wet areas; it is also worth including in the cutting garden when there is space for planting two shrubs for the sake of the effect of one. The Winterberry is well suited to limestone soils, and it is a dependable, common border shrub in central Kentucky. It is possible that this species is mixed with the similar, closely related *I. laevigata*, or Smooth Winterberry.

*Juniperus chinensis pfitzeriana*, Pfitzer Juniper. *Juniperus sabina*, Savin Juniper. The Pfitzer Juniper has been for many years a favorite material for foundation plantings throughout the Southeast. It is an excellent shrub, well suited to almost any kind of well-drained acid or alkaline soil in open sites throughout the region, and it has a distinctive shaggy beauty with its horizontal habit and steel blue color. Generally, however, this Juniper has been much overplanted. It has an exotic appearance, which in mixture with other plants seems incongruous, and upon constant repetition becomes tiresome. Also, this shrub is often crowded. Allowance is seldom made for the 6- to 8-foot height or 10-foot spread which it may achieve with some speed. But the Pfitzer Juniper still has its place in broad masses for sunny, dry, windswept slopes, not in the average home grounds but in large-scale areas. Similar to the Pfitzer, and possibly superior, is the Savin Juniper, which is darker green in color and slightly larger in size. A still newer form is called the Hetz Juniper, which is somewhat more upright in character and has more blue in foliage color. The latter characteristic should disqualify its use in most landscape compositions, however. These plants can be badly damaged by red spider mites, but usually this pest is serious only in confined or shaded locations.

*Kalmia latifolia*, Mountainlaurel Kalmia. The Mountainlaurel is thought of ordinarily as a native of the eastern mountains (where it is commonly called "Mountain Ivy"), but it does creep into the Piedmont and the Coastal Plain, following the water courses, growing on well-shaded banks and hillsides which face north. It does well enough in the Coastal Plain that one garden near Charleston, S. C., can boast of harboring the largest specimen in existence. In any place where it will do well, Mountainlaurel is a choice material for naturalistic masses, informal borders alone or in mixture, in foundation plantings, or as a specimen. In the Upper South it can be generally recommended, its use being limited only by its requirement for an acid soil. Southward its application is much more limited to special locations, generally in some shade where the atmosphere is cool and humid. In cooler sections the plant adapts well to sunny exposed sites where it develops a dense compact habit, often remaining under 5 feet in height for some time. In sheltered places, it may exceed 10 feet in height with an open irregular form which, while it may be rather leggy, is graceful, interesting, and often picturesque. When the plant grows too tall or thin, it can profitably be cut to the ground, preferably in late winter, to sprout up anew. The medium-textured, evergreen foliage is handsome; so are the showy heads of white or pinkish flowers which open late in spring. The plant is pest free save for a leaf spot disease which may be controlled with dusting sulfur.

*Kolkwitzia amabilis*, Beautybush. A showy flowering shrub for the Upper South and the cooler Piedmont, the Beautybush is hardy, vigorous, and fast growing to nearly 10 feet in almost any soil in sun or light shade. It is a deciduous shrub of medium to fine texture which is literally covered in late spring with light pink tubular flowers that are fine for cutting in addition to making a display in the garden. Later the brown bristly seed pods mature, and the plant has no distinction for the remainder of the year. To be kept in good condition it should be pruned annually after flowering. It has little use except in the cutting garden.

*Ligustrum japonicum*, Japanese Privet. *Ligustrum obtusifolium regelianum*, Regel Privet. The Japanese Privet is dependable as far as the colder parts of the Upper South, and it is one of the most used shrubs of the region. Unfortunately, so far as names are concerned, the identity of this plant is commonly confused, being listed rather consistently in the catalogues as the "Glossy Privet," *L. lucidum*, a plant which belongs with the Large Shrubs of Chapter VI. Since this misnomer was pointed out at least fifteen years ago, after which some nurseries did reclassify their stock properly, there seems to be no need for perpetuating an error which could be cleared up within a short time if all growers would recognize it. Be this as it may, the Japanese Privet is a versatile trouble-free plant, having a rather irregular habit of growth, sometimes reaching over 10 feet in height. The evergreen foliage is dark in color, glossy, and coarse in texture. The flowers occur in late spring in panicles of white; these are succeeded in autumn by clusters of blue-black fruits. The Privet grows well in all soils and in almost any exposure from fully open to almost heavily shaded; but the foliage, which is attractive to the white fly in warmer sections, is usually cleaner in an open site. A neat, dependable, amenable shrub, the Japanese Privet is over-planted. It should be grafted on nematode resistant roots for planting in the Coastal Plain or Piedmont.

There are relatives or varieties of the Japanese Privet which deserve mention with the best materials of this size class. The first of these is the Roundleaf Japanese Privet, *L. j. rotundifolium*, often listed as *L. coriaceum*. This is a slow grower, usually smaller than the above, but capable of reaching 10 feet in an upright columnar form which is as intriguing as it is unusual. The dark evergreen foliage is distinctive in the way it is carried, giving a twisted, rather distorted effect. This variety is useful as a specimen for its interesting form, for hedges, or for fitting into cramped quarters in small city gardens. It may not be quite as hardy as the species but it appears safe in Memphis and Atlanta.

Other known varieties of the Japanese Privet include several varie-gated foliage types. In recent years the nurseries of the region have been carrying a number of other forms of evergreen Privet which are perhaps doubtful as to name but which are of some merit. *"Ligustrum erectum"* has most of the design characteristics of the Japanese Privet, but it has very dense foliage, the branches appearing to carry almost twice as many leaves as those of the latter. Another, *"Ligustrum repandens,"* bears slender, sharp-pointed leaves of a bright green color which give a lighter, more graceful character to the plant. Still another of compact character is called "Suwanee River."

The Regel is possibly the best of the deciduous Privets, and it is certainly one of the finest materials for the Upper South for borders, unclipped hedges, and screens where something about 8 feet in height and not overly positive in character is needed. This is a bushy shrub of rather horizontal branching habit, facing down well with pen-dulous branchlets, with light green foliage of medium texture which is colorful in autumn in yellow, dull blue, and purple. It bears small sprays of white flowers in June followed in autumn by dark blue berries which are decorative well into the winter, until devoured by birds. A most dependable performer in all kinds of soils, in sun or in partial shade, this plant is hardy and enduring, requiring a mini-mum of attention. In securing the plants, one should be sure to get this species, cutting grown, which even without pruning will remain in bounds and uniform in character. If grown from seed, the Regel is quite variable. There is a smaller variety called Pygmy (*nanum*) which should be fine for the free form hedge.

*Lonicera fragrantissima*, Winter Honeysuckle. This appears to be the best of the many large-growing Bush Honeysuckles; it is a fine deciduous shrub which is very nearly evergreen in warmer sections. It reaches a height of about 8 feet with a dense twiggy growth which makes it an effective, fast growing, rather long lasting, and inexpensive screen material. The foliage is bluish green in color, medium in texture. One of the shrub's best features is its small white flowers which begin to open in January and continue for a month or so, never making a great display but giving ample evidence of their existence by their spicy fragrance. The plant appears to be pest free, and flourishes even under neglect in unfavorable spots in all kinds of soils and exposures. It is equally at home from the Coastal Plain through the Upper South. One sees it often located in places too small for its normal growth, and consequently its top is barbarously sheared off, so that its beauty is utterly destroyed. Some pruning is necessary to remove old wood, but this should be done by cutting back the over-mature stems to the ground.

*Loropetalum chinense,* Loropetalum. This appears to be successful in the Southeast from the north Florida Coastal Plain through the Piedmont to Knoxville. It does not seem entirely happy in full sun in the very sandy soils of the warmest section of the area. Subjected to severe cold, the plant may be almost defoliated without suffering irreparable damage. It is rather recent in general planting here, but it is being more widely used and seems to be one of the better broad-leaved evergreens of this size. It grows fairly rapidly with little care, possibly attaining a height somewhat over 10 feet with rather rugged and irregular form and small dark leaves of medium texture. The chief beauty of this shrub is its showy display of white or creamy blossoms in early spring. These have fine, feathery petals which are unusual and interesting in effect. The flowers and the later seed pods are similar to those of the closely related Witchhazel. This shrub probably ought to be grown in partial shade in cool, moist situations. It makes a good selection for screens and borders or for the cutting garden.

*Malus sargenti,* Sargent Flowering Crab. This is one member of an outstanding group of flowering trees which retain a shrubby character. Rarely exceeding 8 feet in height, this variety forms a solid irregular mound 10 feet in diameter. Its use on most places is limited by its size, but it is appropriate for estates and parks of gardenesque character. The foliage is rather small, very dense on the twiggy growth, dark green in color, and deciduous. The glory of the plant is in its heavy clusters of pure white flowers appearing with the first leaves of spring. Sometimes it seems to require a long time for this shrub to bloom, but the rugged matured branches, covered with their fragile blooms, eventually make a handsome display. In the fall, the blossoms give way to clusters of tiny scarlet berry-like apples which are colorful into winter. This plant takes sunny exposures, where it will tolerate droughts and poor soils if

the climate is cool. It may be planted in the Upper South and portions
of the Piedmont, but the flowering is not bountiful in warmer areas.
This crab is usually grafted, and it is well to plant it with the union
well underground to eliminate as much as possible troublesome under- *Note*
stock sprouts which must be systematically removed.

*Myrica pennsylvanica,* Northern Bayberry. This grows principally
along the northern seaboard, but it is also adaptable to interior
gardens where it is valued for its handsome semi-evergreen aromatic
foliage and its decorative fall and winter clusters of gray waxy berries
formerly employed in making candles. The sexes are separate in
these plants; both males and females must be planted for fruit production. This is not likely to be one of the most important materials
for this region, but it can be planted in the Upper South in higher
cooler sections in poor soils in either sunny exposed sites or in partial
shade. With its grayish green foliage of medium texture and its
mounding, billowing habit of growth the bayberry is effective either
for naturalizing in masses and borders or in more gardenesque surroundings such as foundation plantings.

*Myrtus communis,* True Myrtle. This is desirable both from the
standpoint of its intrinsic beauty and the long garden history associated with it. It is a plant which varies widely in size and in habit;
thus when buying it, one should try to see a mature specimen of the
stock in question in order to be sure the desired plant is obtained. The
variety *compacta* has been discussed with the Dwarf Shrubs. Standard
forms grow to about 10 feet or more in height in an upright form,
although there are some which are somewhat lower and more oval in
silhouette. The arrangement of the small dark evergreen leaves also
may vary with individuals, being rather loose and open in some,
and close-packed, almost overlapping in others. The foliage is aromatic, and this quality adds materially to the value both of the plant
in the garden and of the cut branches for the house. Small attractive
white flowers are scattered along the stems in late spring, and
these are succeeded by inconspicuous black fruits. The Myrtle is
not used extensively, possibly because it transplants poorly, it is
hard to establish, and it is often thin and leggy. However, it is seen
fairly often in old gardens. It is useful for hot, sun-drenched, dry
sandy soils where not too many plants will thrive. It makes an
excellent hedge or a good specimen for occasional use in architectural
settings and herb gardens. Myrtle is often attractive in old age with
its lengths of smooth-barked stems contrasting with tufts of dark
foliage. It seems to be less hardy than the Dwarf variety, and it
probably ought not to be planted outside the Coastal Plain north of
Charleston, S. C.

*Nandina domestica,* Nandina. This is much planted in the Southeast, where it is sometimes known as the Heavenly Bamboo. It is one of the important ornamentals of the Coastal Plain and the Piedmont, and is planted also in the Upper South to Lexington and Louisville, where it grows well with some shelter but may not always set fruit. The habit of this shrub is distinctive; it tends to become leggy to almost 10 feet in height although it should be maintained at less than this by occasional removal of older stems to the ground to make room for new basal shoots. The compound foliage is evergreen and fine in texture. Two foliage forms are recognized, the leaflets of one being even smaller and more finely divided than those of the normal type. Some growers consider this little-leaved type superior for its more compact habit. The Nandina's foliage is wine red in color on unfolding in the spring, and in the fall, especially in sunny locations, it often turns reddish, even to bright scarlet on some individuals. This color note should be recognized in placing the plant. The flowers appear in mid-spring in rather large and fairly showy panicles of white, but the berry-like fruits of brilliant red make a more bold and handsome splash in autumn and winter. The Nandina thrives in the sun, but it grows thin and fruits poorly in deep shade. It stands drought well, but it does not appear to be happy in excessively sandy soils. It has no pests. It is probably one of the most abused of all plants in this region in that it is so often planted near red brick buildings with which it clashes violently in both color and texture. If its qualities are recognized properly in design, this can be a most attractive and tractable shrub.

*Philadelphus coronarius*, Sweet Mockorange. Mockoranges have been favorite shrubs for gardens since colonial times, and they are still desirable for the cutting garden because of their lovely showy white fragrant flowers of late May. Aside from this display and a remarkable ability to grow under the most difficult of circumstances, these plants have little to recommend them in foliage or form, and they present a constant maintenance problem with their rank growth and their accumulations of old wood. Possibly the best species for general use is the Sweet Mockorange listed here, which was introduced from Europe for colonial gardens. It has a rather satisfactory mounding growth habit to about 10 feet, and its flowers have a fine fragrance. Some may prefer one of the hybrid Virginalis varieties which have large double fragrant blooms. This multi-petalled feature adds little real beauty, however, and the form of these plants is so poor that they should be used only for the cutting garden and should never be placed where they can be seen. There are, as a matter of interest, at least four species native to the Southeastern uplands. They are *P. grandiflorus*, the Big Scentless Mockorange; *P. inodorus*, the Scentless Mockorange; *P. pubescens*, the Hoary Mockorange; and *P. laxus*, the Drooping Mockorange.

*Pieris japonica,* Japanese Pieris. This is another member of the Heath Family which loves acid soils and a cool humid atmosphere. In cooler sections of the Upper South it grows well in sunny places, but in warmer sections here and in the Piedmont it should have some shade. It may also be grown in the Coastal Plain in moist cool sites such as those described for the Kalmia. It becomes a choice and refined ornamental usually within the size limits of this class, but capable of becoming somewhat larger in time. The evergreen foliage is especially attractive, bright or somewhat yellowish green all year, fine in texture; the leaves are arranged in compact whorls around the twigs. Flower buds are formed in late summer in terminal sprays which are effective all winter, opening in the spring into small white bell-like blossoms. In habit this shrub often grows, after some time, into a sort of miniature tree form with an irregular-shaped trunk. It makes a fine restrained informal specimen, and it mixes nicely with other broad-leaved evergreens in borders and masses to give variety in foliage color and texture. It is a choice and reliable selection for city gardens. The Formosa Pieris, *P. taiwanensis,* and the Himalaya Pieris, *P. formosa,* are somewhat more tender species, said to be more showy, probably worth a trial where they may be available.

*Prunus laurocerasus schipkaensis,* Schipka Laurelcherry. *Prunus laurocerasus zabeliana,* Zabel Laurelcherry. The Common Laurelcherry becomes a very large shrub or small tree as high as 20 feet, but these forms are more compact and probably can be safely placed in design to remain within the 10-foot height limit of this category, with a spread of this much or more. Both are relatively new in the nursery trade of this region, and they are being widely planted as if they would not exceed 4 to 5 feet. This will almost certainly prove to be a mistake. The plants are well suited to this region from the Coastal Plain through the Upper South in all but its higher elevations and very severe exposures. Their chief value is in their rich glossy evergreen foliage of coarse texture which is short, oval, and blunt pointed in the Schipka form, and long and narrow oval in the Zabel variety. There are white flowers and blue-black fruits, but they have little effect. These plants like good soils, but they are tolerant of acid or alkaline reactions. They grow in sun or shade and adapt well to city conditions. They are employed widely in foundation plantings where their elegant foliage is most fitting, but they may grow outsize for such places and might better be set out as specimens or in borders. The Laurelcherries take trimming well in hedges or as pieces of topiary.

*Pyracantha coccinea,* Scarlet Firethorn. *Pyracantha koidzumi,* Formosa Firethorn. The Firethorns are extremely popular plants in this area for their brilliant displays of scarlet fruits in autumn and winter. Nurseries of this region commonly offer two species of which the Formosa Firethorn, usually listed as *P. formosana,* is probably the best in both fruiting, color, and habit of growth. Normally this grows as a dense and twiggy, broadly spreading, and somewhat irregular bush to a height of almost 10 feet. The flat clusters of white flowers of late spring are attractive, and the heavy bunches of bright red fruits of fall and winter are truly outstanding. This species is well suited to the Coastal Plain and the Piedmont, but it may not be reliably hardy in all parts of the Upper South. Here the Scarlet Firethorn will be the better choice. Similar to the Formosa with a low rounded habit of growth, this variety is not so colorful and prolific in production of fruits, which are smaller. In buying the Scarlet Firethorn, one must take care to secure cutting grown material from a plant of good berrying habit. Also widely planted is the Laland variety, *P. c. lalandi,* which produces orange berries and which, being more vigorous and hardy than the above, is the form most often planted in areas to the north of this region. In most of the Southeast, however, it will have little use since it grows rapidly to a height of well over 10 feet with great spike-like canes which disqualify it entirely for planting in most places. Other species of Firethorn may be encountered more rarely. Recently the Overlook Nurseries of Mobile, Alabama, have introduced a dwarf form which has been patented (No. 884) under the name of "Low-Dense." Although its fruits are said to be obscured largely by its dense foliage, this variety will doubtless become an important Firethorn for planting on smaller properties and in more refined surroundings. It is slow growing, but its ultimate height is placed by the developers at 8 feet.

The Firethorns are good evergreen (or semi-evergreen in colder climates) shrubs of medium foliage texture with handsome displays of flowers and fruits. They make satisfying specimen materials, they are good in screens and borders, and they are prized for cutting. Set at 3 feet on centers they develop impenetrable borders, but they do not take well to shearing in hedge form. They are easily trimmed and trained against walls and on trellises and are often seen in this interesting form. They suffer, however, from at least one very serious handicap. They are attractive to the lacewing fly which occasionally attacks them in such numbers as to destroy entirely the beauty of the foliage and the plant. To control this pest, at least several well-timed sprays of nicotine sulphate, or one of the newer insecticides such as Malathion, are necessary during the summer. The plants are also subject to fire blight and to scale insects. They are difficult to transplant except in small sizes. Most nurseries sell their Firethorns in cans because of this latter characteristic. Taken altogether, these are heavy drawbacks which might lead one to hesitate to include the Pyracantha among the best shrubs of this group. Still it is a unique and beautiful thing when well grown; and, when it is planted in sunny open windswept sites, the disadvantages seem to be minimized. This is no plant for sheltered quarters; but for large scale compositions, especially where some care may be anticipated, it is excellent. Where privacy is desired its thorny character makes it one of the best for screens, borders, or hedges.

*Rhododendron arborescens,* Sweet Azalea

*Rhododendron austrinum,* Florida Azalea

*Rhododendron calendulaceum,* Flame Azalea

*Rhododendron canescens,* Piedmont Azalea

*Rhododendron catawbiense,* Catawba Rhododendron

*Rhodendron indicum,* Indica Azalea

*Rhododendron nudiflorum,* Pinxterbloom Azalea

*Rhododendron prunifolium,* Plumleaf Azalea

*Rhododendron serrulatum,* Hammocksweet Azalea

*Rhododendron vaseyi,* Pinkshell Azalea

*Rhododendron viscosum,* Swamp Azalea

A number of Rhododendrons or Azaleas are included among the important landscape materials of this size class for the Southeast. In order to simplify the discussion of the preceding list of eleven species, the (1) Catawba Rhododendron and the (2) Indica Azalea are studied first as separate items and the remaining nine species are grouped finally in one class of (3) "deciduous native Azaleas."

(1) Growing in native stands in the southern Appalachians in open areas at elevations of usually 3,000 feet or more, the Catawba Rhododendron itself is hardly ever found in gardens. But this plant is important as one of the parents of the Catawba Hybrids which include many varieties with flower colors ranging from white to lavender and deep rose-red. The named varieties are of separate colors, but many nurserymen offer "hybrid seedlings." Sometimes these can be quite attractive, but the buyer should see them in bloom before buying since the colors may be quite unsatisfactory.

The form of these plants is usually irregular and informal, to a height of 6 or 8 feet but sometimes to 15 depending largely on exposure. They make distinguished specimens, and they are handsome in massive clumps, borders, and screens. For best blooming effect they need sun, preferably a spot under open sky with exposure to the north, sheltered from winter sun and wind from the south and west. They often do well, however, either in fully exposed locations or under the high shade of Oak trees. They need perfect drainage, and they like ample moisture supplies, high humidity, and protection from desiccating wind. Soils should be light, rich in humus, acid in reaction; the shallow roots should be protected with an acid mulch, never disturbed by cultivation. In general the Rhododendrons are well suited to only a relatively small section of the Upper South since limestone soil conditions, excessively hot dry summers, and rapid winter temperature changes make growing them in much of the region a difficult task, to be undertaken only by the specialist.

While the Rhododendrons are generally a group of plants to be used with some discretion, they are among the finest of materials of this size class for the southern mountain areas and cooler localities along the northern edge of the region where acid soil conditions can be met. Once established they can thrive for many years without attention in such unaccountable spots as open cemetery lawns or corners of small city gardens. Their worst insect pest is the easily controlled lacewing fly, which is seldom serious on well grown plants. Occasionally there may be borers to be cut out. If the plants become leggy, long branches may be cut back to the ground in late winter before growth begins to force new shoots from the base. Bloom is better if faded flower heads are removed, but this is practical usually only on small plantings. Once established, Rhododendrons provide year after year a permanent, rich, coarse foliage effect, and an early June flower show of unmatched beauty.

The collector of Rhododendrons in this region should watch for introductions of hybrid strains other than the Catawba which, for design purposes at least, are similar in habit, flower display, and foliage. These include the Caucasian Hybrids, of which the splendid and dependable "Boule de Neige" is a well-known older variety, the Fortune Hybrids, and the Griffithianum Hybrids. Especially interesting are the latter, descendants of a genus from the Himalayas, said to be somewhat tender but outstanding in flower.

(2) One of the greatest satisfactions in the gardening year in the Deep South comes when the Indica Azaleas begin to spread their flamboyant petals in early spring, continuing in increasing splendor until early April. The forms in use today are hybrids of complicated ancestry. Generally speaking they may be divided into several groups. These are (a) the hardier, dependable, common garden types which are recommended for general landscape use in the Coastal Plain and the warmer Piedmont; (b) more tender varieties, often blooming from autumn through the winter and consequently subject to damage when freezes occur; and (c) the so-called Belgian hybrids which are suitable only for pot culture. Some of the best known examples of the first group are "Formosa," "Pride of Mobile," "G. L. Taber," and "Fielders White," all very common, but sturdy and reliable. These Azaleas grow rapidly to 8 or 10 feet in height,

spreading to an equal dimension. The dark evergreen foliage is medium in texture, attractive throughout the year. The plants are well suited to growing conditions in most localities in the Coastal Plain; they succeed equally well in sun or shade, in sandy or heavier soils of acid reaction provided they have a mulch. However, they do not thrive on alkaline soils but suffer from yellowing of the foliage (chlorosis) and general lack of vigor due to malnutrition. They are successful in warmer parts of the Piedmont, but they are liable to be somewhat tender here. They are propagated and transplanted very easily. The Azaleas have several common insect pests which require spraying, including scales, mites, and the lacewing fly; but the petal blight disease attacking the flowers in the lower South is the most disheartening of all. Control of this disease can be achieved in small isolated plantings by rigid sanitation, but usually three sprayings or more of "dithane" or "parzate" each week during the flowering season will be required for good control. The relatively recent appearance of this pest has dampened the ardour of would-be Azalea growers in at least the lower Coastal Plain, and it certainly makes the maintenance of large plantings there very expensive.

(3) This list may be criticized for the inclusion of so many of the native Azaleas with the best plants of this size class, but it is difficult to make a single choice among them. Selection might be made on the assumption that the early flowering species are more showy and more generally appreciated because they bloom before the foliage becomes so heavy as to hide the flowers. However, some of the later flowering types are valuable for giving color and cutting material for a lengthened season. It is said to be possible to have Azaleas almost all summer through skillful selection of species.

Almost everyone who has worked with native Azaleas remarks on the variations to be found among collected specimens of a single species, not only in flower color, but also in quantity of bloom, foliage character, habit of growth, and even in hardiness. A great deal of collecting and selecting needs to be done in order to insure that the best types of the various species reach the market. Here is a challenge both to the commercial nurseryman and also to the amateur in search of a fascinating hobby. The habit of growth of these Azaleas is upright, open, and rather leggy. The thin quality is hardly a drawback, however, because these are airy plants, and they should always be set where their peculiar dainty grace will be appropriate. In favorable circumstances some species reach easily to 15 feet in height, taking them into the next size group. However, it is well to cut back to the ground a cane or two occasionally as they grow overly tall. This practice will keep the plants at about 10 feet or lower, and will improve their vigor.

Most of these species are natives of deep woods, often of ravines or glades where moisture and humus are relatively abundant. It is well to try to duplicate these conditions as nearly as possible when bringing the plants into the garden, although they adapt to sunny sites if close attention is given them when established. Native species are subject to most of the ills which beset other Azaleas, although possibly to a lesser extent. But they are almost certainly the best deciduous shrubs of this group, and their qualities deserve wider attention.

Although it is impossible to give full justice to the subject of native Azaleas here, it may be practical to suggest from the list several species to give bloom over a long season in either one of two color ranges—yellow to red, or white to pink. Although their native habitats vary somewhat, all of the native Azaleas may be considered dependable throughout the Southeast wherever acid soils prevail. Very few are grown in the nurseries, and stock must ordinarily be collected from native stands.

The flowers of three species are in the yellow-orange-red color range. The Florida (*R. austrinum*) and the Plumleaf Azaleas (*R. prunifolium*) are Coastal Plain species, and have the first blooming before leaves appear and the second in midsummer to autumn. The Flame Azalea (*R. calendulaceum*) inhabits the Piedmont and the mountains; it flowers in May just after the leaves have begun to appear. This may well be one of the best-known, most generally available, and satisfactory species of the group.

The Pinxterbloom Azalea (*R. nudiflorum*) flowers in tints of pink before the leaves appear. A variety with a deeper rose flower color is called *R. n. roseum*. The former ranges from Massachusetts to Florida, and the latter is said to grow farther inland. The Pinkshell Azalea (*R. vaseyi*), native to North Carolina, bears pink flowers in mid-spring. It is said to be also a choice and dependable species, outstanding for fall foliage color. The Hammocksweet Azalea (*R. serrulatum*), with fragrant white blossoms, is a late bloomer of midsummer, native to the Coastal Plain; it is considered rather tender.

The Piedmont Azalea (*R. canescens*), a widespread species from North Carolina to Florida and Texas, blooms in early spring before the leaves appear. The Sweet Azalea (*R. arborescens*) bears very fragrant flowers in midsummer and ranges through high lands from Pennsylvania to Georgia and Alabama. The Swamp Azalea (*R. viscosum*) is similar in outstanding flower fragrance and season, but it inhabits low, swampy situations.

*Sorbaria aitchisoni*, Kashmir Falsespiraea. Of interest for their plume-like sprays of white flowers in late summer, the Sorbarias will be little used in most gardens. Having fern-like deciduous foliage of fine texture, they are weedy in growth, needing space and frequent severe pruning. However, they grow well in all soils in sunny exposures, and they do not present other cultural problems. They can be useful for cutting or for naturalizing in the Piedmont or the Upper South.

*Spiraea prunifolia plena*, Bridalwreath Spiraea. *Spiraea vanhouttei*, Vanhoutte Spiraea. The old-fashioned Bridalwreath is one of the best of the Spiraeas. This common shrub makes in time a massive, spreading clump, about 8 feet in height. Its fine-textured deciduous foliage has a good dark glossy green color in summer, often turning an attractive red or orange in autumn. The button-like white flowers, appearing before the leaves in spring, make a good showing, especially in cooler sections of the region, and they are fine for cutting. A very easy shrub to grow in any sunny place throughout the Southeast except in its warmest parts, the Bridalwreath is bothered only by aphids in the spring, never very seriously, and by a tendency to accumulate old wood which needs to be regularly pruned. In character this plant seems appropriate with informal architecture and in foundation plantings of cottages, and it associates happily with other plants in flower and shrub borders, particularly with bush roses and old-fashioned perennials.

The Vanhoutte Spiraea is possibly the more common of the two, although it may be considered somewhat inferior in that elusive quality called character. Growing to a height of about 8 feet in a leggy fountain form, it is much seen in foundation plantings where it is usually lopped off at the top in a vain attempt to keep it low and to make it fill out at the base. Nicely set as a specimen or in a free form border it can be successful. It is a beautiful thing in May, heavily covered with its heads of white flowers. It is easily grown in all soils and in any sunny exposure, flowering better in the Piedmont and the Upper South than in the Coastal Plain. The foliage is gray-green in color, fine in texture, with no fall color, but remaining on the bush until quite late. The plant does require intelligent pruning, but it presents no other problems aside from occasional aphid attacks. The persistence of faded flower heads is a disfiguring characteristic.

*Taxus cuspidata*, Japanese Yew. *Taxus media*, Anglojap Yew. The Japanese Yew is the most valuable needle-type evergreen of this size class for the Upper South. This is frequently planted to fit smaller spaces than would be indicated here. Indeed, with careful pruning it can be maintained for many years in sizes about 3 to 4 feet in height and from 4 to 6 feet in spread; but if allowed to grow unfettered, it may reach well over 10 feet in either dimension. This versatile plant, in its typical spreading form, is more broad than high, inclined to be rangy and open in habit in good soils in sheltered locations. This tendency usually has to be curbed with a shearing in mid-June when the new growth of the season is half complete. This practice does not produce an overly formalized specimen; but, with more frequent cutting, the most precise hedge or topiary forms may be developed. The fine-textured foliage is dark green all year. The inconspicuous male and female flowers occur on separate plants, and the females bear red fleshy fruits in late summer which are occasionally quite showy. For hedges, screens, borders, or as either formal or informal specimens, the Japanese Yew is an excellent plant throughout cooler sections, tolerant of acid or alkaline soils in sun or shade, but needing good drainage. Its southern limits probably will be Washington, Atlanta, and Memphis where it can be grown only in cool, moist shade. An upright form called the Upright Japanese Yew, *T. c. capitata*, fits more narrow spaces, but it tends to grow into a tree form, losing its lower branches in spite of almost anything one can do. These plants are especially valuable in city gardens where they endure poor growing conditions and smog better than other needle-type evergreens.

The Anglojap Yew is the result of a cross between the English Yew, *T. baccata*, which has little if any value here, and the Japanese Yew. The spreading forms are similar in habit to those of the Japanese species, but they are considered to be a bit more tender and refined in habit and of a brighter, fresher green color through the winter. Widely circulated forms of this class are the Hatfield, Anderson, and Brown Yews. Their uses are similar to those mentioned above for the Japanese Yew. Possibly the best of the upright growing Yews is the Hicks, *T. m. hicksi*, which does hold its foliage well to the ground while growing in a narrow columnar form that is particularly fine for hedges, borders, vertical accent, or height in tight places. One form of the English Yew seen fairly frequently in the Upper South is the Irish Yew, *T. baccata fastigiata* or *T. hibernica*. This is an upright columnar plant reaching eventually to 15 or 20 feet, used often as a garden focal point in the vicinity of Washington, the Eastern Shore, and Richmond, and with fair success in Louisville, Kentucky. In larger sizes it is rather weak and liable to snow damage and probably is not as generally useful as the Hicks Yew.

*Viburnum burkwoodi,* Burkwood Viburnum
*Viburnum dilatatum,* Linden Viburnum
*Viburnum odoratissimum,* Sweet Viburnum
*Viburnum rhytidophyllum,* Leatherleaf Viburnum
*Viburnum tinus,* Laurestinus Viburnum
*Viburnum tomentosum,* Doublefile Viburnum

Like the Rhododendrons, the Viburnums present in this size class a wealth of fine materials which can hardly be described with full justice. The above list of six species, however, does cover a representative palette of better forms within this size category adapted to this region.

The Burkwood Viburnum is a vigorous hybrid of rather recent introduction, notable for its very fragrant and beautiful pinkish to white flowers of early spring. The black fruits are of little note. Its habit of growth is open and irregular, eventually becoming rounded to nearly 10 feet in height. The foliage is somewhat sparse, rather small and medium in texture, semi-evergreen or almost evergreen in warmer sections. It is perfectly hardy in the Southeast and well suited to all soils of the region in sunny locations. Of gardenesque character, it makes a fine substitute in flower borders for the old *V. carlesi* although it is larger growing. It lends itself well to pleaching against a wall.

The Linden Viburnum is a superior, sturdy deciduous species with coarse foliage, making a dense growth in a broadly rounded form which is fine for borders and screens. It is best adapted to fertile, well-watered soils in cooler areas where it provides at two seasons a most effective color display with its flat heads of white flowers in May and its bright clusters of red fruits in fall. This shrub is easily grown in fair to good soils in exposed or partly shaded spots, and it is quite clean and free of pests.

The Sweet Viburnum is a tender species suited only to the Coastal Plain. With unusually large, rounded, glossy, coarse-textured evergreen leaves, this plant would be ornamental for foliage effect alone. However, it also bears in mid-spring showy panicles of fragrant white flowers; these are followed in late summer by berries which turn red and finally black. Growing in a robust and rounded form to a height of about 10 feet, Sweet Viburnum makes a splendid screening and border plant in good soils with adequate moisture and in a sunny location where it makes a rapid growth. It is probably hardy to Charleston, S. C.

Another evergreen species with interesting coarse-textured foliage is the Leatherleaf Viburnum, but this is hardy through the Upper South. The leaves are long oval, thick and heavily veined, dark green above and rusty woolly beneath, rather widely and thinly scattered on the upright and somewhat leggy plant. This variety grows well in shade; in colder sections it ought to be planted under or near the shelter of trees or buildings to protect it from excessive wind exposure. During severe winter spells the leaves curl and appear to wilt, but return of mild temperatures restores them. The whitish flowers of early spring are not attractive, and the black fruits of fall are inconspicuous. But this plant is fine for foliage interest through the year for cutting or for displaying against an architectural background. It is one of the rather limited list of broad-leaved evergreens which will do well on the alkaline soils of the colder Upper South.

The Laurestinus is an old garden form coming from the Mediterranean region which is well suited to the Coastal Plain and the lower Piedmont. The evergreen foliage is dense, medium in texture, and dark dull green on the dense bushy plant which may reach to somewhat over 10 feet in favorable sites. Growing in either sun or shade, this shrub must not be planted in very rich soils nor should it be watered in the fall. It is easily stimulated into an autumnal spurt of growth, after which it goes into the winter covered with soft shoots which will usually freeze in this location, possibly killing the plant. The flower buds are formed in late summer, and oftentimes these will start to open, pinkish to white, at any warm season after early December to make a welcome winter display. This is a good material for garden, screen or border, or specimen.

The Doublefile Viburnum is one of the best of deciduous flowering shrubs for the Upper South and the Piedmont. Reaching to about 8 feet, it has an interesting and distinctive horizontal branching habit, rather similar to that of the Flowering Dogwood. The plant presents a rugged effect, added to by the coarse-textured leaves, dark green in color, turning a deep somber red in fall. The flat heads of white flowers in May are beautifully constructed, lace-like in detail, and very effective in uniquely horizontal pattern. These are succeeded in late summer by fruits which turn red, then black as they mature. This plant succeeds in sun or possibly better in lightly shaded sites. The Maries variety, *V. t. mariesi*, is said to be somewhat more floriferous than the Doublefile Viburnum, and ought to be selected where available. The Japanese Snowball, *V. t. sterile*, is a common variety of this shrub and has bright snowball-form blossoms; it also is highly desirable, especially for cutting. With a more vertical habit of growth, it lends itself especially well to training against a wall.

*Vitex agnuscastus*, Lilac Chastetree. The Chastetree is noteworthy chiefly for its pleasant spikes of small fragrant flowers which in its varieties are lilac, white, or rose through the early summer, making a rather good color effect in the flower border and a nice cutting material. This is gardenesque in character and not of great use in other places. Ordinarily it is less than 10 feet in height, but in the South it may become a small tree as high as 15 feet, with a single trunk. Usually it is better to keep old wood cut out and to maintain the plant as a lower, distinctly flowering material. The grayish-green, aromatic deciduous foliage is five-parted, fine in texture, and distinctive in quality. The plant should be grown in sun, it stands poor dry soil nicely, and it has no pests or diseases. It is somewhat tender and may die back to the ground in very severe winters, but it recovers quickly to bloom again, somewhat later than usual, during the ensuing summer. The Negundo Chastetree, *V. negundo*, is a larger growing species also to be found here, and it is about equal in value.

*Weigela florida*, Oldfashioned Weigela. The Weigelas are fine shrubs for the cutting garden but for little else. They include several species and many named horticultural varieties, but none is much superior to the common species listed with its pink blossoms. The red flowering forms, some of which are nearly continuous bloomers, such as "Eva Rathke," are quite popular, but the color is wholly undesirable. These plants are pest free and are easily grown in sunny locations through cooler sections, but they lack distinction after the flowers have faded. They also present an annual pruning problem if they are to be kept in any presentable condition.

## VI. Large Shrubs for the SOUTHERN COASTAL PLAIN

| *Botanical Name* | *Common Name* |
|---|---|
| RECOMMENDED FOR GENERAL USE | |
| Camellia japonica | Common Camellia |
| Camellia sasanqua | Sasanqua Camellia |
| Cleyera japonica | Japan Cleyera |
| Elaeagnus pungens | Thorny Elaeagnus |
| Ilex cornuta | Chinese Holly |
| Ilex cornuta burfordi | Burford Holly |
| Ilex vomitoria | Yaupon Holly |
| Michelia fuscata | Bananashrub |
| Nerium oleander | Oleander |
| Osmanthus fortunei | Fortunes Osmanthus |
| Osmanthus fragrans | Sweet Osmanthus |
| Osmanthus ilicifolius | Holly Osmanthus |
| Pittosporum tobira | Tobira Pittosporum |
| Podocarpus macrophyllus maki | Shrubby Yew Podocarpus |
| RECOMMENDED FOR RESTRICTED USE | |
| Aesculus parviflora | Bottlebrush Buckeye |
| Baccharis halimifolia | Eastern Baccharis |
| Bambusa multiplex | Fernleaf Hedge Bamboo |
| Cassia corymbosa | Flowery Senna |

| *Botanical Name* | *Common Name* |
|---|---|
| Cocculus laurifolius | Laurelleaf Snailseed |
| Cotoneaster salicifolia | Willowleaf Cotoneaster |
| Exochorda giraldi wilsoni | Wilson Redbud Pearlbush |
| Feijoa sellowiana | Feijoa |
| Franklinia alatamaha | Franklinia |
| Hamamelis japonica | Japanese Witchhazel |
| Hamamelis mollis | Chinese Witchhazel |
| Hamamelis virginiana | Common Witchhazel |
| Ilex cassine | Dahoon Holly |
| Ilex pedunculosa | Longstalk Holly |
| Illicium anisatum | Japanese Anisetree |
| Illicium floridanum | Florida Anisetree |
| Lagerstroemia indica | Crapemyrtle |
| Laurus nobilis | Grecian Laurel |
| Ligustrum lucidum | Glossy Privet |
| Ligustrum sinense | Chinese Privet |
| Lindera benzoin | Common Spicebush |
| Myrica cerifera | Southern Waxmyrtle |
| Osmanthus americanus | Devilwood Osmanthus |
| Photinia glabra | Japanese Photinia |
| Photinia serrulata | Chinese Photinia |
| Prunus laurocerasus | Common Laurelcherry |
| Prunus lusitanica | Portuguese Laurelcherry |
| Punica granatum | Pomegranate |
| Stewartia malacodendron | Virginia Stewartia |
| Vaccinium arboreum | Farkleberry |
| Viburnum prunifolium | Blackhaw Viburnum |
| Yucca aloifolia | Spanish Bayonet |

## VI. Large Shrubs for the SOUTHERN PIEDMONT

### RECOMMENDED FOR GENERAL USE

| | |
|---|---|
| Camellia japonica | Common Camellia |
| Camellia sasanqua | Sasanqua Camellia |
| Cleyera japonica | Japan Cleyera |
| Cotoneaster salicifolia | Willowleaf Cotoneaster |
| Elaeagnus pungens | Thorny Elaeagnus |
| Ilex cornuta | Chinese Holly |
| Ilex cornuta burfordi | Burford Holly |
| Ilex vomitoria | Yaupon Holly |
| Lagerstroemia indica | Crapemyrtle |
| Osmanthus americanus | Devilwood Osmanthus |

| Botanical Name | Common Name |
|---|---|
| Osmanthus fortunei | Fortunes Osmanthus |
| Osmanthus ilicifolius | Holly Osmanthus |

### RECOMMENDED FOR RESTRICTED USE

| | |
|---|---|
| Aesculus parviflora | Bottlebrush Buckeye |
| Baccharis halimifolia | Eastern Baccharis |
| Buxus sempervirens arborescens | Truetree Box |
| Cassia corymbosa | Flowery Senna |
| Clerodendron trichotomum | Harlequin Glorybower |
| Cornus mas | Cornelian Cherry |
| Exochorda giraldi wilsoni | Wilson Redbud Pearlbush |
| Feijoa sellowiana | Feijoa |
| Franklinia alatamaha | Franklinia |
| Hamamelis japonica | Japanese Witchhazel |
| Hamamelis mollis | Chinese Witchhazel |
| Hamamelis virginiana | Common Witchhazel |
| Hibiscus syriacus | Shrubalthaea |
| Ilex aquifolium | English Holly |
| Ilex cassine | Dahoon Holly |
| Ilex pedunculosa | Longstalk Holly |
| Illicium anisatum | Japanese Anisetree |
| Illicium floridanum | Florida Anisetree |
| Laurus nobilis | Grecian Laurel |
| Ligustrum lucidum | Glossy Privet |
| Ligustrum sinense | Chinese Privet |
| Lindera benzoin | Common Spicebush |
| Lonicera maacki | Amur Honeysuckle |
| Michelia fuscata | Bananashrub |
| Myrica cerifera | Southern Waxmyrtle |
| Nerium oleander | Oleander |
| Osmanthus fragrans | Sweet Osmanthus |
| Photinia glabra | Japanese Photinia |
| Photinia serrulata | Chinese Photinia |
| Pittosporum tobira | Tobira Pittosporum |
| Podocarpus macrophyllus maki | Shrubby Yew Podocarpus |
| Prunus laurocerasus | Common Laurelcherry |
| Prunus lusitanica | Portuguese Laurelcherry |
| Punica granatum | Pomegranate |
| Stewartia malacodendron | Virginia Stewartia |
| Stewartia ovata grandiflora | Showy Mountain Stewartia |
| Styrax japonica | Japanese Snowbell |
| Symplocos paniculata | Sapphireberry Sweetleaf |

| Botanical Name | Common Name |
|---|---|
| Syringa vulgaris | Common Lilac |
| Viburnum opulus | European Cranberrybush |
| Viburnum prunifolium | Blackhaw Viburnum |

## VI. Large Shrubs for the UPPER SOUTH

### RECOMMENDED FOR GENERAL USE

| | |
|---|---|
| Cotoneaster salicifolia | Willowleaf Cotoneaster |
| Elaeagnus pungens | Thorny Elaeagnus |
| Ilex cornuta | Chinese Holly |
| Ilex cornuta burfordi | Burford Holly |
| Lagerstroemia indica | Crapemyrtle |
| Osmanthus americanus | Devilwood Osmanthus |
| Osmanthus ilicifolius | Holly Osmanthus |
| Rhododendron maximum | Rosebay Rhododendron |
| Syringa vulgaris | Common Lilac |
| Viburnum lantana | Wayfaringtree Viburnum |
| Viburnum opulus | European Cranberrybush Viburnum |
| Viburnum prunifolium | Blackhaw Viburnum |
| Viburnum sieboldi | Siebold Viburnum |

### RECOMMENDED FOR RESTRICTED USE

| | |
|---|---|
| Aesculus parviflora | Bottlebrush Buckeye |
| Baccharis halimifolia | Eastern Baccharis |
| Buxus sempervirens arborescens | Truetree Box |
| Camellia japonica | Common Camellia |
| Camellia sasanqua | Sasanqua Camellia |
| Clerodendron trichotomum | Harlequin Glorybower |
| Cleyera japonica | Japan Cleyera |
| Cornus mas | Cornelian Cherry |
| Cotinus coggygria | Common Smoketree |
| Exochorda giraldi wilsoni | Wilson Redbud Pearlbush |
| Franklinia alatamaha | Franklinia |
| Hamamelis japonica | Japanese Witchhazel |
| Hamamelis mollis | Chinese Witchhazel |
| Hamamelis virginiana | Common Witchhazel |
| Hibiscus syriacus | Shrubalthaea |
| Ilex aquifolium | English Holly |
| Ilex pedunculosa | Longstalk Holly |
| Ilex vomitoria | Yaupon Holly |
| Ligustrum lucidum | Glossy Privet |
| Ligustrum sinense | Chinese Privet |

| Botanical Name | Common Name |
|---|---|
| Lindera benzoin | Common Spicebush |
| Lonicera maacki | Amur Honeysuckle |
| Osmanthus fortunei | Fortunes Osmanthus |
| Photinia serrulata | Chinese Photinia |
| Photinia villosa | Oriental Photinia |
| Rhus copallina | Flameleaf Sumac |
| Stewartia ovata grandiflora | Showy Mountain Stewartia |
| Styrax japonica | Japanese Snowbell |
| Symplocos paniculata | Sapphireberry Sweetleaf |
| Vaccinium corymbosum | Highbush Blueberry |
| Viburnum trilobum | American Cranberrybush Viburnum |

### RANGE CHART FOR GROUP VI. LARGE SHRUBS

|  | Coastal Plain | | Piedmont | | Upper South | |
|---|---|---|---|---|---|---|
| Camellia japonica | x x x | x x x | x x x | x x x | - - - | |
| Camellia sasanqua | x x x | x x x | x x x | x x x | - - - | |
| Cleyera japonica | x x x | x x x | x x x | x x x | - - - | |
| Cotoneaster salicifolia | | | x x x | x x x | x x x | x x x |
| Elaeagnus pungens | x x x | x x x | x x x | x x x | x x x | x x x |
| Ilex cornuta | x x x | x x x | x x x | x x x | x x x | x x x |
| Ilex cornuta burfordi | x x x | x x x | x x x | x x x | x x x | x x x |
| Ilex vomitoria | x x x | x x x | x x x | x x x | - - - | |
| Lagerstroemia indica | - - - | x x x | x x x | x x x | x x x | x x x |
| Michelia fuscata | x x x | x x x | x x x | - - - | | |
| Nerium oleander | x x x | x x x | - - - | | | |
| Osmanthus americanus | x x x | x x x | x x x | x x x | x x x | x x x |
| Osmanthus fortunei | x x x | x x x | x x x | x x x | - - - | |
| Osmanthus fragrans | x x x | x x x | x x x | - - - | | |
| Osmanthus ilicifolius | x x x | x x x | x x x | x x x | x x x | - - - |
| Pittosporum tobira | x x x | x x x | x x x | - - - | | |
| Podocarpus macrophyllus maki | x x x | x x x | x x x | - - - | | |
| Rhododendron maximum | | | | - - - | x x x | x x x |
| Syringa vulgaris | | | | - - - | x x x | x x x |
| Viburnum lantana | | | | - - - | x x x | x x x |
| Viburnum opulus | | | - - - | x x x | x x x | x x x |
| Viburnum prunifolium | - - - | - - - | - - - | x x x | x x x | x x x |
| Viburnum sieboldi | | | | - - - | x x x | x x x |

Recent work with Camellias is extending the range of these ever-greens so that varieties may be available some day for all of the region. At present they can be grown well in the Piedmont only with special care, and they are of doubtful value in the Upper South. Special soil conditions should be noted for these and for the Rhododendron, but others on the list are very tolerant. The Elaeagnus and the two

Chinese Hollies are quite hardy in all parts of the region, but the latter may fail to set fruit in the Upper South. The *Lagerstroemia* is a dependable Large Shrub in all parts of the Southeast although it would not be considered first choice in the Coastal Plain. (Note that it and *Ilex vomitoria* are also rated with the Small Trees of Group VII.) *Osmanthus americanus*, native to the Coastal Plain, is an evergreen having endurance to cold. In its home section it is not appreciated widely, and it is possibly better treated as a Small Tree here. The latter note might be applied also to *Viburnum prunifolium*, which is native as far south as Florida. In warmer sections it is shown with a broken line because it is not considered first choice here even though it is dependable.

*Aesculus parviflora*, Bottlebrush Buckeye. This native of the Southeast from South Carolina to Alabama probably cannot be used extensively, but it is a very special plant for spacious sites. Growing to a height of 10 to 12 feet, it forms a broad mound of dense foliage facing down to the ground well. The fact that the foliage is deciduous may cause some people to shy away from this shrub in areas where many evergreens are available. However, the large, coarse-textured, palmately-compound leaves are most rich and handsome for summer effect; and in winter, when the plant is bare, the sturdy branches form an interesting structural pattern. The plant grows rather slowly and is difficult to obtain and to transplant, but it flourishes without care in any fairly good soil, either acid or alkaline, in lightly shaded sites. In early summer when there are few other flowers in bloom, the Bottlebrush Buckeye sends up its flashy, massive, terminal spikes of white. The seeds, maturing in autumn, are small brown "buckeyes." This is at its best as a specimen plant, either in architectural settings of massive scale or in naturalistic woodland glens. It is perfectly hardy throughout the Southeast from the Gulf to the Ohio River.

Another attractive native of this area is the Red Buckeye, *A. pavia*, which occurs in moist woodlands from Virginia to Florida and Louisiana. It grows to a height of 20 feet, becoming tree-like, of open habit, and bearing reddish flowers in early spring. This plant should not be confused with *A. carnea*, a red flowering form of the European Horsechestnut growing to a height of 40 feet. The Red Buckeye is not common in nurseries, and the demand for it will be slight.

*Baccharis halimifolia*, Eastern Baccharis. More commonly called the Groundsel Bush, this inhabits swampy areas and tidal marshes of the Coastal Plain, but it is quite hardy and will grow under garden conditions throughout the Southeast. It reaches just over 10 feet in height, with an open leggy habit. The leaves are medium-textured evergreen of a bright fresh color; the flowers, not very pretty in detail, are borne in large heads which, with the following seed heads, are very showy in mass in autumn and early winter. This plant is not an important ornamental, but it can be useful for wet places and in seashore sites subject to salt spray. It has some good qualities for quick effects in full sunlight wherever there is a fair moisture supply. It needs an annual pruning to maintain it in a vigorous state. It is not usually grown in nurseries, and it must ordinarily be collected.

*Bambusa multiplex*, Fernleaf Hedge Bamboo. Often listed as *B. disticha*, this is a "clump-type" Bamboo, so called because it spreads slowly and remains fairly well within bounds. This shrub is deservedly popular in warmer parts of the Coastal Plain although it is not hardy in cooler sections. Left to itself, it reaches a height of 10 to 15 feet with many graceful slender stems in a massive clump; but it lends itself admirably to shearing, making a dense and satisfactory hedge in narrow places from 5 to 10 feet high. The evergreen foliage is delicately cut, so as to give a fine texture effect, and this appearance is heightened by a light to grayish green color. Generally the Bamboos are not useful in the majority of landscape projects because they tend to spread so rapidly. This species does not have this fault, however, and it is a disease free, fast-growing, tolerant material for use as a specimen or for borders in all soils in sun or shade.

*Buxus sempervirens arborescens*, Truetree Box. Various forms of the Common Box have been discussed in previous chapters, but the Tree Box is a good large shrub for evergreen foliage of fine texture in the Piedmont and the Upper South. Possibly it should be included among the best for the latter region. This is the most vigorous and hardy of the Common Box varieties, and therefore is widely grown in nurseries, where it is clipped to make formal specimens of 4 to 6 feet in size. The plant is only partly satisfactory for this purpose, however, since it thins out in the center and is difficult to restrain within the set bounds. This variety is easily recognized by its leaves, which are quite narrow with a triangular round point. It is better left to itself as a tall screening material, taking on a loose, irregular, and informal habit. There is a weeping form characterized by a pendulous branching habit. The plant takes well to acid or alkaline soils, likes light shade, a mulch around its shallow roots, adequate moisture, and shelter from winds and winter sun. It is widely adaptable, however, and one may see fine old specimens in fully exposed sites as far north as Louisville and the Ohio River. Once established in a place suited to it the Tree Box is a permanent material requiring little care, although it must be watched for trouble with leaf miners and scale insects.

*Camellia japonica*, Common Camellia. *Camellia sasanqua*, Sasanqua Camellia. Certainly the Camellias are the favorites in many gardens of this region. They are easy to grow, being perfectly hardy through the Coastal Plain, much of the Piedmont, and into warmer parts of the Upper South. They are so generous with their almost infinitely varied floral returns through the long dull winter season that they well deserve their popularity. They are abused, however, and overplanted. A great deal has been printed about blossom variations and culture, but very little on correct arrangement in a landscape composition. In fact not too much is known, or at least not much has been published, concerning form and habit of growth, rate of growth, and size in the different varieties; and these are the major factors in arrangement for landscape effect. Until these factors have been investigated thoroughly and the information made known, collections of Camellias will remain rather hit-or-miss aggregations of assorted specimens without much unity or harmony. Unfortunately not much help on this score can be given at this writing.

The Camellias are essentially specimen plants, cultured and aloof in character, formal, and not mingling happily in close contact with other plants. This is not so true, however, with the fall-blooming Sasanquas. The latter fit admirably into informal borders and shrubbery clumps, making excellent screening materials and suiting almost any purpose which one might conceive for a shrub. These are exceptionally vigorous growers, rapidly reaching to 10 feet or more, and so they do require space. The Common Camellia has quite a different character, however. It needs an essentially formal setting, a place obviously designed to receive it, or it looks out of place. Nothing can have a more dismal effect than a small yard spotted with specimens of these plants in meaningless array. If one wishes to grow Camellias for cutting, he should place them in the vegetable or cutting garden, well screened from public view. A word should be added concerning their use in foundation plantings too. There is nothing wrong with this practice if the effect is well studied, but one needs to remember that these plants grow to over 10 feet in height and that they have a broad spread. They cannot be planted under bay windows, nor can they be spaced only 2 or 3 feet away from a wall without unfortunate results. They grow too large for such places. So much has been circulated concerning varieties and culture that to deal further with these subjects here would seem a useless repetition. But so many of these shrubs are planted with such little consideration for design that they threaten to become overly common.

These plants are best adapted to warmer sections including the Coastal Plain and the lower Piedmont. With proper siting, some of the more hardy varieties can be grown throughout the Southeast, however. The Common Camellia is now considered more easily adapted to cooler climates than the Sasanqua varieties, although the reverse was once thought to be the case. In the Coastal Plain the plants are best set in a light shade, doing very well under Pine trees. They will grow well in full sun, but the foliage often burns in winter. In cooler sections, the plants like full exposure to the sun in summer, but they must have shade in winter, and they ought to be protected from full blasts of freezing winds from the west. For localities north and west of Washington, Richmond, Atlanta, and Memphis special recommendations on the selection of varieties should be sought from local nurserymen or the publications of the American Camellia Society. In these locations Camellias can hardly be relied upon for landscape effect, but they are subject for the hobbyist. Generally they prefer acid to neutral soils, and they are shallow rooted, requiring to be set somewhat above soil level and well mulched. Scales are the only serious insect pests although die-back disease is a problem in some areas. The plants should have a good bit of seasonal care. These chores are simple, however, and are the sort of thing which any gardener loves to do to occupy his interest.

Some collections in the Coastal Plain include the Netvein Camellia, *C. reticulata*, but it is tender and not at all common. It is being employed in hybridizing, and its varieties may be much more important in the future.

*Cassia corymbosa*, Flowery Senna. A good shrub for flower color effect in late summer and autumn, the Flowery Senna is rather tree-like in habit, thin at the base and often with one trunk, attaining a height of just over 10 feet. The deciduous compound foliage is light in color and fine in texture. The flowers are produced over a long season in clusters which make a bold showing of golden yellow; these are followed in turn by small beanpod-like seed vessels of little interest. There are few pests to bother the Senna, and, although it is short-lived, it grows rapidly from seed in all well-drained soils in sunny spots, enduring drought and heat very well. It is not the most choice of materials, but for giving a spot of cheerful color at the rear of a border it is excellent. There are other Cassias for fall color listed in this area, namely, *C. berriana* and *C. splendida*. All of these are tender, and are confined to the Coastal Plain or the lower Piedmont. They are not widely distributed but they are worth a trial.

*Clerodendron trichotomum*, Harlequin Glorybower. This is a coarse, rank-growing shrub which may well be trained to tree form with one trunk, reaching about 15 feet in height, in a broad squatty form. The deciduous leaves are large, light green in color, somewhat resembling those of the Catalpa, but differing in their arrangement in opposite pairs. This would be an undistinguished plant were it not for its interesting fragrant white flowers of late summer and its spectacular display of fruits, bright blue in conspicuous red calyxes, in September. Easily grown in sunny locations in dry soils, this plant is hardy in the Piedmont and the Upper South where it makes a good cutting material or a rather interesting specimen where space is no consideration.

*Cleyera japonica*, Japan Cleyera. The shrub which is generally known in this region by the name of Cleyera is commonly used throughout the Coastal Plain and the Piedmont. At least some of the stock, however, probably is of a closely related species called *Ternstroemia gynnanthera*. The differences between the plants are minor. The flowers and fruits of the latter are yellow, while those of the Cleyera are white and red. There is also a difference in the leaf arrangement, but this character may not be reliable for identification. Leaves of the Ternstroemia are said to be clustered at the ends of the branches, while those of the Cleyera are alternate along the stems. The Cleyera may also be found listed as *Eurya ochnacea*.

The Cleyera (or *Ternstroemia*) is interesting chiefly for its evergreen foliage which has a very dark tone, turning purple or sometimes wine red in winter, making a rich color contrast in the medium texture range. The arrangement of the leaves in compact whorls is also unusual and effective. The habit of growth is upright, enabling the plant to be fitted into narrow places, but specimens which have good soils and ample water supplies become thin and leggy. Some cutting back is recommended where the shrubby habit is desirable, for left alone the Cleyera becomes a small tree. In late spring the clusters of white, faintly fragrant flowers break out, and the dull red fruits mature in autumn. This shrub is dependable through the Piedmont, and it may succeed as far north as Knoxville. It likes heavy soils in sun or light shade, and it is free from pests and tolerant of urban discomforts. It is fine for mixed shrub clumps, borders, or screens; it also makes an excellent specimen played against architectural details. A variegated form called *C. j. tricolor* has leaves which are striped with yellow and red.

*Cocculus laurifolius*, Laurelleaf Snailseed. This is of interest primarily as a foliage plant for use in the warmer parts of the Coastal Plain. Growing to a height of about 15 feet, this plant becomes a dense, spreading, round-headed shrub with gracefully drooping branches, somewhat inclined to become leggy with age. This is a good material for borders or screens of large dimensions, and it takes shearing well. The large, lance-like, coarse-textured leaves of a bright evergreen color and a waxy gloss make this plant outstanding in any group and a very fine material for cutting. It does well in sun or partial shade, in alkaline or acid soils, preferring good feeding and watering.

*Cornus mas*, Cornelian Cherry. This is a hardy, vigorous, clean, and tolerant plant of bushy or tree-like habit to almost 20 feet, occasionally useful for screen or cutting material for exposed sites in the Upper South and cooler parts of the Piedmont. The foliage is deciduous, medium in texture, lacking any distinctive quality. There are very small flowers borne in profusion in early spring before the leaves appear to make an effective display of yellow color when the landscape is bleak. For its early bloom, this shrub is often desirable for colder climates. Cherry-like fruits mature during the summer, but they are well concealed by the foliage and are soon eaten by birds. This plant usually becomes leggy, and it is too large for the average garden.

*Cotinus coggygria*, Common Smoketree. An old-fashioned garden favorite, this is known for the cloud-like effect produced through a long period of midsummer by the fruiting panicles found on female plants. It is closely related to the Sumacs and, like them, prefers full exposure to sun and tolerates drought and poor soils. The foliage is medium in texture, and deciduous, turning red or orange in fall. The form is open and irregular, reaching a height of almost 15 feet, depending on growing conditions, with a broad spread. Although it is not widely useful, the Smoketree can be an interesting specimen, or it can fit nicely at the back of a border. It is best adapted to cool sections of the Upper South.

*Cotoneaster salicifolia*, Willowleaf Cotoneaster. This is an outstanding ornamental for form, foliage, and fruit, certainly one of the most beautiful members of this versatile genus. The habit of the plant is weeping. It grows to about 12 feet in height with an equal spread. It needs ample space, but it is often planted where it must be cut back and its form is therefore mutilated. The foliage is evergreen, but it may be only semi-evergreen in cooler seasons in the Upper South. The long, narrow, and pointed leaves are dark and rich in color, of medium to coarse texture. The clustered white flowers are not very showy, but the bright red fruits are spectacular in autumn and early winter. This plant will be hardy to the Ohio Valley, but should have a somewhat sheltered site with partial shade. With this species too, one needs to watch for the usual Cotoneaster pests: fire blight, scale, and lacewing fly. The variety *C. s. floccosa* is considered more hardy than the species; it is also more vigorous and has larger leaves.

*Elaeagnus pungens*, Thorny Elaeagnus. This is a very common shrub in the Southeast, hardy from the Coastal Plain to Charleston, W. Va., broad and spreading in form with pendulous branches, reaching just over 10 feet in height and girth. Where the branches have a chance to scramble into some low tree, the plant becomes vine-like, climbing to a considerable height, and may be trained readily as a vine against walls or on treillage. The medium-textured foliage is dark green, but there are several colored foliage forms, all characterized by a metallic sheen on twigs and the undersides of the leaves. The small cream colored flowers of October and November are inconspicuous to the eye, but their fragrance is noticeable all over the garden. The dull red fruits maturing in spring are hardly conspicuous. The Elaeagnus seems to thrive under almost any conditions of soil or exposure, tolerating limestone, the salt of seashore, or the smoke of cities, never affected by usual pests. For its tolerance of surrounding conditions, as well as for its beauty, the plant is used a great deal, but it should be given sufficient room in which to spread. Sometimes it is clipped as a hedge rather satisfactorily, but the growth is almost too irregular and rampant for this purpose. It makes an excellent large scale bank cover, screen, free growing border plant, or occasional specimen. There are several foliage forms of the species, of which the variety *E. p. maculata*, with bright yellow splotches on the leaves, is rather widely planted. Still more useful is the Fruitland Elaeagnus, *E. p. fruitlandi*, originated at the Fruitland Nurseries of Augusta, Ga. For the Coastal Plain and the Piedmont, the Fruitland is a superior variety having a symmetrical habit and luxurious foliage of a silver-green cast, but it probably is not as hardy in the Upper South as the species.

For cooler sections there are two other Elaeagnus species of some interest. *E. angustifolia*, the Russianolive, is rather commonly grown for its silvery deciduous foliage of fine texture. Being a very rapid grower on all soils in severe exposures to sun, wind, and drought, the Russianolive has some value for a quick showing. The color is only rarely desirable, however, and the plant is weedy in character. Somewhat more valuable is *E. umbellata*, the Autumn Elaeagnus, which is a sturdy, long-lived, and dependable shrub for screens and borders in difficult exposed locations. Its deciduous foliage is grayish green in color and fine in texture; the profuse crop of small tart, edible, dull red fruits in autumn is interesting. Of rather weeping habit, this variety has a broad spread and faces down well.

*Exochorda giraldi wilsoni*, Wilson Redbud Pearlbush. Several forms of the Pearlbush are good spring flowering shrubs for the Southeast, but the variety above is recommended for a superior display of panicles of white blooms. The Pearlbush is almost equally satisfactory in all parts of the region, but after its brief flowering season it has little to commend its use. It is easily grown in any sunny to lightly shaded situation and has no pests, but it is a formless leggy open plant of no character with thin deciduous foliage of little distinction.

*Feijoa sellowiana,* Feijoa. Often called the Pineapple Guava, this has become fairly common in the Coastal Plain within rather recent years, and it seems to be gaining popularity for use in large borders, screens, and even for clipped hedges. The plant is seen usually at a height of about 10 feet although it may grow to almost twice that. It is spreading and rather horizontal in habit. The grayish evergreen leaves have prominent silver undersides which give the shrub a pleasing tone in the landscape. The red flowers are about an inch in diameter, appearing in early summer, and the subsequent greenish fruits are edible in autumn. The Feijoa loves sun, and it seems to grow well in droughty, sandy, acid or alkaline soils. It appears not to be affected by insects or diseases, although it will probably require some pruning to keep it in good form. It is hardy throughout the Coastal Plain and will survive as a smaller shrub through most winters to Atlanta and Norfolk wherever it has some protection and a well-drained soil.

*Franklinia alatamaha,* Franklinia. The story of the Franklin Tree is fairly familiar—how it was discovered along the banks of the Altamaha River in Georgia by the botanist, John Bartram, in the 18th century, taken to Philadelphia and grown there, while the original native growths apparently have disappeared completely. The Franklin Tree, named for Benjamin Franklin, has much historical interest; it is attractive for its large, white saucer-like flowers of late summer and its reddish to orange autumn foliage color. The leaves are deciduous, and coarse in texture, turning red in autumn. Although it is native to the swampy areas of the Coastal Plain, it is reported to be difficult to establish under any conditions in that section, slow to develop, and altogether not a very satisfactory ornamental there. It is fair in cooler parts of the Upper South for late summer flower interest, but the plant is usually ungainly, unattractive, and hard to handle.

*Hamamelis japonica,* Japanese Witchhazel. *Hamamelis mollis,* Chinese Witchhazel. *Hamamelis virginiana,* Common Witchhazel. The Witchhazels present at least two excellent species in this size class which have unique landscape interest for bloom in earliest spring and late fall. Both are deciduous shrubs, broadly spreading and gracefully leggy in form, reaching heights of 15 to 20 feet, with coarse foliage of bright yellow fall color. The Chinese Witchhazel is possibly the most showy of the very early spring flowering shrubs with its large, spidery, fragrant, bright yellow blooms almost covering the plant on the first warm days. For some reason this is quite rare in the nurseries as compared with the Japanese Witchhazel which, with reddish blossoms at the same season, is not nearly so effective in color. The Common Witchhazel is a widespread native of the eastern states, usually found in woodlands. Its flowers, also yellow, spidery, and fragrant, are quite small, but they have a peculiar value in that they come out in late fall after the leaves have fallen. This characteristic, as well as the graceful, open, horizontal branching habit and the ability to thrive in rather deep shade, give this shrub importance for naturalizing. These plants can be employed successfully in all parts of the Southeast although they may be better adapted to the cooler sections.

*Hibiscus syriacus*, Shrubalthaea. Although it is common enough to be thought of practically as a weed, this shrub nevertheless has possibilities when used imaginatively. The plant grows to about 15 feet in height, at first quite vertical in habit, but becoming broad spreading and rounded with age. The foliage is rather sparse, medium to fine in texture, dark in color, and deciduous. The chief interest is in the Hollyhock-like flowers, single or double, which open in an almost constant succession from June until frost, ranging in color from white through various tones of rose and magenta. Brown seed pods persist through the winter, and these may be considered unattractive. The plant is hardy from the Coastal Plain throughout the Upper South, tolerant of poor soils and neglect, resistant to pests, and in general is one of the easiest of plants to grow for quick effect in sunny to lightly shaded sites. It makes a good hedge or border plant although it tends toward legginess, and it can be an attractive specimen. All in all, this is a first rate material for places where speed of growth, color effect, and low maintenance are prime considerations. In warmer parts of the Coastal Plain, some people try to grow the more exotic Chinese Hibiscus, *H. rosa-sinensis*, with varying degrees of success. The spectacular flowers can be produced here through the summer, but the plant is not quite hardy. With heavy covering it can be wintered in some areas, but this requires extra care, and the plant never approaches its normal size of 20 feet or so.

*Ilex aquifolium*, English Holly
*Ilex cassine*, Dahoon Holly
*Ilex cornuta*, Chinese Holly
*Ilex pedunculosa*, Longstalk Holly
*Ilex vomitoria*, Yaupon Holly

The English Holly is normally a small tree, but in the Southeast it is seen as a shrub up to 15 feet in height if it is seen at all. While this is among the most beautiful of plants, with its rich and glossy leaves and brilliant red winter berries, it is also one of the most exasperating to site and to coax into satisfactory performance in this region. Apparently it will grow fairly well in a north exposure in the vicinity of Norfolk and Washington where humidity is relatively high because of proximate bodies of water. In other localities it may grow in shade, but it becomes thin and straggly; in the sun it is stunted, burned, and continually plagued by frost-killed tips. It is also very liable to destruction by the cottony cushion scale. Altogether this is a questionable selection in this region, to be undertaken only by the specialist.

The Dahoon and the Yaupon Hollies are species native to the Coastal Plain, shrubby in form, often becoming with age tree-like with several trunks that lose their lower branches. The Dahoon differs from the Yaupon in having slightly larger leaves with smooth instead of toothed edges. This species is interesting for having a number of foliage forms, some in which the leaves are very small and narrow, almost hairlike (*I. c. angustifolia*, the Alabama Dahoon, and *I. c. myrtifolia*, the Myrtle Dahoon). There is also a handsome yellow-fruited form with dark green foliage called *I. myrtifolia lowi*. This is probably a Dahoon variation, but the nomenclature of the Hollies is not always clear. All of these are best suited to the Coastal Plain or the Piedmont where they do well in either wet or normal soils, making fine materials for tall screens or borders. The Foster Holly, *I. fosteri*, is a hybrid of the Dahoon and American Hollies and is highly regarded for its dark green foliage of fine texture, its rapid growth, and its heavy fruit production. This hybrid is also more hardy than the Dahoon species, being a favorite as far north as Nashville and in much of the Upper South.

The Chinese Holly is probably best known for its variety the Burford Holly, *I. c. burfordi*. In habit these plants are identical, differing materially in landscape effect, however, because of foliage variances. The leaves of the Chinese species are cut into sharp-pointed lobes, almost bristly in appearance, while those of the Burford are nearly entire, ending in one blunt point at the tip to give it a more subdued and refined foliage effect.

The Burford Holly is one of the most planted shrubs of the Southeast, and seems to be quite hardy from the Coastal Plain to the Ohio Valley although it usually fails to set fruit in the northern part of this range. It is apparent everywhere that a reminder as to the growth habits of this shrub—large, dense, and bushy, reaching rather quickly a height of 8 feet or so and, ultimately, 15 feet—needs to be made. The Burford is set often in foundation plantings and in other restricted areas where, as it approaches its normal stature, it can only be cut back or transplanted. A dwarf Burford, which is needed for small spaces, is said to exist, but it is little circulated. The wonderful waxy sheen of the medium-textured foliage of the Burford Holly is one of its finest qualities, and another, of course, is its prolific and colorful fruiting habit which provides almost annually a brilliant winter show of scarlet. This appears to be one of the few female Hollies which will set fruit even if a male plant is not stationed nearby. It is easily grown in any good soil with a clay base; it needs little spraying, pruning, or other maintenance; and it likes sun, but it does well also in light shade. It is ideal as a specimen plant or for border or screen. The parent Chinese species is scarcely inferior to the Burford variety. In buying this species one should take care to secure both the female and male forms in order to be sure of a display of fruit. There is a yellow fruiting form of the Chinese Holly. Seedlings of this species show a great variety of leaf forms and fruiting habits. Hence it is not always so reliable as the Burford which is reproduced from cuttings and always comes up to certain standards. These plants are rarely attacked by scale insects, which, once established, are difficult to control.

With the interest in Holly species in recent years, several new ones have been introduced. This discussion cannot begin to cover adequately the subject, which is treated in several available specialty volumes. Of the newer species, the Longstalk Holly appears to be one of the most attractive. Growing in a bushy form which seems to hold its foliage well to the ground, this plant reaches to somewhat over 10 feet with a rather vertical form, and is said to be capable of attaining 30 feet. The plant is hardy from the Coastal Plain through the Upper South and is distinctive for its medium to coarse-textured leaves, which are entire, glossy, of a light green color, densely covering the bush. The red fruits too are unique in their large size and their carriage on long stalks to give a loose and graceful effect. This may be a particularly fine material for screening.

The Perny Holly, *I. pernyi*, is another Oriental species which may be mentioned here. It also may reach 30 feet in a dense pyramidal form with spiny leaves and bristling effect. This species is, however, relatively poor in this region; both it and its English Holly cross called *I. aquipernyi* will have little use here.

The Yaupon Holly is native to swampy areas near the coast, forming a rather open shrub to about 20 feet in height. The trunks and twigs are usually gray in strong contrast to the small dark evergreen leaves of fine texture. Flowers are inconspicuous, but the female plants bear in winter a bright profusion of tiny scarlet berries. Although it naturally inhabits wet spots, the Yaupon is perfectly at home in well-drained soils too. It is hardy throughout the Coastal Plain, the Piedmont, and into the Upper South to Nashville where it usually fails to set fruit. It is more dense and attractive in sunny sites but grows well also in light shade. It has no insect or disease enemies. For landscape use there is hardly a more versatile plant than the Yaupon. It lends itself to clipping very well, making excellent hedges, even as small as 2 feet in height, and fine topiary specimens. In hedge form it must be carefully shaped, for it tends to become leggy. It is good in screens, borders, and informal groups, and it forms a graceful, picturesque small tree. It is one of the most reliable of materials for seaside locations.

*Illicium anisatum,* Japanese Anisetree. *Illicium floridanum,* Florida Anisetree. Two species of Anisetree are commonly grown in warmer parts of this region and both are fine ornamentals, possibly worthy of including with the selected species were there not so many others of greater value. The Japanese Anise is a rounded, open, bushy plant growing to a height of nearly 15 feet with a large spread. The evergreen foliage is aromatic, thick, and coarse-textured, but the color is a light olive green that is somewhat unusual. This plant grows well in all sections and all soils of the Coastal Plain and the Piedmont to Memphis and Atlanta, and apparently it is free of all pests. Since it rarely, if ever, produces flowers the plant is grown for foliage effect, mostly in borders, in sunny or lightly shaded sites. In many ways the Japanese Anise could rank with the best materials of this class.

The Florida Anise, native to the lower Coastal Plain, grows to just over 10 feet in height in a vertical, sometimes arborescent form. It is not as hardy as the Japanese species. It probably should be confined to well-watered acid soils in lightly to heavily shaded locations in the Coastal Plain, although with protection it will survive to Memphis and possibly to Norfolk. The evergreen foliage is coarse, dark in color, and aromatic. This species bears in April attractive deep red flowers, not unlike those of the distantly related *Calycanthus* or Sweetshrub.

*Lagerstroemia indica,* Common Crapemyrtle. One would scarcely know how to plant a garden in the South without the Crapemyrtles, as essential here as are the Lilacs to New England. The effect of their sinewy trunks gleaming in the winter sunlight is as decorative in that season as are their massive heads of blossom in white, pink, red, and lavender through the long summer. The habit of growth is upright, occasionally more round-headed in very exposed sites; and with their several vertical trunks, the Crapemyrtles often have a strong upward effect in plant compositions. The foliage texture is fine, light, and airy. These may be considered either as shrubs or small trees, reaching a height of about 20 feet. Always somewhat too leggy and thin to be considered for screening, they are at their best treated as specimens. They take almost no care, although it is well to cut off old seed heads where that is practical, and they are attacked by Japanese Beetles where these insects have been introduced. About the only disease which is common is a mildew that disfigures the foliage in damp weather in shaded locations. Plants grown in the full sun, however, are hardly ever affected. Sometimes people will cut back their Crapemyrtles in winter with the thought of forcing larger flowers the following summer. To anyone who appreciates the natural form of this shrub, however, this is a brutal practice, and it is very doubtful whether in the end it brings about any greater total bloom effect. Some of the colors of these plants are trying in combination with those of others; the reds and magentas must be placed with special care. In general the Crapemyrtle is not recommended for the seacoast, but inland it thrives on any heavy soil almost to the Ohio River. It can be grown in even colder regions, but is likely to be frozen back in winter, losing its character even though it recovers readily from the root.

*Laurus nobilis*, Grecian Laurel. The Laurel, hallowed in history and in gardening traditions, grows with fair success in the Coastal Plain and the Piedmont, possibly reaching as far as Washington in sheltered sites. It forms a rather upright, irregular shrub to about 15 feet in height. The foliage is its chief asset, being coarse in texture, evergreen, bright in color, and aromatic. The dried leaves are used as a seasoning. The Laurel grows best on well-drained acid or alkaline soils in the sun in open sites, for the leaves may be covered with a sooty mildew in shade, particularly in warmer sections. This plant makes a thick screen and stands shearing well in both hedges and topiary. Pot-grown specimens, clipped into ball shape, have been characteristic features of certain period gardens. There are many foliage forms of the Laurel in cultivation, but none of them is easily obtained in the nurseries of the region.

*Ligustrum lucidum*, Glossy Privet. *Ligustrum sinense*, Chinese Privet. The widespread confusion existing in the naming of the Glossy and the Japanese Privets has been pointed out in the discussion of the latter in Group V. The Glossy Privet is a rank growing coarse evergreen, rapidly reaching 20 feet in height with a leggy habit often useful in tall screens where quick height is desirable. However, it adapts better to use as a small tree than as a large shrub. It is therefore discussed more fully in Group VII.

The Chinese Privet is the common hedge plant of the lower South, where it is often called the Amur Privet South. It is a weed in most of the region, the seeds being widely scattered by the many birds which feed on the prolific fruits during the winter. The plant is therefore common and generally despised, and in warmer sections one would plant it only as a last resort because of its frequent and heavy infestations of white flies which can damage other ornamentals although they seldom harm the Privet to any extent. This shrub can be an effective material, however, for quick screening effect under the most inhospitable urban conditions. The fine foliage is almost evergreen in warmer areas and into the Upper South to Nashville and Lexington; the small spikes of white flowers in June and the blue fruits of winter are effective. Like other Privets, this takes clipping well in hedges from 4 feet in height and up; but left to itself it becomes a graceful, many-trunked small tree of about 15 feet in height. The true Amur Privet, *L. amurense*, is also planted in this region, where it is called the Amur River North Privet because of its hardiness. A weeping variety, *L. a. pendulum*, is seen frequently in sections of the Upper South where it is sometimes interesting for form contrast in borders or in mass cover plantings for banks under difficult soil and exposure conditions.

*Lindera benzoin*, Common Spicebush. This is a common native shrub of the eastern woodlands, usually found there in moist areas or creek bottom sections. Growing as high as 15 feet in a many-stemmed, leggy, spreading form, this plant is usually open and quite picturesque in character. It makes a rather good pest-free naturalizing and border material for damp shade in all parts of the region. It is not particularly showy nor easily procured from the nurseries, but it has several interesting qualities. The medium-textured deciduous foliage is a clean, glossy dark green, turning yellow in autumn. The minute flowers open in great numbers in early spring before the leaves, making a dainty yellow mist in the bare woodland. In the fall female plants display sizable red berries after the leaf-fall. The entire plant, leaves and stems, is aromatic; the twigs are spicy to chew and make fine flavoring spits for roasting wieners.

*Lonicera maacki*, Amur Honeysuckle. Most of the large Bush Honeysuckles are weedy shrubs of very little value, but the Amur Honeysuckle is one of the better ones for color and for early results in screen plantings. A fast growing shrub, it reaches a height of about 15 feet with rather upright branches. The handsome deciduous foliage is medium in texture, dark and glossy green in color, persisting well into the early winter. In late May the small white flowers appear in the axils of the leaves with attractive effect, but the shrub provides its chief display in the autumn when it is well covered with small, shiny, red berries which last until late winter. Like most of the Honeysuckles this one is easily grown; it makes a quick effect; it is free from pests; and it is well adapted to difficult soils and conditions so long as it has a fair amount of sunshine. It is, however, weedy in habit, and requires regular pruning of older wood. A variety, *L. m. podocarpa*, is equally desirable.

*Michelia fuscata*, Bananashrub. This old-fashioned plant is one nearly always found in older gardens of the Coastal Plain and the lower Piedmont. Here there are splendid specimens, often 15 feet high with a spread of 20 feet, showing the fine endurance and staying power of the plant even under total neglect. The habit is broad, massive, dense, rounded, and somewhat leggy, and the medium-textured, dark, evergreen foliage is rich and handsome. The flowers open rather early in the spring, their small brownish petals never making much of a show; but their strong fragrance, like that of ripe bananas, produces an unforgettable impression. People like to pick the flowers and warm them in their hands or pockets to bring out a more pungent perfume. Rarely, there are fleshy orange seeds produced in small brown pods in autumn. The Bananashrub seems to have no insect or disease enemies. Without any care at all, it may be considered a permanent material after it has once been established. It grows well, although slowly, in sunny or lightly shaded locations in well-drained soils. It has a dignified, rich, refined character which makes it a choice specimen plant for the flower garden. It might be used effectively in screening, but it is too choice for such a merely utilitarian purpose.

*Myrica cerifera,* Southern Waxmyrtle. The Southern Waxmyrtle or Bayberry abounds in native growths throughout the Coastal Plain, mostly in swampy lands. It forms a broad, open, more or less leggy shrub up to 20 feet or more in height, sometimes becoming a small tree. The leaves are evergreen, linear in shape and fine in texture, light green in color, and fragrant when crushed. There are no flowers of note, but the female plants bear clusters of tiny gray berry-like fruits which are often sufficiently numerous to be very decorative. The wax coating of these seeds was used at one time in the making of Bayberry candles. The Waxmyrtle grows well in almost any kind of soil and almost without care wherever it has a sunny site. It provides a good foliage contrast in mixed shrub borders and makes a fair hedge although it tends to thin out at the base. Even though it may not be so choice as some other materials, the plant is probably not used as much as its carefree nature would justify. It is reliable throughout the Coastal Plain and the lower Piedmont. It is also planted in the Upper South where it grows somewhat smaller and where its performance is likely to be more erratic. It is especially fine near the seashore.

*Nerium oleander,* Oleander. Fragile in appearance but sturdy in fact is the Oleander, so common along the seacoast. Here it grows to as much as 20 feet in height in a rounded form, always maintaining its shrubby character. The leaves are long, but their line and shape, their gray green color, and their placement on the stems give this plant a fine or fine-medium texture effect. The flowers, either single or double, occur throughout the summer in showy clusters in colors ranging from white through pink to rose and a sort of apricot yellow;

nearly all forms are fragrant. There are not many plants which will endure so well the heat and glare, and the poor, dry, alkaline sandy soils of the coastal region. The Oleanders require no care, but will benefit from an occasional pruning in spring to remove old wood or to promote more dense growth. They are not reliably hardy above the Coastal Plain, at least not all forms. There are some, such as the single white, the red variety "Cardinal," and the single pink, which are reported to be more resistant to cold damage than others. These varieties can be planted safely as far north as Atlanta, but in such cooler sections these plants may be restricted by climate to heights of 10 feet or less and their use confined to decorative flowering interest in protected gardens and patios. Oleanders should always be grown in the sun; and, if water is withheld in late summer so that new growth is hardened properly, the hardier forms will be quite safe in the areas suggested. These plants are excellent as specimens, especially effective against architectural settings, and make fine, fast-growing free form hedges and borders. As ornaments for flower garden or terrace Oleanders are handsome in large pots or tubs. The milky sap of these plants is said to be poisonous, and smoke from the burning wood is irritating.

*Osmanthus americanus*, Devilwood Osmanthus
*Osmanthus fortunei*, Fortunes Osmanthus
*Osmanthus fragrans*, Sweet Osmanthus
*Osmanthus ilicifolius*, Holly Osmanthus

The Devilwood is the one species of this group native to the United States, being found in swampy areas of the Coastal Plain from North Carolina to Louisiana. It is not much planted as an ornamental in the Deep South, where it can become a small tree of nearly 30 feet in height, but in the Upper South as far north as Lexington and Louisville it is much planted and widely esteemed as a broad-leaved evergreen shrub of the Medium to Large Shrub class. In form, it makes an irregularly rounded specimen, often with a rather open and thin habit. The leaves are long and slender, entire edged, coarse in texture, and light green in color. There is a wide variety of leaf forms to be found ranging in length from 2 to 6 inches with strongly differing texture effects. Flower buds formed in the fall open in early spring in great profusion. These are noticeable although not very showy, but the delightful lemon-like fragrance is a decided asset in the garden. The blue-black fruits are produced in autumn. This plant is a fast grower, free of troubles. It should be planted in good deep soils, acid or alkaline, where it will have some shade and moisture in the Coastal Plain, but in the cooler Upper South it looks best in sunny locations.

The latter three Osmanthus, or Tea Olives as they are better known, are among the finest materials for the Coastal Plain and the Piedmont. The Sweet Osmanthus is unique because of its tiny white flowers which are produced freely throughout the winter, giving off an unforgettable perfume which is one of the delights of the southern garden. It has faintly toothed or entire leaves of medium texture, and a vigorous upright habit of growth which may in time carry it to 25 feet in height. In the Coastal Plain the Tea Olive may become a small tree, but it is the least hardy of these three species, hardly safe to Atlanta in the Piedmont, where it will rarely reach more than 10 feet.

The Fortunes Osmanthus is a hybrid of the Sweet and Holly species, characterized by light evergreen leaves similar to those of the Sweet Osmanthus, but more prominently toothed, with spiny tips. This hybrid is also more bushy and compact, rounded in form, facing down well, reaching to 15 feet in height and girth, but capable of being maintained lower by good pruning. The small white flowers are fragrant, profuse, and showy, appearing in the fall. This is a more hardy form, quite reliable throughout the Coastal Plain and the Piedmont, and probably safe in the Upper South as far as Knoxville.

The Holly Osmanthus differs from the two varieties above in bearing much darker and smaller leaves, resembling miniature Holly leaves with their strongly spined tips. All the varieties of Osmanthus bear their leaves in opposite pairs. This species has white or yellowish fragrant flowers in autumn. Its form is rounded and shrubby, adapting to clipping very well to make a formal specimen; and its ultimate height is about 18 feet. The foliage is fine in texture and a beautiful dark green in color. Several interesting horticultural varieties are mentioned with the Small Shrubs of Group IV. This is a hardy species, well suited to normal garden conditions from the Coastal Plain through the Upper South except at its higher elevations.

All three varieties of these Osmanthus are first class, choice evergreen shrubs within the ranges of climatic adaptation indicated. They require no spraying and very little pruning or other maintenance. They grow well in sun or in light shade, asking only reasonably fertile soils and protection from severe drought. The Sweet Osmanthus is especially delightful as a specimen near a terrace, porch, or pathway where its perfume will be appreciated through the winter. It is too leggy to be employed in screens, and it does not take shearing well. The other two are excellent for screens or borders. They also adapt well to clipping for hedges, and they can be shaped into formal specimens which are almost as refined in character as the more difficult Boxwoods.

*Photinia glabra,* Japanese Photinia. *Photinia serrulata,* Chinese Photinia. *Photinia villosa,* Oriental Photinia. There are two evergreen Photinias of some importance in landscape work in the lower South. The Japanese is the smaller and more tender of the two, reliable in the Coastal Plain and in warmer parts of the Piedmont. Here it reaches a height of just over 10 feet with a loose, upright, leggy, and rather ungainly form. It is useful chiefly for the cutting garden because the new foliage opens with a bright red color, effective in flower arrangements. As they mature, the leaves, which are medium in texture, turn a dark dull green of no particular distinction. The plant should be grown in the sun because the red leaf coloration is not so pronounced in the shade. With frequent cutting the plant can be kept in bright new growth and in a smaller size class. Where the color fits, this shrub can be employed in a hedge.

The Chinese Photinia is a bolder shrub, much more common than the above, more generally useful, and more hardy throughout the Piedmont and into warmer parts of the Upper South. With a sheltered location it will succeed in Charleston, W. Va. It may reach over 20 feet in height, developing very rapidly and taking on a broadly oval, occasionally arborescent form. The foliage is dense and heavy, coarse-textured, and, in this species, the newly expanding leaves in the spring take on an attractive coppery tone which later turns to dark green. In April the large flat heads of white flowers make a fine show, and the clusters of red fruits which follow in autumn are effective into the winter. This shrub has many attractive qualities, and makes a hardy, fast-growing screen or border for sunny or lightly shaded sites. Unfortunately it is not usually given enough space to develop properly. It has a leaf disease which is reported to be very destructive and hard to control in some sections; it also suffers sometimes from blight which kills out some of the branches much as does fire blight on certain fruits of this family.

The Oriental Photinia is a hardy deciduous species which will be planted only in the Upper South for its showy clusters of red fruits and good foliage color in the fall season. It is well suited to sunny, exposed, dry hillside sites. Otherwise it has little merit, growing to 15 feet in an open, irregular, and rather leggy form with medium-textured, yellow-green leaves. It also is said to be subject to the fire blight disease. This may be planted in the cutting garden or for color at the back of a shrub border.

*Pittosporum tobira*, Tobira Pittosporum. Some plantsmen regard the Pittosporum as the most valuable single shrub for all-round use in the lower South, and it is very widely planted in consequence. Well suited to the Coastal Plain and to warmer parts of the Piedmont, this shrub is reasonably satisfactory to Memphis and Atlanta. It has an interesting form, strongly inclined toward a rather rugged, horizontal pattern, becoming ultimately tree-like, from 15 to 20 feet in height. It has beautiful foliage, bright evergreen in color with a clean glossy sheen and medium texture. In mid-spring it has flowers in clusters of white and dull yellow, exceedingly fragrant; and it bears occasionally rather ornamental fruits in autumn. In addition to these good qualities, the Pittosporum grows rapidly, making it a good subject for quick effects in even the poorest of soils. It tolerates well the heat of a sunny exposure and accompanying droughts but locations on fertile moist soils in shade should be avoided. A good subject for clipping into hedges or topiary, it makes either a fine screen or an interesting specimen. Ordinarily this shrub is healthy and free of disease, but it must be watched for attacks of the cottony cushion scale which, once established, is almost impossible to control. It is small wonder that Pittosporum is one of the most important plants of this area. Somewhat smaller than the species and interesting for its cream and gray-green foliage color is the Whitespot Pittosporum, *P. t. variegata*, also rather widely grown here.

*Podocarpus macrophyllus maki*, Shrubby Yew Podocarpus. At least two species of Podocarpus are grown in parts of the Coastal Plain, but the Shrubby Yew Podocarpus is the one which is hardy and dependable throughout this section and into warmer parts of the Piedmont. Grown in sheltered environs on patios and in plant boxes, it succeeds as a smaller evergreen as far north as Birmingham. Sometimes this plant is considered a broad-leaved evergreen, but the designation is not accurate since the plant is more closely related to the Yews and the cone-bearing evergreens. In milder climates this shrub becomes a tree up to 50 feet in height, but in this area it usually grows 10 to 20 feet tall with a dense form like a squatty spire. The dark evergreen leaves are narrow, 2 to 3 inches long, and fine to medium in texture. The plant seems to grow equally well in the sun or in quite dense shade. It has no flowers or fruits of merit, but it is included among the best of this size class because of its simple cultural demands and the contrast in foliage and form which it can provide in plant composition. Since it takes clipping admirably it makes one of the best hedge and screening plants for narrow spaces, excellent for small city gardens. The Japanese Podocarpus, *P. nagi*, is more tender and of a coarser texture, but it is an interesting specimen or border material occasionally seen in warmer portions of the Coastal Plain.

*Prunus laurocerasus*, Common Laurelcherry. *Prunus lusitanica*, Portuguese Laurelcherry. The two Laurelcherries listed here are beautiful for their large, coarse-textured, glossy, evergreen leaves. Although they are rather satisfactory in the Coastal Plain and the Piedmont, they are not considered quite first rate because they are occasionally subject to blight and because they are overly rank, coarse growers for most places. The Common, often called English, Laurelcherry is the more often seen of the two, and has several varieties which are most useful, such as the Schipka Laurelcherry discussed in Group V. The Schipka appears to be more hardy than its parent, which probably ought not to be relied upon north of Atlanta. The species grows to nearly 20 feet in height with a broad crown, making a handsome specimen where it is given space. It likes fertile soil, moisture, and sunshine, and it is a rapid grower and a voracious soil robber. The Portuguese form is said to grow even larger, with leaves somewhat smaller than those of the above. Both species bear white flowers in long clusters or racemes in late fall or early spring, and blue-black fruits. The flowering effect is sometimes quite attractive. Both species suffer occasionally from borers as well as from blight. These plants have been in cultivation for centuries with the result that there are many varieties, including dwarfs, which would make an interesting collection to serve as a source for propagating stock. The Carolina Laurelcherry, *P. caroliniana*, is often planted as a Large Shrub, but it is better classed as a Small Tree. Hence it is described in Group VII.

*Punica granatum*, Pomegranate. This is one of the very interesting deciduous shrubs for the Coastal Plain and the Piedmont. Its usefulness is limited because it is large growing, requiring a generous space for development, as it reaches a height of about 15 feet with an even greater spread. The leaves are small, fine in texture, and rather gray green in color. The flowers appear in early summer and make a brilliant show. The typical color is an orange-scarlet, but there also are other varieties with blossoms of white, yellow, and variegated red and white, single or double. The fruits, maturing in autumn, are equally decorative yellow to reddish globes, 3 to 5 inches in diameter, containing numerous fleshy scarlet seeds of pleasant tart flavor. The Pomegranate is pest free, perfectly hardy in this region, thriving with no care in sunny exposures on droughty, heavy, acid or alkaline soils. Its color is difficult to adapt to most places, but the plant makes a splendid specimen for the herb, flower, or fruit garden. The Dwarf variety *nana* has been mentioned in Chapter III.

*Rhododendron maximum*, Rosebay Rhododendron. Native to the southern mountains and to the hilly country of the Upper South, this plant is restricted to acid soil localities of cooler regions where it is among the best of materials for foliage effect and for massing or screening. It is an excellent shrub for shaded to partly sunny areas in woodlands, whereas the Catawba Rhododendron should be grown in more sunny situations. This is effective chiefly in its coarse-textured evergreen foliage since the white to pinkish flowers, which open in late June, are not very conspicuous although they are lovely in detail. Though Rhododendron should be grown in areas of acid soils, it is surprisingly tolerant of limestone regions provided it is planted very shallow, almost on top of the ground, surrounded with a bed of light soil rich in acid humus, protected with an acid-forming mulch of peat, oak leaves, or rotted sawdust, and given a cool, well-drained but humid situation protected from wind and winter sunshine. A major fault of the Rosebay in most places is the tendency to grow thin, open, and straggly, occasionally reaching 30 feet in height. Unattractive growth form can be prevented by cutting to the ground an occasional branch; if pruning is done in midwinter, it will usually encourage new shoots to fill in later. Attacks of spider mites and lacewing flies can be troublesome although they are seldom serious on vigorous plants. This shrub is somewhat unpredictable, and finding a spot to its liking is the key to success with it. Therefore it may be considered somewhat inferior to some other evergreens, but for cooler sections and higher elevations this has a beauty and character hardly to be matched. There are at least two hybrids of this species which are strong fine evergreens for the Upper South. These are "Cunningham's White," and "Album elegans."

*Rhus copallina*, Flameleaf Sumac. Several Sumacs are native to the eastern United States, making rather exotic looking and colorful large shrubs or small trees, usually growing in clumps or masses in old fields. Possibly the best of these, more easily controlled for ordinary landscape work, will be the Flameleaf or Mountain Sumac. This forms a clump of spindly, graceful, naked stems rising to a height of 10 feet, sometimes more, supporting a top-heavy tuft of luxurious compound leaves which are a rich glossy green in summer and deep ruby red in autumn. Greenish white flowers in showy spikes appear in mid-summer and these are followed in autumn by conspicuous red fruits which persist into the winter until they are finally picked off by birds. This plant may be too weedy for many places and its character too rugged and strong, but it is excellent for massing on poor dry banks in exposed situations for naturalistic effect, chiefly in the Upper South and possibly also in cooler parts of the Piedmont.

*Stewartia malacodendron*, Virginia Stewartia. *Stewartia ovata grandiflora*, Showy Mountain Stewartia. It is not easy to explain why the Stewartias are not seen in the landscape work of this region more than they are unless it be that they are rather large materials for including on the average small place. They are not easily obtained although they should prove thoroughly reliable throughout this region and probably ought to have a place in many larger gardens and parks. They are rather slow growers, requiring good, well-watered soils, and a place with some sunlight. They may be partial to acid peaty soils and to locations sheltered from desiccating winds. The foliage is deciduous, of medium texture, giving a good autumn color effect. The habit is rather thin, upright, tending to become tree-like, and in winter the bare branches are interesting for the colorful patterns of the flaking bark. These plants are particularly notable for their large single flowers of midsummer, resembling those of the single Camellias, which are of the same family. Two species of merit are natives of the Southeast. The Showy Mountain Stewartia is a desirable one of these, with 3-inch blooms of white with prominent purple stamens. The Virginia Stewartia is similar although it may not be so hardy. The Japanese Stewartia, S. *pseudo-camellia*, is hardly as desirable as the native species.

*Styrax japonica*, Japanese Snowbell. This is a large deciduous shrub becoming eventually tree-like to 20 feet or more in height which may be rarely seen in the Southeast. It is grown chiefly for its pendulous, bell form, fragrant white flowers which are quite attractive in detail, rather similar to those of the common native Silverbell or *Halesia* of the same family. The bloom is appreciated where it can be seen from below as it might be near a terrace, but it is not very effective in the landscape because it occurs in midsummer when the plant is largely covered by the medium-textured foliage. This plant is not outstanding in other respects and so, although it is well suited to growing conditions in sunny locations in the Upper South and the cooler Piedmont, it probably will be little used here. The American Snowbell, *S. americana*, a native shrub of the Coastal Plain from Virginia to Louisiana, growing to about 10 feet in height, may be of interest for naturalizing in this section if it can be procured.

*Symplocos paniculata*, Sapphireberry Sweetleaf. The Sapphireberry is not much grown in this region, and it hardly merits more attention than it receives. It is interesting, however, for its small fragrant white flowers of late spring and its unusual bright blue fruits of late summer. The fruits are not very showy because they are covered by the foliage, and they soon drop. The form of the plant and the rather coarse deciduous foliage have no special beauty.

*Syringa vulgaris*, Common Lilac. Lilacs are not well adapted to most parts of the Southeast, but they grow well in the Upper South and gardeners in cooler parts of the Piedmont persist in trying them, with fair results. In the spring season the opulent clusters of single or double florets of delicious and characteristic fragrance, in white, lilac, blue, purple, or pink, are among the finest of garden productions. The deciduous foliage is coarse in texture, dark green in color, and in this area the plant grows from 10 to 15 feet in height, forming large clumps of leggy, often interesting forms. Lilacs require a good bit of care if they are to be at their best, although old bushes are often seen in abandoned farmyards where they have had no attention for many years. Old stems should be periodically removed after flowering, and new suckers should be selected and thinned to maintain a process of constant renewal. Borers are an unremitting threat, particularly in warmer sections, and dormant spraying may be required at times to control scale insects. If the plants are set in sites which are shaded or where air circulation is poor, the foliage may be disfigured with mildew fungus. These shrubs should be set in open sites in good soils with good drainage in cool sections; they are particularly good in limestone regions. Despite the care necessary for growing them, where they do succeed the Lilacs make the finest kind of cut flower material and are excellent ornamental shrubs for specimens or for borders of garden areas. Often they are fitting in foundation plantings, and their simple charm is always appropriate around farm houses where one might hesitate to use plants of more exotic character. When one is selecting varieties, it is usually worthwhile to take the pains to secure named varieties which are superior in flowering habit. These should be bought as "own root" plants, however. The commonly available hybrids are grafted on Privet understocks which become a nuisance with their sprouting, and the plant is liable to be ruined if a borer gets into the top. A number of Lilac species of this size class can be grown in this region and they are of some interest for prolonging the blooming season. Few of these are as attractive as the Common Lilac, however, and they are not likely to be much used except in collections.

*Vaccinium arboreum*, Farkleberry. *Vaccinium corymbosum*, Highbush Blueberry. The Farkleberry or Sparkleberry is common in the sandy coastal areas and it has value here as a screening, border, or naturalizing material in places where it is sometimes difficult to find other choicer plants which will maintain themselves. Growing to a height of 20 feet or more with an open shrubby form, this plant carries fine-textured, glossy evergreen leaves, small white flowers in summer, and glistening black fruits in winter. It likes the light shade of Pines and a mulch of humus, but it will endure either dry, well-drained, or swampy sites. It is not grown in nurseries and planting stock must be collected.

The Highbush Blueberry is fine for naturalizing in areas of acid soils in the Upper South, but it is more likely to be employed in gardens in one or another of its many varieties developed especially for the edible fruits. As such it is attractive as an occasional specimen in the cutting garden or in an unclipped border for the vegetable plot or small orchard. When planting these for fruit production, several varieties should be included for good cross pollination. The

Blueberry has shy but attractive bell-like flowers in early spring, fine-textured deciduous foliage with good fall color, and an interesting informal and picturesque habit of growth. It requires little care, but it does benefit from some pruning. Bag worms and Japanese Beetles do attack it occasionally.

*Viburnum lantana*, Wayfaringtree Viburnum

*Viburnum opulus*, European Cranberrybush Viburnum

*Viburnum prunifolium*, Blackhaw Viburnum

*Viburnum sieboldi*, Siebold Viburnum

*Viburnum trilobum*, American Cranberrybush Viburnum

The large and invaluable genus of Viburnum presents several of the finest of the deciduous shrubs of this class, mostly for the Upper South and the cooler Piedmont. They have in common the desirable ability to adapt themselves to almost any soil; the species listed are thoroughly hardy, preferring sunny or lightly shaded locations, requiring little or no care if they are given space in which to develop their normal forms. All of them are recommended for screening, massing, or for specimens, for all have that elusive quality called "character" in their habits of growth in addition to outstanding displays of flowers, fruit which is important bird food, and autumn foliage color. The above list does not attempt to exhaust the possibilities but only to suggest some outstanding species with special characteristics and design values.

The Wayfaringtree is distinctive for its coarse foliage of gray green color, new growth which is woolly and silvery, and for a somewhat stoloniferous habit of growth. It is vigorous and fast-growing, reaching a height of about 15 feet, but in the garden it is well to cut one or two of the older stalks to the ground every year or so to encourage new shoots which will face down well and form ultimately a broad and massive clump. This is recommended only for the Upper South where it should be given full exposure to sun, wind, and drought since more sheltered environments favor a looser and somewhat straggling habit. The flat heads of white flowers of late spring are not particularly effective, but the developing fruits through the summer turn a bright coral red for a time, particularly fine with the grayish foliage, before they become black in autumn. The fall foliage color is dull red.

The Blackhaw has a similar cousin, the Rusty or Southern Blackhaw, *V. rufidulum*, and the two are considered by some botanists to be regional variations of one basic species which is found growing naturally throughout most of the eastern states as far south as Florida. This plant often takes on the habit of a small tree of several trunks, forming a broad head of rather horizontal character and losing its lower branches. The foliage is medium in texture, rather rounded, glossy and dark green in color, turning bright red in autumn. The white flowers in flattish heads are numerous and effective in late spring. The blue black fruits are not very showy although they are good to eat and have been used in earlier times for making preserves. This is well suited to all soils and exposures of the region, but it will be more compact with exposure to the sun.

The American and the European Cranberrybushes are of almost equal value. Indeed, it is difficult to distinguish the two in the field, and practically the only real difference is that the fruits of the former are made into jellies while those of the latter are not. New growth on the latter is also quite subject to damage by aphid attacks, but these seldom do any permanent harm and may be considered to be of little consequence. The European Cranberrybush is very common in nurseries and widely planted. The American, a native of our northern states from Maine to Washington, is comparatively difficult to locate. These plants grow into massive bushes over 10 feet in height with attractive lobed foliage of medium texture, turning dull red in autumn. Their flat-headed flower clusters are showy in spring, interesting for bearing a ring of larger sterile florets around the typical assemblage of smaller perfect blooms. The bright red berries mature in late summer, and they are decorative until winter's frosts have withered them or until birds have made off with them. The plants are sturdy and tolerant in sun or partial shade in the Upper South or the Piedmont, making fine materials for screening and cutting. The European species has two interesting varieties, one with yellow fruits, *V. o. xanthocarpum*, and another called the European Snowball, *V. o. roseum*, with rounded heads made up entirely of the showy sterile florets. Although these plants require little care, they should be given some pruning as they mature to remove older wood. The Snowball is especially liable to infestations of aphids which can be disfiguring if not controlled by sprays.

The Siebold Viburnum is considered by Dr. Wyman of the Arnold Arboretum to be the most beautiful single member of this genus. In habit it is somewhat upright, irregular, occasionally tree-like, to a height of 15 feet or more. Its outstanding features are the large, glossy, bright green leaves turning dull red in autumn, the showy massive heads of white flowers in late spring, and the changing color of the fruits from green to red and finally black through the summer. It should be grown in sunny spots, where it makes an excellent specimen, probably only in the Upper South.

*Yucca aloifolia*, Spanish Bayonet. This is one of the very common and also very spectacular plants of the Coastal Plain. Its rugged form, sometimes reaching a height of 15 feet, its bold white plumes of summer flowers, and its coarse-textured, sword-like, evergreen leaves are well known here. It is tolerant of city conditions, and it is much planted in Charleston, S. C., Savannah, and as far north as Birmingham, Ala. The Spanish Bayonet thrives in any well-drained soil, even of poorest quality, in the sun or in light shade, making a striking specimen in contrast with architectural features. It is not quite so useful as *Y. gloriosa* because it grows large, sprawly, and untidy; but it is a very good material of its type where ample space is available.

Magnolia

# 5

# TREES

Group VII - Small

Group VIII - Large

SHADE trees are most important elements of planting in all landscape work, and the choice of species and the study of their placement should be almost the first consideration in any planting design. It need hardly be added that existing trees should be protected in any construction work since they represent values which cannot be replaced except at great cost.

In all planting design the science of plant ecology has some bearing, but it is in the selection of tree varieties and their handling that knowledge of ecological principles is most helpful. The plant ecologist knows, for example, that the native Sugar Maple is the "climax" tree of much of this region, and that normally it germinates and develops only in soils that contain some humus and under fast growing "nurse trees" which invade a raw site before it to modify and temper the environment, giving it protection from sun and drying winds. This species the plant ecologist would not usually specify for an open, dry, windy hilltop; or if, for some particular reason, the Maple should be especially desired, he would first plant, possibly, Black Locusts, and then follow with the Maple after some years. Under this procedure, those trees set out much later will far outstrip those planted directly in full exposure, which for many years may develop only inches during each season. The same knowledge of "ecological succession" tells the plantsman that the Shortleaf and Loblolly Pines will grow well on raw clay, but they will not compete with taller deciduous trees. Each of our native trees has its ecological niche which is rather sharply defined. On small home projects such considerations are not vital because conditions can be controlled to some extent. But in parks and roadside development they are factors of design which permeate every part of the fabric.

Trees are grouped here in two classes, Large and Small, chiefly in order to emphasize the appreciation of a difference in size which is vital as far as landscape design is concerned. As houses become lower and smaller and residential subdivisions are increasingly crowded with both overhead and underground utilities, it is important to select trees which can be relied upon to fit within specified limits. The same consideration applies to streets. City street departments are siding with utility companies in demanding plantings of trees carefully chosen for low upkeep and proportioned to rather precise dimensions.

There are five common uses to which plantings of trees will be devoted in landscape design. These are (1) to provide shade in the home grounds development; (2) to furnish shade and ornament along city streets, parking areas, highways, and parkways; (3) to give screening for privacy and for windbreak; (4) to decorate and enrich parks, larger private places, and other large scale designs either as specimens or in clumps or masses; and (5) to conserve land and provide an economic return through the building up of forests. The latter impinges upon the realm of forestry, and so it is somewhat outside the scope of this discussion. The other four uses do present very definite demands on the landscape designer which ought to be borne in mind throughout any consideration of this group of materials.

(1) Trees for home grounds. It is obvious that today's house is being built smaller and lower and on a smaller lot. For this reason most modern home sites will accommodate only one of the major trees from Group VIII with possibly a number of the lesser species from Group VII. Usually the large specimen should be planted to the west to protect house and outdoor living areas from afternoon sun. The tree should be clean, free from insect and disease damage, and it should shed little litter to clog roof gutters. It should be high branching to permit free circulation of air and open vision. As a general rule, it should be deciduous so that winter sunlight will reach the dwelling when the foliage has disappeared for the dormant season. In some cases, especially in new and raw subdivisions, the selection of varieties characterized by rapid growth will be highly desirable. In almost all cases major trees should be located at least 15 feet away from buildings, and they must be sufficiently far from sewer lines and septic tanks that there will be little danger of damage to these from probing roots.

In most home grounds landscapes and housing developments of all kinds, the Small Trees of Group VII will be of great value after the selection of possibly one or a few Large Trees. The former have the double advantage of proportion and scale fitting for such residential problems, and also of attaining mature effect rather quickly. A planting near one of today's small houses might possess more dignity if it consisted principally of one or two small trees and some ground-covers in place of the typical overstuffed composition of many standard or dwarf shrubs. Oftentimes one small tree may be substituted for several bushes with improved effect. For screen planting in cramped quarters, the increasingly popular practice is to use rows of small trees, backed up by hedges or fencing of one kind or another, and underplanted with groundcovers and bulbs, or Hemerocallis and other shade-tolerating perennials. Small trees give scale and significance to the tiniest of landscapes.

(2) Trees for streets, highways, and parkways. Plantings of this type should be considered first of all as relatively permanent community investments. Longevity and freedom from maintenance demands, whether for general cleanup or spraying or pruning, should be of first importance. Speed of growth is secondary.

Street tree programs are being developed in many progressive communities. As a consequence, the problems associated with such programs are receiving intensive study. They have been inspired generally by the realization that good street tree plantings have a great deal to do with making a town or city an attractive place in which to live. However, they have also had their beginnings, paradoxically, as a result of trees becoming a nuisance, as in places where the breaking of old, soft-wooded specimens has become a public menace, or in towns where there were many Elm trees stricken suddenly by disease, presenting all at once a removal problem of staggering cost. The care of street trees is a community responsibility. This responsibility entails planting programs for new streets and maintenance and replacements on old ones. Sometimes it is said that street tree plantings should consist of mixed varieties so that if disease attacks any one, not all will be damaged or destroyed. On the other hand, it may be said that spraying, pruning, and feeding will be required anyway, and that this work is simplified materially if only one variety is planted along any one street. No doubt there is truth in both viewpoints, and plant selections will be made primarily with regard to the desirability for formal avenue effects on certain major streets, for informality in outer subdivisions, etc.

Although longevity and freedom from maintenance are of prime importance in the selection of street tree varieties, consideration of size is equally vital. In some cases trees must be sized in proportion to the maintenance equipment available—the reach of spray machines and of pruning equipment. In all cases the size of the tree should be proportioned to the size of the street. The width of the standard street paving of many of today's subdivisions is 26 feet in a 50 to 60 foot right-of-way. Since most of the major shade trees have an ultimate spread of at least 40 feet, here too the smaller types of

Group VII have a place, while the larger species fit better on wider primary traffic arteries and boulevards. Pole lines for telephone and electricity have to be reckoned with. So also do other elements of the average city street including water, gas, and sewer lines. Generally the Small Trees should be spaced at least 30 feet apart, and the Large Trees at about 50 feet or more. There should be at least three feet between the tree and the curbing on one side and the sidewalk on the other to prevent damage to either from expanding roots. Where streetside planting strips give less than 6 feet, it will be better in the long run to omit trees. Circumstances are different in many ways when highway and parkway plantings are in question. Generally, more space is available, and one's choice is not limited to species which will tolerate the cramped quarters, the inadequate feeding and watering, and the fumes of the city. Here conditions approximate more closely those encountered in park work and forestry. Usually native species consistent with those existing in the area will be selected here.

(3) Trees for screening. In order to secure screening and protection from noise and severe winds, the evergreen trees are most desirable for the year-round protection they provide. On smaller properties shelter belts of large growing species will, of course, be impractical on account of space limits, and shrubs of Groups V and VI might be substituted. Some instances where screening trees are most desirable are in borders separating residential neighborhoods from major traffic arteries and railroads; in shelter belts shielding farm homes and outbuildings, swimming pools, and recreation areas from north winds; and in screens to diminish the light and noise of neighborhood shopping centers and night baseball game areas which might annoy homeowners in the vicinity. In most cases the materials for this kind of function should be low branching, dense, and quickgrowing as well as evergreen. Occasionally those species bearing thorns will be helpful. Close planting for early effect is often desirable, and the fully developed, perfect specimen is not important.

(4) Trees for decoration. Along with groundcovers, trees of all sizes are of major importance in all larger landscape compositions for both maintenance and aesthetic reasons. As a general rule, shrubs must have a certain amount of pruning and care, without which most borders and mass plantings of any size soon become untidy heaps of tangled branches, both living and dead. Generally trees do not require as much upkeep. It is safe to say that in park plantings, groundcovers and small and large trees should largely make up the nursery list because of the scale of the compositions involved and the lower maintenance costs.

Although functional considerations have been emphasized in the foregoing paragraphs, it is to be hoped that all tree plantings are for embellishment also. From all sides one is bombarded with statistics proving how effective trees are in directing wind currents, deflecting noise and superfluous light and heat, and tempering the atmosphere in which we live and breathe. In more ample landscape compositions, qualities of form, texture, and color become indeed the major factors governing choice, and many more practical considerations may be sidetracked.

## VII. Small Trees for the SOUTHERN COASTAL PLAIN

| *Botanical Name* | *Common Name* |
|---|---|
| RECOMMENDED FOR GENERAL USE | |
| Cercis canadensis | Eastern Redbud |
| Cinnamomum camphora | Camphortree |
| Cornus florida | Flowering Dogwood |
| Eriobotrya japonica | Loquat |
| Ilex cassine | Dahoon Holly |
| Ilex opaca | American Holly |
| Ilex vomitoria | Yaupon Holly |
| Juniperus virginiana | Eastern Redcedar |
| Magnolia virginiana | Sweetbay Magnolia |
| Malus angustifolia | Southern Crabapple |
| Prunus caroliniana | Carolina Laurelcherry |
| Quercus acuta | Japanese Evergreen Oak |
| Sabal palmetto | Cabbage Palmetto |
| RECOMMENDED FOR RESTRICTED USE | |
| Acer palmatum | Japanese Maple |
| Albizzia julibrissin | Silktree Albizzia |
| Broussonetia papyrifera | Common Papermulberry |
| Butia capitata | Brazilian Butiapalm |
| Chaenomeles sinensis | Chinese Floweringquince |
| Chionanthus virginicus | White Fringetree |
| Citrus limon variety | Meyer Lemon |
| Citrus paradisi variety | Duncan Grapefruit |
| Crataegus phaenopyrum | Washington Hawthorn |
| Cryptomeria japonica | Cryptomeria |
| Cunninghamia lanceolata | Common Chinafir |
| Cupressus sempervirens | Italian Cypress |
| Diospyros kaki | Kaki Persimmon |
| Ficus carica | Common Fig |
| Firmiana simplex | Chinese Parasoltree |

| *Botanical Name* | *Common Name* |
|---|---|
| Gordonia lasianthus | Loblollybay Gordonia |
| Halesia carolina | Carolina Silverbell |
| Ilex decidua | Possumhaw |
| Ilex purpurea | |
| Ilex rotunda | |
| Koelreuteria paniculata | Panicled Goldraintree |
| Lagerstroemia indica | Common Crapemyrtle |
| Ligustrum lucidum | Glossy Privet |
| Magnolia soulangeana | Saucer Magnolia |
| Magnolia stellata | Star Magnolia |
| Melia azedarach | Chinaberry |
| Musa species | Banana |
| Olea europaea | Common Olive |
| Osmanthus americanus | Devilwood Osmanthus |
| Osmanthus fragrans | Sweet Osmanthus |
| Oxydendrum arboreum | Sourwood |
| Parkinsonia aculeata | Jerusalemthorn |
| Persea borbonia | Redbay Persea |
| Phoenix canariensis | Canary Date Palm |
| Pistacia chinensis | Chinese Pistache |
| Poncirus trifoliata | Trifoliate Orange |
| Prunus mume | Japanese Apricot |
| Prunus persica scleropersica | Flowering Peach |
| Pyrus calleryana | Callery Pear |
| Sapium sebiferum | Chinese Tallowtree |
| Ulmus parvifolia | Chinese Elm |
| Ulmus pumila | Siberian Elm |
| Viburnum prunifolium | Blackhaw Viburnum |
| Washingtonia robusta | Mexican Washington Palm |

## VII. Small Trees for the SOUTHERN PIEDMONT

### RECOMMENDED FOR GENERAL USE

| | |
|---|---|
| Acer palmatum | Japanese Maple |
| Cercis canadensis | Eastern Redbud |
| Cornus florida | Flowering Dogwood |
| Crataegus phaenopyrum | Washington Hawthorn |
| Ilex opaca | American Holly |
| Juniperus virginiana | Eastern Redcedar |
| Lagerstroemia indica | Common Crapemyrtle |
| Magnolia soulangeana | Saucer Magnolia |
| Magnolia virginiana | Sweetbay Magnolia |
| Malus angustifolia | Southern Crabapple |

| *Botanical Name* | *Common Name* |
|---|---|
| Malus floribunda | Japanese Flowering Crab |
| Malus purpurea | Purple Flowering Crab |
| Prunus caroliniana | Carolina Laurelcherry |

### Recommended for Restricted Use

| | |
|---|---|
| Acer campestre | Hedge Maple |
| Acer ginnala | Amur Maple |
| Albizzia julibrissin | Silktree Albizzia |
| Asimina triloba | Common Pawpaw |
| Betula nigra | River Birch |
| Broussonetia papyrifera | Common Papermulberry |
| Carpinus caroliniana | American Hornbeam |
| Cercidiphyllum japonicum | Katsuratree |
| Chaenomeles sinensis | Chinese Floweringquince |
| Chionanthus virginicus | White Fringetree |
| Cladrastis lutea | American Yellowwood |
| Cryptomeria japonica | Cryptomeria |
| Cunninghamia lanceolata | Common Chinafir |
| Eriobotrya japonica | Loquat |
| Ficus carica | Common Fig |
| Firmiana simplex | Chinese Parasoltree |
| Halesia carolina | Carolina Silverbell |
| Ilex decidua | Possumhaw |
| Ilex purpurea | |
| Ilex vomitoria | Yaupon Holly |
| Koelreuteria paniculata | Panicled Goldraintree |
| Ligustrum lucidum | Glossy Privet |
| Melia azedarach | Chinaberry |
| Osmanthus americanus | Devilwood Osmanthus |
| Oxydendrum arboreum | Sourwood |
| Pistacia chinensis | Chinese Pistache |
| Poncirus trifoliata | Trifoliate Orange |
| Prunus cerasifera pissardi | Pissard Plum |
| Prunus persica scleropersica | Flowering Peach |
| Prunus serrulata | Oriental Cherry |
| Pyrus calleryana | Callery Pear |
| Quercus acuta | Japanese Evergreen Oak |
| Sassafras albidum | Common Sassafras |
| Ulmus parvifolia | Chinese Elm |
| Ulmus pumila | Siberian Elm |
| Viburnum prunifolium | Blackhaw Viburnum |

## VII. Small Trees for the UPPER SOUTH

*Botanical Name*                                    *Common Name*

### RECOMMENDED FOR GENERAL USE

| | |
|---|---|
| Acer palmatum | Japanese Maple |
| Cercis canadensis | Eastern Redbud |
| Cladrastis lutea | American Yellowwood |
| Cornus florida | Flowering Dogwood |
| Crataegus phaenopyrum | Washington Hawthorn |
| Ilex opaca | American Holly |
| Juniperus virginiana | Eastern Redcedar |
| Magnolia soulangeana | Saucer Magnolia |
| Magnolia virginiana | Sweetbay Magnolia |
| Malus floribunda | Japanese Flowering Crab |
| Malus hupehensis | Tea Crab |
| Malus purpurea | Purple Flowering Crab |
| Oxydendrum arboreum | Sourwood |

### RECOMMENDED FOR RESTRICTED USE

| | |
|---|---|
| Acer campestre | Hedge Maple |
| Acer ginnala | Amur Maple |
| Albizzia julibrissin | Silktree Albizzia |
| Amelanchier canadensis | Shadblow Serviceberry |
| Asimina triloba | Common Pawpaw |
| Betula nigra | River Birch |
| Broussonetia papyrifera | Common Papermulberry |
| Carpinus betulus | European Hornbeam |
| Carpinus caroliniana | American Hornbeam |
| Castanea mollissima | Chinese Chestnut |
| Cercidiphyllum japonicum | Katsuratree |
| Chaenomeles sinensis | Chinese Floweringquince |
| Chamaecyparis species | Falsecypress |
| Chionanthus virginicus | White Fringetree |
| Cornus alternifolia | Pagoda Dogwood |
| Cornus kousa | Kousa Dogwood |
| Crataegus intricata | Thicket Hawthorn |
| Cryptomeria japonica | Cryptomeria |
| Cunninghamia lanceolata | Common Chinafir |
| Euonymus europaeus | European Euonymus |
| Euonymus yedoensis | Yeddo Euonymus |
| Evodia hupehensis | Hupeh Evodia |
| Halesia carolina | Carolina Silverbell |
| Halesia monticola | Mountain Silverbell |

| Botanical Name | Common Name |
|---|---|
| Ilex decidua | Possumhaw |
| Koelreuteria paniculata | Panicled Goldraintree |
| Laburnum species | Laburnum |
| Lagerstroemia indica | Common Crapemyrtle |
| Libocedrus decurrens | California Incensecedar |
| Magnolia fraseri | Fraser Magnolia |
| Magnolia macrophylla | Bigleaf Magnolia |
| Magnolia stellata | Star Magnolia |
| Magnolia tripetala | Umbrella Magnolia |
| Malus coronaria | Wild Sweet Crabapple |
| Morus alba variety | White Mulberry variety |
| Prunus cerasifera pissardi | Pissard Plum |
| Prunus persica scleropersica | Flowering Peach |
| Prunus serrulata | Oriental Cherry |
| Pyrus calleryana | Callery Pear |
| Sassafras albidum | Common Sassafras |
| Sorbus americana | American Mountainash |
| Sorbus aucuparia | European Mountainash |
| Syringa amerunsis japonica | Japanese Tree Lilac |
| Thuja occidentalis | Eastern Arborvitae |
| Ulmus parvifolia | Chinese Elm |
| Ulmus pumila | Siberian Elm |
| Viburnum prunifolium | Blackhaw Viburnum |

Five native species of the following chart are suited to all climatic and soil conditions of the Southeast. These are the Redbud, Dogwood American Holly, Redcedar, and Sweetbay (*Cercis, Cornus, Ilex opaca, Juniperus, Magnolia virginiana*). The first two are deciduous and the last is semi-evergreen, at least in warmer sections. The Holly is a broad-leaved evergreen, and the Redcedar is a needle-type evergreen. Warm climate species, all evergreens, are the Camphor (*Cinnamomum*), Loquat (*Eriobotrya*), Dahoon (*Ilex cassine*), Evergreen Oak (*Quercus*), and Palmetto (*Sabal*). The Yellowwood (*Cladrastis*) is probably least able to endure heat. The Flowering Crabs (*Malus*) will grow well in warm sections, but they require a minimum number of days of frost for proper maturing of the flower buds. After warm winters in the Lower South the bloom display is often disappointing, and thus the Crabs are only fairly useful here. Throughout the region the Saucer Magnolia, representing a number of deciduous oriental forms, is likely to bloom so early in the spring that its flowering effect is destroyed by late frosts. *Ilex cassine* and *vomitoria*, and the *Prunus* are broad-leaved evergreens of the Coastal Plain which are

fairly hardy in cooler sections; but here, along the upper limits indicated, they are generally more shrubby than tree-like in character.

### RANGE CHART FOR GROUP VII. SMALL TREES

| | Coastal Plain | | Piedmont | | Upper South | |
|---|---|---|---|---|---|---|
| Acer palmatum | | - - - | x x x | x x x | x x x | x x x |
| Cercis canadensis | x x x | x x x | x x x | x x x | x x x | x x x |
| Cinnamomum camphora | x x x | x x x | - - - | | | |
| Cladrastis lutea | | | - - - | - - - | x x x | x x x |
| Cornus florida | x x x | x x x | x x x | x x x | x x x | x x x |
| Crataegus phaenopyrum | | - - - | x x x | x x x | x x x | x x x |
| Eriobotrya japonica | x x x | x x x | x x x | - - - | | |
| Ilex cassine | x x x | x x x | - - - | | | |
| Ilex opaca | x x x | x x x | x x x | x x x | x x x | x x x |
| Ilex vomitoria | x x x | x x x | x x x | - - - | | |
| Juniperus virginiana | x x x | x x x | x x x | x x x | x x x | x x x |
| Lagerstroemia indica | - - - | x x x | x x x | x x x | x x x | x x x |
| Magnolia soulangeana | - - - | x x x | x x x | x x x | x x x | x x x |
| Magnolia virginiana | x x x | x x x | x x x | x x x | x x x | x x x |
| Malus angustifolia | x x x | x x x | x x x | x x x | - - - | |
| Malus floribunda | | - - - | x x x | x x x | x x x | x x x |
| Malus purpurea | | - - - | x x x | x x x | x x x | x x x |
| Oxydendrum arboreum | | - - - | - - - | x x x | x x x | x x x |
| Prunus caroliniana | x x x | x x x | x x x | x x x | x x x | - - - |
| Quercus acuta | x x x | x x x | x x x | - - - | | |
| Sabal palmetto | x x x | x x x | - - - | | | |

*Acer campestre,* Hedge Maple. *Acer ginnala,* Amur Maple. *Acer
palmatum,* Japanese Maple. The Maple genus includes many species
and varieties which have been little tested in the Southeast but which
may well prove most useful in this region when they are better
known and generally available. Three species are discussed here, but
this list does not do justice to the group, and it is especially weak
in omitting a number of promising oriental species. Of these the
Paperbark Maple, *A. griseum,* growing to about 25 feet, is noteworthy
for its peeling red-brown bark and its coarse three-parted leaves, although its hardiness is questionable; the David Maple, *A. davidi,*
has elegant rather linear leaves and greenish bark marked with white
stripes; and the Nikko Maple, *A. nikoense,* and the Devil Maple,
*A. diabolicum,* are attractive in habit. Upon further testing, some
of these may be found highly desirable for street plantings, clean
and long lasting.

Among the small Maples, the Hedge Maple is not uncommon.
This makes a good shade tree for the small place. It comes· from
Europe and bears small deciduous leaves which are lobed rather
like those of our native species, fine in texture. The habit is densely

twiggy, distinctly tree-like with one trunk, and the form is ir-regularly upright oval. It is considered a superior material for tall clipped hedges. The Hedge Maple is slow growing, but it appears to be pest free, long lasting, and tolerant of urban conditions, so that it should be a good selection for the small street in the Upper South.

The Amur Maple is almost shrubby, particularly in exposed loca-tions. Normally it will reach about 15 feet with several trunks, a broad spread, and a quite irregular horizontal form. The leaves are rather like spear points with barbs at the bases, dark and glossy green in color, turning deep red in autumn. The plant is often colorful through the midsummer, providing a fine cutting material at this season, when the seeds with their prominent red wings are maturing. Adapted to sunny locations in the Upper South and the cooler parts of the Piedmont, this plant is probably best in screens or as a speci-men. However, one could not expect to be able to walk under its branches.

Fourteen varieties of the Japanese Maple are listed in *Standarized Plant Names*, and nearly all of these are superb materials of their kind for landscape use. They vary in size from small types of about 6 feet, often with very picturesque branching forms, to about 20 feet, which is normal for the species. All are deciduous and of fine texture value, but the lobings and cuttings of the leaves are of many patterns, and the foliage colors range from green to yellow-green and pink or red. Some of the green foliage forms are most outstanding for their fall coloration of red or yellow. Possibly nothing growing in this region can compete with them in this respect. With such a collection to choose from, the ultimate selection, which is further complicated by a general mix-up in nomenclature, often must be left to consultation with the local nurseryman on the desired scale or size and leaf form or color. The smaller types make excellent specimens for rock gardens, often displaying the contorted forms which are being appreciated once again as natural sculptural elements. Larger types, including the green-leaved species, although they are slow growers, can hardly be equalled as clean shade trees of refined character and classic beauty for the small yard or terrace. The colored foliage types are the best of their class, although the average garden has little proper need for them, popular as they are. These trees are hardy and well suited to all but the sandy coastal strip of this region. They prefer good soils, however, and they need ample water and protection from over-exposure to desiccating winds which may cause tip burn and generally poor growth. In much of the Southeast late frosts often nip the first shoots of spring, and this makes the selection of some types, especially those with colored foliage, somewhat questionable. Weak specimens may be damaged by borers, but otherwise they are pest free.

*Albizzia julibrissin,* Silktree Albizzia. Often called the Mimosa, this is a somewhat weedy plant, often making a nuisance of itself because its seedlings volunteer so numerously. Still it forms a handsome tree which grows very rapidly, even under severe soil and drought conditions. When one needs a quick shade, as in some of the new treeless subdivisions where there is nothing but subsoil to plant in, the Albizzia could be a good temporary solution. It reaches a height of 30 feet in a broad, spreading horizontal form. The foliage is fine in texture, light and gray-green in color. In the late spring the cottony tufts of rosy flowers are quite showy. The Albizzia has its faults, for it is short-lived, and the foliage in many sections is invariably attacked by web worms which require spraying at least twice during the summer. In some sections a "Mimosa blight" has attacked, and to combat this a blight resistant strain has been developed which should be planted wherever it is available. This tree is well suited to all parts of this region except its higher elevations. A smaller growing variety called *A. j. rosea* has blooms of brighter pink and is said to be more hardy than the species.

*Amelanchier canadensis,* Shadblow Serviceberry. In the mountainous section of the Southeast the Shadblow is a familiar native. It is often a shrubby many-trunked tree which is lovely in early spring before the leaves appear, with its loose trusses of small white flowers, and again in June when its edible red to purplish fruits mature. Possibly its finest landscape quality, however, is its graceful form which emphasizes a delicate tracery of thin trunks and stems only lightly clothed by the fine-textured leafage. The trunks are sleekly covered with a smooth gray bark. The Serviceberry will be successful only in cooler sections, preferably in sunny exposed places where the soil is thin, poor, and rocky. It is liable to the depredations of beetles, borers, scale, and fire blight, but where it thrives it provides a light arabesque of much beauty. The Allegheny Serviceberry, *A. laevis,* is a larger growing species separated from the above by its hairless instead of woolly flower racemes and its purplish new growth. A hybrid of the two, the Apple Serviceberry, *A. grandiflora,* produces more showy flowers. Neither of these is to be preferred to the Shadblow, however.

*Asimina triloba,* Common Pawpaw. Of little practical value in landscape work, the Pawpaw is nonetheless an interesting small native tree widely distributed in the Southeast. Growing on well-watered fertile soils, either acid or alkaline, it usually forms clumps, occurring rarely as an isolated specimen, the individuals reaching to about 20 feet in a narrow oval form. Outstanding characters of the Pawpaw include a rich coarse deciduous foliage with oval leaves up to a foot long turning yellow in autumn, rather inconspicuous but fascinating bell-form flowers of chocolate brown in early spring before the leaves open, and the characteristic edible fruits of late summer of strong banana-like fragrance. This plant is not available in nurseries but it may be collected for those rare times when one might select it in either the Upper South or the Piedmont.

*Betula nigra*, River Birch. Gardeners who are familiar with the picturesque clumps of white barked Birches employed with such charming effect in northern gardens and in spring flower shows are often tempted to bring them into their own domains. But these trees are not well suited to climatic conditions of the Southeast except for the River Birch which is native along stream banks from the Gulf to the Ohio River. It may grow taller than 40 feet, but under ordinary conditions it is less than this. Susceptible to borers like the rest of the genus and rather short-lived, it will usually die out before exceeding 40 feet. Despite this hazard, it is a good species for quick effect. Its foliage is light-textured, clean, with yellow autumn color; the form is upright, oval, and informal; the branching is delicate and graceful; and the exfoliating reddish bark is colorful. It is not sufficiently reliable for street tree use, but it makes a desirable lawn or garden tree throughout the region in all good, well-watered soils. White barked Birches such as the Paper, *B. papyrifera*, and the European White, *B. pendula*, may be satisfactory for transitory effect in the mountains and cooler parts of the Upper South.

*Broussonetia papyrifera*, Papermulberry. The Papermulberry is generally regarded as a weed in the Southeast where it thrives in all sections. It is difficult to control because of its persistent suckering and rampant habit. However, as a street tree of about 30 feet in height, or as a decorative and shading material for areas largely paved or where growing conditions are exceptionally difficult, it has some possibilities. The deciduous foliage is coarse-textured and heavy, providing a dense shade, and it has no pests. This would be classified as a fast-growing, possibly rather short-lived tree for quick effects, but one sees old specimens occasionally which are characterized by exceptionally handsome trunk and branch forms. Reliable in all parts of this region, it is much used in the old gardens of Williamsburg, Va., and it is hardy up to Charleston, W. Va.

*Butia capitata*, Brazilian Butiapalm. *Phoenix canariensis*, Canary Date Palm. *Washingtonia robusta*, Mexican Washington Palm. Several Palms are widely grown in the Coastal Plain area, all somewhat less hardy than the common native Palmetto (see *Sabal* below) but fairly reliable locally in warmer sections. The most common of these are (1) the Butiapalm, almost universally listed as *Cocos australis*, which is a smaller, usually 15 feet or less, pinnate type with gracefully arching or reflexed fronds of a distinctive blue or gray-green color; (2) the Canary Date Palm, a robust, heavy tree to 40 feet or more, with long, drooping, dark green pinnate leaves and showy orange fruit clusters; and (3) the Mexican Washington Palm, a species growing very fast in rich soil, attaining about 40 feet in height, and rather closely resembling the Palmetto with its fan-shaped leaves. Both of the latter species may exceed 40 feet in height, but this size is unlikely in most sections of the Coastal Plain. When properly placed as accents, all of these strike an exotic note in the landscape, but they are often misused. Generally they require little care and endure poor growing conditions well. The question of their hardiness is the chief factor limiting their usefulness here, but all of these may be planted as far north as Charleston, S. C.

*Carpinus betulus*, European Hornbeam. *Carpinus caroliniana*, American Hornbeam. Although they are not common in cultivation, the Hornbeams include two species which are good small shade trees for this region. Related to the Beeches, these trees are characterized by a similar refined character, deciduous foliage of good dark color and medium texture, smooth gray bark which is decorative in winter, and a general preference for good growing conditions, fertile soils of either acid or alkaline reaction, ample moisture, and cool situations. Both bear inconspicuous flowers in catkins, and the seeds develop in midsummer in leafy bracts which are interesting in detail. The European Hornbeam is a round-headed tree with dense foliage which may reach over 40 feet in height. Adapted only to cool parts of the Upper South, it is an excellent material for tall hedges clipped to 8 or 10 feet. It is also interesting for a number of garden varieties, including a fine columnar form, *C. b. columnaris*, rather frequently seen in flourishing condition in central Kentucky. The American Hornbeam is lighter in character with a more informal, horizontal branching habit. The foliage has fine autumn coloration. Usually it grows to about 25 feet in height with two or more trunks of interesting sinewy form which are quite sculptural. This tree is native throughout the Southeast from Florida to the Ohio Valley, but it is said to be difficult to transplant and should be located in cool, damp, but well-drained, partially shaded sites. On exposure to sun and wind it is not vigorous, and in a weakened condition it is liable to borer damage. This species may be listed as *C. virginiana*.

*Castanea mollissima*, Chinese Chestnut. Since the magnificent American Chestnuts, formerly so common in this region, have been wiped out by blight, plantings of the Chinese Chestnut have been made rather widely for the sake of nut production. While the fruits are worthwhile in themselves, the tree might also be considered as a small shade tree for small properties in cooler parts of the Piedmont and the Upper South. Growing about 30 feet tall with an equal spread in an oval, low branching form, it is heavily clothed with handsome, coarse, dark green deciduous foliage. The white tail-like flowers of June are quite decorative, but they do cause some litter as do the prickly husks of the maturing nuts in autumn. For good nut production spraying is necessary in order to forestall the attacks of worms, and two or more varieties should be planted for cross pollination.

*Cercidiphyllum japonicum*, Katsuratree. This oriental tree is interesting chiefly for its habit of developing several trunks which rise rigidly and with few side branches to its full height of about 30 feet, giving it a unique if somewhat awkward character. Trained to a single trunk, it is said to reach 60 feet or more. The foliage is rather thin, casting a light shade, and the leaves are rounded or somewhat heart shaped, gray-green in color, medium in texture, deciduous, turning dull red in autumn. The flowers and the small brown seed pods are of no importance. While this tree does not appear to have any particular quality, it can be employed occasionally as a small shade tree for yard or park, mostly in the Upper South. It is a clean and pleasant subject which probably needs further testing in warmer sections.

*Cercis canadensis*, Eastern Redbud. One of the few good spring flowering trees for the entire extent of this region is the Redbud. Growing to a height of about 30 feet, this tree takes on a loose open form when grown in shade, and develops a dense, symmetrical round head in the open. The foliage is large, coarse-textured and deciduous, turning brown and sometimes rather unsightly for a brief period in early autumn. The flowers appear in early spring before the leaves, often nearly clothing the bare branches in tight clusters of bright rose, pea-like blooms. A variety called *C. c. alba* with white flowers may be considered the better form for many places where the strong color of the species is objectionable. The Redbud is difficult to transplant in larger sizes and quite disheartening to try to move from native stands, but it is especially valuable where one wants a native flowering tree for exposed, dry, rocky, limestone, or acid sites where the Dogwood may be difficult to establish and very slow to develop.

It may be noted here that the European Redbud or Judas-tree, *C. siliquastrum*, native to the Mediterranean region, also grows well on the Coastal Plain. For all practical purposes, it is almost identical with the American species, however, and it is not generally available. The Chinese Redbud, *C. chinensis*, is seen occasionally in gardens. More shrubby in habit, it has little to recommend it in preference to the American species.

*Chaenomeles sinensis*, Chinese Floweringquince. This plant becomes a small, many-trunked tree nearly 20 feet in height with a rather vertical form. The foliage is somewhat thin, casting a light shade, medium in texture, deciduous, and colorful in autumn. Pink flowers appear in spring shortly after the leaves and are therefore inconspicuous, but the large yellow aromatic fruits of autumn are showy and are useful for jellies. This is not an important material, and it is rarely available in nurseries. However, it grows very rapidly from seed and thrives without care in the Coastal Plain and the Piedmont in sun or light shade. As a garden ornament, it has much character in habit, in fruiting, and in its colorful flaking-barked branches.

*Chamaecyparis species*, Falsecypress. It was not many years ago that the commonly called Retinosporas were used in great numbers in foundation plantings. These places they quickly outgrew since they are, for the most part, trees, and the result is that they are now in almost complete discard. Most of them are more curious than beautiful with their weird forms and colors of foliage, but a few are worth mention for limited use largely in the Upper South where they occasionally make good screens and interesting specimens. The Lawson Falsecypress, *Chamaecyparis lawsoniana*, is a forest giant of the Pacific Northwest, but here it has a modest, narrow conical form with excellent blue-green foliage, making a fine screen. The Thread Sawara Falsecypress, *C. pisifera filifera*, is a curiosity with thread-like foliage of green or gold, a unique plant for a certain spot. Forms of the Hinoki Falsecypress, *C. obtusa*, are interesting, some quite dwarf, and choice for use as specimens. The foliage of this has an excellent color, reminiscent of the common Arborvitae except that it is more dense, somewhat twisted, and has much more character.

*Chionanthus virginicus*, White Fringetree. A common native of the swamps and river banks of the lower South is the Fringe Tree, often called "Grandsir-Graybeard." It is used as an ornamental throughout all parts of the Southeast, being quite hardy and easily adapted to any normal garden soil. Its feathery flowers of late spring are very showy, but the blue fruits of late summer are hardly noticeable. The plant remains somewhat shrubby in habit, although it may reach 25 feet in height with coarse deciduous foliage of little distinction which turns yellow in autumn. For moist to wet soils in sun or light shade this makes an attractive spring show, a good possibility for the woodland garden but somewhat coarse for refined settings. Individuals encountered in their native haunts show wide variation in flowering effect, but good ones are about as handsome as any flowering tree of this region, requiring no care whatsoever.

*Cinnamomum camphora*, Camphortree. The Camphor is one of the larger growing small trees although it will hardly exceed 40 feet in height in this region. In fact, in the upper portion of the Coastal Plain it reaches the limits of its cold endurance, and it is frozen back periodically there. Still, this is a good material for warmer sections, one of the most handsome of evergreen trees, fast growing, said to be something of a soil robber, requiring little care. The leaves, of medium texture value, are glossy and olive green in color, and they give off the characteristic camphor odor when crushed. Flowers are not noteworthy, but the blue black, berry-like fruits are often numerous, and they are apparently liked by birds. The Camphor is often seen as a several-trunked tree because of being cut back by cold, and it forms a handsome specimen, hedge, or windbreak. It is a rather common street tree in New Orleans, but its fruits are not desirable in such surroundings.

*Citrus limon* variety, Meyer Lemon. *Citrus paradisi* variety, Duncan Grapefruit. In warmer coastal sections of this region from Charleston, S. C., southward, there are some varieties of Citrus which may be grown successfully to make decorative specimens, ornamental in both flower and fruit. Two of the most hardy of these are listed here, both growing to heights of 10 to 20 feet with rounded form and handsome glossy, evergreen foliage. Neither can be recommended for the congested city because of the difficulty of controlling invasions of pests, as both will require considerable spraying and care under the best of conditions, to combat scale and white fly infestations.

*Cladrastis lutea*, Yellowwood. This is a handsome, spreading, round-headed tree about 30 feet high, native to portions of the southern Appalachians. The deciduous compound foliage is medium in texture, dark green, turning a beautiful glowing yellow in autumn. The bark is smooth and gray, or sometimes reddish on younger branches. In June the tree produces long drooping clusters of faintly fragrant white flowers which are quite attractive. Unfortunately the leaves are somewhat prone to scorch in poor dry soils, and unless sprayed regularly are sometimes inviting to chewing insects which damage the tree's beauty. Otherwise it is a choice specimen or shade tree material for small properties in fertile moist soils in the Piedmont and the Upper South. It may be especially recommended for alkaline regions. It is a good ornamental for parks, but it probably is not suitable for streets since it is low branching and may not take well to inhospitable growing conditions and cramped quarters.

*Cornus alternifolia*, Pagoda Dogwood. *Cornus florida*, Flowering Dogwood. *Cornus kousa*, Kousa Dogwood. The Pagoda Dogwood is native to the southern mountains and the upper Mississippi Valley, liking cool, well-watered places in either sun or shade. It is not much planted but it has a fine character which could be useful for landscape work in the Upper South. It is particularly attractive for its habit of growth, which is marked by a horizontally tiered branching pattern which sweeps the ground gracefully, and a rounded outline of 15 to 20 feet in height. The deciduous leaves of medium texture are pale green in color, arranged in whorls at the ends of the yellow-green twigs. The flowers, appearing in flat heads of white in late spring, are not very conspicuous, but the fruits maturing through the summer are interesting as they turn from green to yellow and dark blue on the red stemlets. This is not suitable for difficult growing conditions, but it is a choice material for detail interest in select places. It is said to be rather subject to damage by a blight disease.

Possibly the finest single Small Tree of this region is the Flowering Dogwood. Native to all sections except the highest elevations, this tree is beautiful for its flowers and fruits, foliage and fall color, habit of growth, and for its general adaptability to a wide variety of soils, to sun or shade, and to almost any use conceivable for a small tree of 20 to 30 feet in height. The only real flaw in the excellent qualifications of this plant is in several minor but vital cultural difficulties. Even when they are nursery grown, Dogwoods do not transplant easily in sizes of 8 feet or more. It is nearly always better, if at all practical, to plant smaller specimens with a good ball of earth. With feeding, these will overtake much larger plants set out at the same time which will usually fail to start out well. Moving sets back growth seriously under the best of conditions, rendering the plants more vulnerable to attacks of borers, which are a universal pest to be successfully controlled only by maintenance of vigorous and healthy condition. New plantings of Dogwoods should be considered for exposure too. Generally they do not take kindly to searing winds or to confined hot, dry, city situations, and in the Coastal Plain particularly they will be better in partial shade. In cool sections they will endure poor soils and some drought, and they bloom better and at an earlier stage of development in sun than in shade. But, generally speaking, they will respond well to some shelter and to good soils. The pink flowering variety, *C. f. rubra*, is showy and deservedly popular, but its color must be handled with discrimination. For some reason this variety does not bloom satisfactorily in the warmer Coastal Plain section. A double flowering form, *C. f. plena*, is something of a curiosity, but it is not as beautiful in the landscape as the species.

The Kousa Dogwood is the oriental counterpart of the above, similar to it in horizontal habit of growth, in size, and in foliage, differing chiefly in that the showy white flowers appear somewhat later after the leaves have come out. For this reason its blooming is not so effective in the landscape. However, it is quite attractive and it does have the virtue of prolonging the season. In autumn this is spectacular for its foliage coloration and also for its large pink fruits which look like prickly crabapples. This variety probably will be successful only in cooler areas in the Upper South.

*Crataegus intricata,* Thicket Hawthorn. *Crataegus phaenopyrum,* Washington Hawthorn. There are many species and varieties of Hawthorn, as many as several hundred being included in some lists. Many of these are quite interesting, but the Washington Thorn may well be taken as representative of the tree types with a well-defined trunk. It is one of the best and one which is widely available. The native forms are superior to the popular English Thorn and its variety, Paul's Scarlet.

Of the many bush-like types, the Thicket Hawthorn, often listed as *C. coccinea,* is rather typical. This retains its branches to the ground, making a beautiful specimen and the finest of tall barrier-screens. Growing to about 15 feet, this is dense, rounded, with rather coarse foliage and the typical white flowers and red fruits. It is best adapted to the Upper South where it is especially good on poor dry soils in very exposed situations where there is ample space. The English Hawthorn, *C. oxyacantha,* in its varieties with double white or pink flowers (the Paul's Scarlet Thorn) is popular in some sections. However, it is usually infested with aphids, and at best, it is inferior to the native species in habit and in fruiting.

The Washington Thorn is another native species of outstanding merit for the Upper South and the Piedmont. It is colorful in flower in late spring, and it is brilliant in fall and early winter when it is often nearly covered with clusters of small red berries. The glossy, dark green foliage is medium in texture, turning orange to red in autumn, and the plant is interesting at all seasons for its rather symmetrical, round-headed form to 25 feet in height with thorny twigs and branches of silver gray. This plant is valuable for screen, border, or specimen needs, but its thorns are not comfortable for the close quarters of a small yard or terrace. Sizable specimens can be moved with ease by taking reasonable precautions, and the plant adapts well to any sunny place in soils of fair quality. This beautiful tree does have some pests. The most common is the lace-wing fly which may disfigure the foliage, particularly in warmer sheltered locations. This nuisance can be controlled by two or three sprayings in the summer. The grower must also watch for signs of borers, fire blight, and scale insects, but these are seldom serious.

*Cryptomeria japonica,* Cryptomeria. In some localities of the Piedmont and the warmer Upper South, Cryptomerias are fairly common, usually seen at 20 to 30 feet in height although in their native Japan they grow to 100 feet or more. In form these are roughly conical, densely covered with the loose sprays of dark green, needle-like foliage which is quite desirable for cutting. In both form and color this plant makes a strong accent in the landscape, but it is hardly better for such purpose than the native Juniper. Often the tree is disfigured by persistent clumps of dead foliage. Usually it is cleaner and more attractive if located in a fully exposed site and left to itself without extra watering and feeding.

*Cunninghamia lanceolata,* Common Chinafir. This is a pyramidal cone-bearing evergreen growing to large size but here rarely seen over 20 feet, with a stiff and formal habit of growth and interesting heavy linear leaves on graceful drooping side branches. It can be grown from the cooler Coastal Plain through most of the Upper South in sunny places. It too is usually unattractive in the landscape because dead branchlets and leaves hang on the tree instead of falling. Hence this is useful only for cutting.

*Cupressus sempervirens stricta,* Italian Cypress. A few strikingly handsome specimens of the Italian Cypress growing in the Coastal Plain section prove that this tree will do well here under the right conditions. No other plant preserves so well the narrow, pointed exclamatory form so characteristic of this tree. It is resistant to drought, and probably it should be grown only in dry soils, possibly with a neutral to alkaline reaction, in full exposure to sun and wind. In more favorable damp spots, it tends to become weak and willowy, losing its character. For an occasional accent specimen in warmer sections up to the lower Piedmont, this species would probably succeed. It is both unusual and distinctive. There is some variation in habit among seedlings of the species; the variety listed should be obtained if possible for the narrow form.

*Diospyros kaki,* Kaki Persimmon. The Kaki or Japanese Persimmon is grown occasionally in the Coastal Plain for its large, orange-red, edible fruits; but like many other fruit trees, this one may be used as an ornamental also. It makes a broadly spreading, low-branching specimen to 40 feet in height, with good medium-textured deciduous foliage. Where the fruit crop is a major consideration it is advisable to plant two varieties, including one good pollinizer such as "Gailey" to insure the setting of fruit because many of the better forms do not fertilize themselves. Local nurserymen can usually furnish information on this point regarding the varieties which they carry. The tree should be reliably hardy throughout this region, but it may not bear fruit in colder sections.

*Eriobotrya japonica,* Loquat. The Loquat is a small tree which is notable for its edible fruits as well as its decorative character. Growing to a height of 20 feet, it has an irregular form which may vary from round headed to rather flat topped, usually low branched. The evergreen leaves are especially handsome, large, sometimes nearly a foot long, and coarse-textured, leathery, dark green above and covered with a rusty wool beneath. The creamy white flowers appear in late autumn in showy and fragrant clusters on the ends of the current year's twig growth. The bright yellow fruits of sharp flavor mature in early spring. The Loquat likes a good soil, a position in full sun or only light shade, and ample water supply, although it will not endure wet feet. Its lush tropical appearance makes it a handsome accent and a fine material to contrast with architectural features. It is good for screening, but it would hardly be recommended for shade. Ordinarily it is pest free, but a pear blight affecting scattered branches is reported to be troublesome in some localities. The Loquat is well suited to all parts of the Coastal Plain. In the Piedmont up to Birmingham it can be grown in sunny sheltered sites on dry soils as a large shrub to 10 or 15 feet for foliage and flower interest, but the fruits will not mature here.

*Euonymus europaeus*, European Euonymus. *Euonymus yedoensis*, Yeddo Euonymus. In the Euonymus genus there are at least two species which should be mentioned even though they are not likely to be important materials here. Both will probably be confined in their usefulness to the Upper South. The European Euonymus grows to about 20 feet with a low-branching, round-headed form, and light, medium-textured foliage on green twigs and branches. The greenish flowers are not conspicuous; this tree is grown instead for its display of pink fruits which make a bright show in autumn. This plant is not uncommon in cooler sections, and it is vigorous, fast growing in any soil, a good screen material, but rather subject to scale infestations. The Yeddo Euonymus, although not so well known, may be the more useful of the two. Growing to 15 feet with a horizontal branching habit which lends itself well to trimming to one trunk, this plant is rather widely grown as a tall shrub in central Kentucky and Tennessee. It bears deciduous leaves of coarse texture which have a handsome orange-red fall color along with its colorful fruits. It seems relatively resistant to the scale, and it is a fine material for the small garden or terrace. There is a native Euonymus of small tree stature called the Eastern Wahoo, *E. atropurpureus*, which is not handled by the nurseries but which may be encountered from New York to Florida and Texas. It has an open informal habit, reaching 20 feet in height with rather fine-textured foliage and red fruits which are attractive for a brief time in autumn.

*Evodia hupehensis*, Hupeh Evodia. A few plants of the Evodia apparently flourishing in Bristol, Virginia, suggest that this plant might warrant further trial in the Upper South. It bears deciduous compound leaves rather similar to those of the Ash, and it is interesting for the showy clusters of white flowers in midsummer followed by red fruits in autumn. Growing in a low-branching, rather shrubby form to 20 feet, this is likely to be better for screening than for shading.

*Ficus carica*, Common Fig. In general the ornamental qualities of the Common Figs are not exploited fully. It would be unwise to recommend them for common usage in landscape compositions, yet there are many garden settings into which they fit nicely. Normally, such varieties as the hardy "Brown Turkey" or the "Celeste" will attain heights of 15 to 20 feet, depending on the climatic zone, with an equal spread in a many-trunked, low-branched form. On smaller properties they may be cut back severely each year to keep them within bounds, and they may also be trimmed flat against the side of a wall or building with interesting effect. The coarse deciduous foliage of the Figs is a distinctive and handsome material in the designer's palette. When the leaves have dropped in winter, the simple heavy branch structure thus revealed is also decorative. Specimens or avenues of Figs are most appropriate, of course, in vegetable and fruit gardens. They are exceedingly easy to grow in any dry and sunny location, and they are hardy throughout the Coastal Plain and the lower Piedmont. Farther north they may be grown as shrubs to Memphis, Knoxville, and Washington, coming up readily from the root even when they may be occasionally frozen to the ground during a severe winter. They are objectionable in tidy areas because the fruits are messy, and the plants are subject to nematode damage in lighter soils in warm sections.

*Firmiana simplex*, Chinese Parasoltree. This is a tree almost 40 feet in height of coarse and exotic appearance which is occasionally seen in the Coastal Plain and the Piedmont as far north as Memphis and Atlanta. It has been planted for its very large deciduous leaves, often a foot in diameter and boldly lobed, and for its showy upright clusters of small whitish flowers of early summer. The smooth green bark of the branches is noteworthy. A fast and aggressive grower which has escaped in some sections, this tree is not widely applicable although it can be employed for foliage interest in an accenting position if it is cut back periodically to keep it in scale. It may be listed also as *Sterculia platanifolia*.

*Gordonia lasianthus*, Loblollybay Gordonia. This is a native of the southeastern Coastal Plain from Virginia to Louisiana, but it is rarely seen in cultivation despite its excellent glossy evergreen foliage of medium to coarse texture and its showy white fragrant flowers of midsummer. It is rather shrubby in habit, reaching possibly over 40 feet in height, and it might well be used for screening. In its native state it frequents moist lowlands, and it is said to grow best in fertile, well-watered soils, in sun or light shade, with some protection from wind. It can be grown throughout the Coastal Plain and to a limited extent in the Piedmont where it remains lower and more shrubby in habit. It is employed as a garden specimen in Memphis. It is rather difficult to transplant and slow to become established. The Franklinia, discussed with the Large Shrubs, is also listed often under the name of Gordonia.

*Halesia carolina,* Carolina Silverbell. *Halesia monticola,* Mountain Silverbell. Both of the above Silverbells grow naturally in this region and they are of occasional interest for their bell-like white flowers of mid-spring. The Carolina species is fairly common in moist woodlands from the Ohio Valley to the Gulf. It may reach 40 feet in height although it is usually nearer half this size in an open, irregular, and indefinite form. The flowers are not often showy because they open after the leaves are expanded. The winged seed pods are rather interesting in autumn. This plant has little value, but it can be grown anywhere in the region in borders and naturalistic designs. It is said to need shade and some shelter from winds. The Mountain Silverbell is a more robust plant, growing possibly to over 40 feet in height in a pyramidal form, making a fine display of its white flowers, which come out before the leaves, and of its yellow foliage color in the fall. This variety is limited in its growing range to the cool moist uplands of the Upper South where it is probably one of the better trees for shade as well as for color in gardens, small properties, and parks.

*Ilex cassine,* Dahoon Holly
*Ilex decidua,* Possumhaw
*Ilex opaca,* American Holly
*Ilex purpurea*
*Ilex rotunda*
*Ilex vomitoria,* Yaupon Holly

Of the Holly species listed here, the Dahoon and the Yaupon are discussed in some detail as to foliage and fruit among the Large Shrubs of Group VI. Both of these tend to become tree-like if left to themselves, reaching as high as 20 feet under favorable circumstances in rather narrow pyramidal forms. This tendency is encouraged if one cuts off the lower branches. Both species have gray bark which is colorful and attractive in the landscape, especially valuable in winter to give life to dull masses of evergreen foliage. The Dahoon commonly grows to one trunk, but the Yaupon often forms a clump which, with its several graceful stems, is attractive for free-standing specimen use. These are perfectly trouble-free plants in any spot in which a small tree may be used, and they are well adapted to almost all conditions of soil or exposure in the Coastal Plain. In this section the Yaupon is especially valuable where seacoast exposure is a problem. Both species are somewhat tender and therefore they may remain more shrubby in the Piedmont. As shrubs they will grow fairly dependably to Nashville and Lexington but they do not often set fruit here. The Dahoon hybrid (crossed with the American Holly) called *I. fosteri,* the Foster Holly, appears to be somewhat more hardy. It is a vigorous plant, characterized by extraordinary fruit production, with fine-textured, dark green, spine-tipped foliage. It promises to become a favorite here.

Volumes are written about the American Holly and its many varieties, its adaptability, and its culture. It has quite a different character from the above, and it is one of the very choice materials of this size class for all parts of the Southeast. Normally it becomes a stout tree of about 40 feet in height with a trunk up to as much as a foot in diameter, dense and twiggy in habit, irregularly narrow and upright or ruggedly broad and horizontal in a bewildering variety of forms. The flowers are small and white, very pretty but hardly noticeable, but the bright ·red fruits of autumn and winter are highly ornamental. In the Hollies the male and female flowers are borne on separate plants; so it is usually necessary to plant a male, which bears no fruit, fairly close to groups of the females in order to insure that the latter will bear. These plants like good soils and adequate moisture. Given these they will thrive in most exposures. Fruit production is heavier where the plants have sun, but the evergreen foliage often burns and turns yellowish if it is exposed to much winter sun and severe winds. There are a few pests of more or less local importance. Leaf miners can disfigure the foliage; for control two or more sprays of DDT in mid-spring may be required. A leaf spot disease may be cleared up with dusting sulfur. American Hollies are often considered difficult to move. With proper care, they are, however, transplanted in sizes to 20 feet or more.

There are in the nursery trade many named varieties of the American Holly which have been selected for superior foliage and fruiting qualities, and these are the ones which should be selected for most uses, especially when there is space for only one or two specimens. However, care should be taken that the varieties chosen are suited to the climate, for those originated in the warm Coastal Plain are not always successful in the colder Upper South and vice versa. For the Coastal Plain, "Howard" is considered one of the best with its small dark colored leaves and its abundant fruits. "Taber No. 3" and "Taber No. 4" are both good ones with spine tipped leaves, and "Savannah" is interesting for its lighter green foliage color. "East Palatka" has almost spineless entire leaves of excellent color, and abundant fruits, giving an almost completely different plant character. For the Upper South and especially its more severe sections, the better selections might be "Old Heavyberry," "Firecracker," or "Arden," which are a few of the good forms originated in the north. These are, of course, only a small percentage of the total named varieties of the Holly, and the local nurseryman should be consulted concerning the adaptability and the availability of forms for a particular locality. There is a yellow fruited variety, *I. o. xanthocarpa*, in addition to the many with typical red berries. Considering the placing of these plants in the landscape, they are probably best employed as isolated specimens with their lower limbs coming down to the ground. Older specimens are often seen with their lower limbs removed, treated as shade trees, but they often look top heavy and tend to shade out grass. In clumps they make superior border and screening plants. They take to shearing in simple topiary very well, and, planted 2 feet apart, they make an impenetrable hedge of superior quality.

*Ilex purpurea* is sold in a few nurseries in this area, and some older specimens show what attractive possibilities the plant has to offer. This tree may grow to nearly 40 feet in height, upright oval in form, retaining its branches to the ground. The elliptical leaves, dark in color and evergreen, lack the spiny teeth commonly associated with the Hollies, but the foliage effect is coarse and very rich. The large red berries are produced in profusion in winter to make a handsome show. This is a vigorous plant under conditions of the Coastal Plain; it is hardy in the Piedmont and as far north as Memphis, Atlanta, and Washington, D. C. It will almost undoubtedly be a favorite for specimen and screen plantings when it becomes better known. It frequently goes under the name here of *I. oldhami*, properly a variety of *I. purpurea;* it may also be called *I. chinensis*.

Another newcomer just becoming available at a few nurseries is *Ilex rotunda*. This is a smaller, rather flat-headed tree to about 25 feet in hight. The evergreen oval leaves of this species are also entire, considerably smaller than those of the *Ilex purpurea*, and medium in texture. The small red berries are profuse, making a brilliant show on plants set in the open. Growers recommend, where space is very limited, that both male and female specimens of this may be included in one hole, and that the male may be kept minor in stature through pruning. This plant is beautiful in the Coastal Plain. It may not be hardy in the Piedmont, although it needs further trials.

The Possumhaw is a native of most of the Southeast, commonly neglected in landscape work, perhaps because it has deciduous foliage. Yet it has an appealing form with a horizontal branching habit sometimes quite like that of the Hawthorns, compared to which it is much superior in immunity to insects and diseases. It may become an attractive spreading tree to 20 feet or more in height, often with several trunks. The bark is light gray in color and the branches of the females are well covered with colorful red berries in winter when the leaves are down. This plant, easy to grow under almost all conditions of soil and exposure throughout this region from the Coastal Plain to the Ohio River, should be a nearly ideal subject for a small terrace where shade is desired only in summer. It is excellent also in high screens and borders. It is rarely found in the nurseries, and like many native plants it is very variable. Selections for habit of growth, foliage, and fruiting characteristics should be made so that better types become available.

*Juniperus virginiana*, Eastern Redcedar. In the varying environments of this region, the native Redcedar shows an interesting variety of forms and foliage characters. Usually conical in form, especially as a young plant, the adults commonly retain this shape, although some are rounded and others may be quite flat headed in exposed sites, as along the seacoast. Some forms are outstanding for production of the colorful blue fruits of autumn, but it should be noted that the sexes are separate and only the females produce the berries. Foliage colors may be dark green to yellow green or gray. The leafage may be dense and compact, especially in specimens grown in the open, but under crowded conditions or in old age the foliage is often sparse and open.

The Redcedar was planted formerly a great deal around plantation houses where many picturesque old specimens survive. It is not now so highly favored, possibly because it is fancied that more exotic materials will be better. This is a plant of positive character which should be placed with care. It can hardly ever be set successfully in foundation plantings, but in clumps or as an isolated specimen it is often excellent in close relation to architecture. It is impressive in avenues or for punctuating and framing views, and it is fine in tall narrow screens, although it is not happy in clipped hedges. In the many sections where it is native, it can be spotted about in the landscape with a freedom which might, on first thought, seem incongruous.

This plant should be used only in exposed sites in full sun and in poor soils. These locations may be very dry, yet the Redcedar will also stand "wet feet" in poorly drained spots. It is an excellent evergreen for alkaline soils. The wood is superior for all outdoor construction and its fragrance and color for indoor work are well known. Practically speaking the Redcedar has no pests and requires very little care. Waves of bag worms appear in periodic cycles to cause occasionally rather serious although rarely fatal damage. A disease called the Cedar-Apple Rust always attacks it when it is placed near apple trees. To avoid this it is only necessary to avoid the combination of the two genera.

Some of the horticultural varieties of the Redcedar, of which there are many, are well worth trying where uniformity of effect in a planting scheme is required. Among these are *J. v. canaerti* with picturesque form and dark green color, *J. v. keteleeri* bright green, and *J. v. glauca* gray. These are more compact in form and generally superior to native collected stock.

*Koelreuteria paniculata,* Panicled Goldraintree. A fast-growing small tree, good for quick effect in dry hot exposures, the Goldraintree becomes round headed to irregular in form to about 25 feet in height, with a sparse open branching habit, and heavy, compound, deciduous, rather coarse-textured foliage. It is especially interesting for its showy plumes of tiny yellow flowers in mid-summer and for the large brown bladder-like seed pods which mature a little later in the season. The Goldraintree is not long lived; but it is free of pests and diseases, is tolerant of poor soils and drought, and is a lover of sunshine. It benefits from an annual pruning to remove old blossom heads and weak growths, but this is not absolutely necessary and the tree can thrive with about as little care as any. It is a good small tree for shade or for street planting for temporary use, and it also makes a decorative specimen. It is equally at home from the Coastal Plain to the Ohio Valley. The Flame Goldraintree, *K. formosana,* is said to be equally desirable, but it is not so widely available.

*Laburnum* species, Laburnum. The Laburnums are often attempted for their attractive drooping clusters of yellow flowers of late spring, but they are so often unpredictable that they seem hardly worth recommending for any but very rare use. The habit of growth is stiff and upright, and the range of adaptability is largely confined to cooler sections and limestone soils. The foliage is often scorched and unattractive in locations subject to drought and searing winds. The Waterer Laburnum, *L. watereri* (usually listed as *L. vossi*), is a hybrid which is rated as superior to the Scotch (*L. alpinum*) or the Goldenchain (*L. anagyroides*).

*Lagerstroemia indica,* Crapemyrtle. The Crapemyrtles have been discussed more fully with the Large Shrubs of Group VI, but it may be noted here that they also form excellent Small Trees attaining heights of 20 to 30 feet in the Coastal Plain and the Piedmont. Some nurserymen offer Crapemyrtles grown to a single trunk and pruned high in standard tree form. Their trunks are quite as effective in winter as are their bright flower plumes in summer, providing a sparkling contrast against a foil of somber evergreens. This is primarily a decorative material, not sufficiently dense to make a heavy shade or screen. It is rather pest free, tolerant, and long lived, but the foliage is likely to mildew in shaded locations and Japanese Beetles relish the flowers through the summer. The Crapemyrtle should not be counted on as a tree in the thin sandy soils which are common along the coast, nor in colder parts of the Upper South. In these locations it is likely to remain shrubby in form although tall specimens are found in sheltered sites to Charleston, W. Va., and Louisville.

*Libocedrus decurrens*, California Incensecedar. This is a coniferous evergreen tree growing in a narrow columnar form rather similar to that of the Juniper to a height of 20 or 30 feet. There are not many instances where such positive and distracting forms as this tree has are needed in landscape design, but this is an excellent material for such few cases. It is fast growing and vigorous in any fertile, well-watered soil in a sunny location in the Upper South. It has a good dark color in the aromatic foliage through the winter, and on older specimens the trunks have a rich red-brown color which is quite handsome.

*Ligustrum lucidum*, Glossy Privet. Although it is commonly classed as a large-growing shrub, this plant has little application in that category. However, it is fairly satisfactory treated as a small tree. Growing to a height of 30 feet, it may have one trunk or several trunks, a rather upright form, and dense evergreen foliage of medium green color and medium to coarse texture. It bears attractive clusters of fragrant white flowers in June and beautiful bunches of dark blue fruits on bright orange stems in winter. The Privet is a fast grower and makes a handsome early show under trying growing conditions; it is valuable for city work. On the other hand, it is a greedy feeder, its wood is weak, it makes some litter, it harbors the white fly pest, and it cannot be considered one of the choice materials. This species is usually confused with *L. japonicum* in the nurseries. An upright form called *nobilis* is not uncommon and, with its strongly ascendant branching habit, it makes a handsome specimen. It is used mostly for fitting into narrow borders for a high screen. As a tree form it is best suited to the Coastal Plain and the lower Piedmont, although as a shrub it can be planted into the Upper South.

*Magnolia denudata*, Yulan Magnolia
*Magnolia fraseri*, Fraser Magnolia
*Magnolia kobus*, Kobus Magnolia
*Magnolia macrophylla*, Bigleaf Magnolia
*Magnolia salicifolia*, Anise Magnolia
*Magnolia soulangeana*, Saucer Magnolia
*Magnolia stellata*, Star Magnolia
*Magnolia tripetala*, Umbrella Magnolia
*Magnolia virginiana*, Sweetbay Magnolia

The subject of Magnolias in this size class presents many possibilities in the Southeast. For the sake of discussion, these plants may be divided into three groups according to design characteristics as follows: (1) the Sweetbay, (2) several oriental species which bloom before the leaves appear in early spring including the Saucer Magnolia, the Anise, Star, Kobus, Yulan, and the Lily Magnolias, and (3) several species native to the southern mountains, mostly with

very large deciduous leaves and flowers of late spring including the
Bigleaf, the Fraser, and the Umbrella Magnolias.

The Sweetbay is native to coastal lowlands from Massachusetts
to Texas. Despite the swampy nature of its homeland, it performs well
in all good garden soils, and it is perfectly hardy throughout this
region from the Gulf to the Ohio Valley. It becomes a round-
headed tree, often with several trunks, up to about 25 feet or even
to 40 feet in warmer sections, with an open and irregular branching
habit. The leaves are long oval, about 3 inches long, gray green with
silver undersides which glitter brightly in breezes, turning golden
brown in autumn, or, in warmer areas, persisting almost until spring.
The flowers are not very conspicuous, being quite small and somewhat
hidden among the leaves, but they are lovely in detail, creamy white
and cup shaped; they make their presence known to some distance
by their heavy rich fragrance throughout a long blooming period in
late spring. The cucumber-like fruits are red in the fall. Occasionally
the Sweetbay, like most of this family, suffers attacks by a soft-shelled
scale which is readily eliminated by a dormant spray of oil or by
a summer dosage of malathion, but the plant is ordinarily care free.
With intelligent pruning, which it takes very well, almost anything
can be done with this plant since it sprouts readily from the root
when cut to the ground to make a many-stemmed, smaller, more
shrubby screening or specimen material. This is rather light, open
and airy in effect, never heavy and massive, and thus at its best
supported by architectural constructions or dense evergreens as a
background.

In contrast, the above listed Asiatic species of Magnolia are quite
heavy in character with dense, coarse-textured, dark green, deciduous
foliage, and with flowers that make a spectacular display in early
spring before the leaves appear. These plants are not perfectly suited
to lower parts of the Coastal Plain but they will grow here in places
partially shaded and well watered. They thrive from the Coastal
Plain to the Ohio Valley in any good well-drained soil in the sun. In
all areas the bloom effect is liable to be destroyed by an occasional
late frost, an everpresent possibility somewhat diminishing the value
of these trees. The Star Magnolia is the first of these to open, with
its profuse small white blossoms with narrow strap-like petals. It
is rather small, about 15 feet, remaining somewhat bush-like, rounded,
dense, compact, and branching to the ground. The Pink Star variety
has a pinkish tint in the blooms, and this species is said to be a dependable bloomer in the Coastal Plain. The Anise Magnolia is comparatively rare in this region, but there are good specimens in Bristol,
Va. It seems worth further trial for its early, showy, white fragrant
flowers characteristic of this group and especially for its neat lance-

like foliage of comparatively fine texture and its rather vertical conical form. The Saucer Magnolia, a hybrid produced in France, is the most widely grown and, with the Star, probably the most hardy of this group. Its large, cup-shaped flowers are typically light pink to cream, but there are both pure white and deeper purple-rose varieties available. This becomes a round-headed, sometimes irregular tree up to 25 feet. Its winter silhouette of thick branches covered with silver-gray bark and ending in the fat, furry bloom buds is often attractive. It grows well in city gardens, and it espaliers well in close quarters. The Kobus and Yulan Magnolias are considered by many to be superior to the above with their large pure white blossom effect, but in other respects they are similar. They may be rather tender in the colder parts of the Upper South, and they are more difficult to locate in the nurseries. The Lily Magnolia, *M. liliflora*, is mentioned here since it is widely listed; but it is of relatively little value, as it is smaller and more shrubby in habit and produces flowers with an outer surface of deep red-purple which is ineffective if not disagreeable in the garden.

The native Magnolias listed in group (3) are suited only to the Upper South and they will not be important materials here. However, they may add interest occasionally in sheltered places with deep moist soils where the exotic tropical effect of their large coarse leaves can be exploited to advantage. A leaf of the Bigleaf Magnolia can be as much as 3 feet long and nearly a foot wide. The flowers of all are white, and large in size but not very showy because they appear after the foliage, fragrant but rather disagreeably so in the case of the Umbrella Magnolia. The pod-like fruits are quite showy, being rose colored on the outside and splitting to expose the orange-red seeds. These are all rank growers to heights of 30 or 40 feet and would need careful pruning and management to fit in most gardens.

*Malus angustifolia*, Southern Crabapple
*Malus coronaria*, Wild Sweet Crabapple
*Malus floribunda*, Japanese Flowering Crabapple
*Malus hupehensis*, Tea Crabapple
*Malus purpurea*, Purple Crabapple

There are so many good Crabapples available that to treat the subject with justice would require a separate volume. These trees have so much to offer and there are so many varieties with good qualities that they deserve attention far beyond the scope of this survey. It must suffice here to say that there is a Crabapple for every garden, and almost every garden should have a Crabapple of one variety or another. Only a few varieties will be discussed, chiefly for the purpose of suggesting the range in form, color, and habitat.

The sizes of these trees vary from 15 to 30 feet and the forms are generally round headed with rather horizontal branching habits. A few varieties are somewhat columnar, desirable for street planting; there are also weeping forms of which the variety Red Jade, with pink flowers and showy fruits, is recommended. The deciduous foliage is medium to fine in texture, from yellow-green to purplish in color, sometimes with good fall color. In all the best varieties the flowers are so numerous as to cover the plants year after year in white, pink, or rosy purple, and many are quite fragrant too, so that these are possibly the most showy and most dependable of all trees for flower display. In many varieties the fruits are effective in autumn, ranging in color from yellow to rose and bright red, lasting until the birds finally pick them off. Some with larger fruits furnish material for excellent jellies. These trees are best suited to the cooler Piedmont and the Upper South, and only one species, the Southern Crabapple, is adapted to the Coastal Plain. They grow well in any average soil with normal water supplies, preferably in open sunny spots, and they can endure drought and severe exposure to wind and cold as well as any ornamentals. Most of our best Crabapples are descended from oriental species which are resistant to the Cedar-Apple Rust disease. Aside from this, they should be watched for fire blight, which is seldom serious, and for borers, tent caterpillars, and scales. They are easily transplanted in all sizes and are excellent for borders, massing, and individual specimen use, and some varieties have been employed with good results as street trees.

Although the subject of varieties cannot be covered adequately here, some general notes on some of the species and on the variety of characteristics available may be helpful. Of the natives, the Southern Crabapple is the one to be planted in warmer sections because it does bloom well here whereas other species do not receive a sufficient number of frosty days in the Deep South to mature their buds properly and to make a good show. As a rule this is a good choice for any area considered too warm for commercial apples. It must not be planted in association with the Eastern Redcedar. The green fruits are a nuisance in tidy areas, but the flowers, coming just after the first leaves, transform the tree into a pink to white cloud of the most delicious fragrance. As it sprouts readily from the roots, it can be a nuisance in a border; but with its lower branches trimmed high, it can be a good lawn specimen, needing only occasional pruning of dead wood to keep it in good condition.

The Wild Sweet Crabapple will be found in native stands throughout cooler parts of this region, usually in thickets, and the gardener is fortunate who finds it at hand. Again the flowers are very fragrant, pink in color, but this is not a plant which would be widely cultivated and circulated in the nurseries, because the Oriental Crabs are superior in growing range for most purposes. The Prairie Crab, *M. ioensis*, is another native to be mentioned because of its common variety, the Bechtel Crab. Although it has a beautiful flower, the Bechtel Crab should be avoided here.

Of the Asiatic species, possibly the best white is the Tea Crab, often listed as *M. theifera*. This grows to about 25 feet in height with a stiffly out-thrusting, almost awkward, but often picturesque, branching habit, bearing fragrant white blooms and small yellow fruits. Pink tints are possibly best represented in the Japanese Flowering Crab. This is rather large growing, round headed to 30 feet, with a massive display of flowers in pink fading to white, followed by tiny bright yellow fruits. However, it is a parent of the Arnold Crab, *M. arnoldiana*, which is similar in flower and fruit but somewhat smaller in stature, and the Scheidecker Crab, *M. scheideckeri*, noteworthy for a rather upright habit of growth and semi-double flowers of pink to white. Many of the rose to purple flowering types are descendants of the Purple Crab, *M. purpurea*, itself a splendid form of hybrid origin. Growing to 20 feet, it is characterized by flowers of deep rose, showy fruits of an inch in diameter in purple-red, and foliage which is purplish on first opening, rather bronzy green through the summer, and deep rose in autumn. Selections of this are many, usually considered to be improved on one count or another. Some of these are Lemoine, Eley, Aldenham, etc.

While the varieties mentioned do not cover the list available by any means, they do give a fair cross section of reliable forms which should fill most normal landscape requirements. For more detailed recommendations, any one of several references may be consulted, and it is often well to consult the local nurseryman on his experience and the varieties available.

*Melia azedarach*, Chinaberry. One of the most familiar trees of the Coastal Plain and the Piedmont is the Chinaberry, casting a dense and welcome shade over the hottest farm yard and softening the most inhospitable city alleyway. This tree grows rapidly under the worst conditions, producing attractive, feathery deciduous foliage along with clusters of heavily scented violet flowers in late spring followed by showy yellow berry-like fruits in the fall. These are all good qualities which would seem to make this a most valuable plant. However, many people object to it because it is short-lived and because it continually drops fruits, flowers, leaves, or brittle twigs, thus requiring much clean-up work. Although unaffected by pests, it fosters the white fly nuisance. The species grows to an irregular upright oval form of about 40 feet in height, while the common Umbrella variety, *M. a. umbraculiformis*, reaches 20 feet with a broad, flattened head and a stiffly formal branching pattern. These are weedy trees, but the imagination should be able to conceive of some use for them in inhospitable urban environments.

*Morus alba*, White Mulberry. The Mulberry was planted in colonial times in attempts to establish a silk industry, and later its weeping variety, *M. a. pendula*, enjoyed a great vogue along with Victorian architecture. It is a hardy, vigorous, disease-free tree of dense, round-headed form to nearly 40 feet, which is widely regarded as a weed and a nuisance for its great quantities of staining purple fruits of midsummer so relished by birds and children. Now a new variety called "Kingan" is offered which produces no fruits. This is suggested as a fast-growing, hardy small tree for poor soils and inhospitable surroundings for the Upper South. It is possible that it will be a good find for new subdivisions, school yards, and parking lots where a quick but not necessarily permanent material is desirable.

*Musa* species, Orinoco or Horse Banana. Few plants can rival the Banana for giving the final tropical touch to a garden patio. Nurseries in the Coastal Plain commonly offer a relatively hardy variety which is listed as the Orinoco or Horse Banana. These plants survive the winter's cold in sheltered locations through much of this region; even when they are cut down by frost, they shoot up quickly in the spring and may even produce fruits during the following summer. Naturally, to do this the plants must have rich soil and ample moisture. The foliage is very coarse in texture. The height of the stems, which commonly grow in clumps, varies from 6 to 12 feet. The flowers of summer and the fruits, as they mature in autumn, are interesting. The latter have no value as food, however, and this plant will be used only rarely as an exotic specimen.

*Olea europaea*, Common Olive. The Olive has not been successful in the several trials made in the Coastal Plain for fruit production, but a few old specimens survive here and there to demonstrate its ornamental quality. These are shrubby trees, often with several trunks, with an open straggling form to about 15 feet in height. The evergreen foliage is the Olive's chief ornamental asset, possessing a fine texture and a silver-gray color which are distinctive. Since the fruits can make a litter, it is probably just as well that they do not develop in this region. The tree should be grown only in dry soils in open sunny exposures in the warmest sections of the Coastal Plain. The Olive is not commonly available.

*Osmanthus americanus*, Devilwood Osmanthus. *Osmanthus fragrans*, Sweet Osmanthus. Both of these have been discussed more fully among the Large Shrubs of Group VI, but in the Coastal Plain they may be considered as Small Trees. The Devilwood especially might well be planted with this use in mind. It reaches as much as 40 feet in height, making an irregularly rounded and open specimen, with medium to coarse-textured, light green evergreen foliage of good quality. Flower buds formed in the fall open in early spring in profusion and with delightful fragrance. These are noticeable although not very showy, but their perfume is a decided asset in the garden. Blue-black fruits, like small cherries, are produced in autumn. The plant is a fast grower in this region, rather free of troubles, and it should be planted in good deep soils where it will have some shade and moisture. The Sweet Osmanthus, on the other hand, may be too slow in reaching its full size of 25 feet to be much used as a tree. It does develop with some vigor, however, and it should be mentioned here to call attention to its size if nothing else; it might be employed occasionally as a lawn specimen or in screening.

*Oxydendrum arboreum*, Sourwood. The Sourwood is a native of acid soils in the Southeast from Pennsylvania to Florida and Louisiana, usually growing on cutover land and along the edges of fields or woodlands. It develops into a rather narrow form to 40 feet in height, sometimes more in shaded fertile sites, with coarse deciduous leaves of dark glossy green color, turning flame red in autumn. In early summer it produces rather showy clusters of small white bell-like flowers which are the source of the fine Sourwood honey produced in quantity on mountain farms. The blossoms are followed by decorative seed pods of plume-like appearance. This plant is quite pest free, but it is difficult to transplant in larger sizes and therefore is not found in cultivation as much as it might be. It can hardly be used as a shade tree because of its slight spread, nor is it well suited to limestone areas or to urban conditions. In parks and suburban areas almost anywhere in the region where poor dry soils are a problem, this tree is desirable for border plantings.

*Parkinsonia aculeata*, Jerusalemthorn. This is interesting in form, flower, and foliage. It is possibly the best of this class for the Coastal Plain for those occasions where the exotic Weeping Willow form would be used in cooler climates. The Jerusalemthorn grows to a height of about 30 feet with branches that are thin, wiry, and pendulous, bearing small thorns. The leaflets are almost minute, of unusual construction, fine textured, yellow-green in color, and semi-evergreen in warmer sections, casting a very light shade. A more or less evergreen effect is characteristic of this species, however, because of the green twigs which prolong the color after the leaves have dropped. In late spring the tree is covered with bright yellow flowers, hanging in clusters up to 6 inches long. This member of the Pea Family is a sun lover, growing rapidly in those hot dry sandy soils common in much of the coastal area. For such sites it is an excellent choice for gardens or patios under urban conditions. Although it is not generally considered to be long lived, it is valuable for early results under poor growing conditions.

*Persea borbonia,* Redbay Persea. This is a native of the Coastal Plain which is a good pestfree small evergreen tree for borders and screens and occasionally as a lawn specimen. It is also quite hardy in most of the Piedmont to Atlanta where it remains rather shrubby and is best suited to screening. It bears heavy, olive green, coarse-textured foliage which is aromatic, and it attains to 20 feet in height with a rounded head. It may be trimmed to one trunk or allowed to branch to the ground with many stems. The small flowers are inconspicuous, greenish in color, appearing in late spring, and the small blue fruits mature in autumn. The Persea is grown in some nurseries and may be confused with the Swampbay Persea, *P. palustris,* similar in landscape quality. The latter is hardy into the Piedmont, and is said to be the more common and more hardy of the two. Both plants are of easy culture, disease free, and well suited to the sandy soils of the coast in sun or light shade.

*Pistacia chinensis,* Chinese Pistache. This tree is being tested in the Coastal Plain and the Piedmont where it shows attractive qualities for wider use in the future. There are good specimens of 20 to 30 feet in height in the vicinity of Washington, D. C. Growing to 40 feet or possibly to 60, it is characterized by an open habit of growth and a light foliage of fine-textured compound leaves. This tree is a member of the same family as the familiar native Sumacs, and like them, has good red fall foliage color; the female plants bear showy clusters of red to purple berry-like fruits. The plant is said to be quite pest free and particularly valuable where poor soils, heat, and drought are problems to be solved. It is rare in the nurseries of the region.

*Poncirus trifoliata,* Trifoliate Orange. The Trifoliate or Hardy Orange is hardly an important ornamental, but it is very common in the Southeast and does have some interesting qualities. Normally it grows into a rounded mound to 20 or 30 feet, branching densely to the ground with rather thin, dark green, deciduous foliage. There are showy fragrant white flowers in spring, and in the fall numerous decorative orange colored fruits of one to 3 inches in diameter. While these are attractive qualities, the numerous heavy thorns and the difficulty in restraining the plant within reasonable bounds make it unacceptable for close quarters. It is often planted in clipped hedges, but it is only fair for this purpose. It grows beautifully in hot, dry, infertile sunny places in the Coastal Plain and the Piedmont, and it is hardy with some shelter to the Ohio River although the fruits may not develop in the cooler sections.

*Prunus caroliniana,* Carolina Laurelcherry
*Prunus cerasifera pissardi,* Pissard Plum
*Prunus mume,* Japanese Apricot
*Prunus persica scleropersica,* Flowering Peach
*Prunus serrulata,* Oriental Cherry

The Carolina Laurelcherry is a native of the Coastal Plain from South Carolina to Texas and is used extensively in cultivation throughout this section, the Piedmont, and into warmer parts of the Upper South. It varies in height from 20 to 30 feet, normally growing into tree form with one trunk and a dense globular head, but often it is cut back to make it more shrubby. The evergreen foliage is exceptionally handsome, medium in texture, glossy, and rich dark green in color. The small white flowers appear in showy panicles in early spring, followed in autumn by the inconspicuous, black cherry-like fruits. The Laurelcherry ordinarily has no pests of consequence but it is liable to borer damage in some sections. It is valuable because it is one of the fastest growing materials of its class in any reasonably good soil. It is at its best in sunny sites, but it will also grow well in partial shade. In larger sizes it does not transplant well, and one is usually ahead in setting out small seedlings. The plant takes shearing well, and is used a great deal in hedges of 3 feet or more in height, and in topiary; but it is most handsome in its natural tree form, used in screening, in borders, or as a specimen. It might also be used as a small street tree, but it may break badly in ice storms in areas where they may occur. In warmer sections of the Coastal Plain this plant is said to be infested rather heavily with white flies. It cannot be planted in poorly drained spots. It is considered a choice and reliable evergreen as far north as Lexington, Ky., but in this colder climate it remains rather shrubby in habit to about 12 feet in height, and needs some shelter from winter winds which will usually sear the new growth.

The Pissard is one of the commonest of the purple-leaved Plums. Growing to a height of 15 feet, it forms a round to flat-headed tree with deciduous red to purplish foliage of medium texture. The leaves make a strong color effect throughout the summer, and in early spring there is a bright showing of pale pink flowers which are soon followed by red edible fruits. There are many other varieties of this tree as well as an improved hybrid, *P. blireiana,* the Blireiana Plum, all characterized by similar colored foliage. The latter differs in bearing more attractive double flowers, and because of this it is widely considered the best of the lot. These plants are satisfactory in the

Upper South, the Piedmont, and in cooler parts of the Coastal Plain. They should be set in the sun since the color is not effective in the shade. These plums are plants of limited use because of their color and because they are generally short lived because of borer attacks. They are valuable for their quick growth in some cases.

The Japanese Apricot is probably the one usually sold here under the name of Flowering Apricot. It is apt to be better suited to the Coastal Plain climate than most other flowering trees of the Cherry genus. This Apricot may reach over 20 feet in height. It bears in its several varieties handsome displays of single or double pink, rose, or white flowers before the leaves appear. However, the blooms often come out so early that they are set back by late frosts. The fruiting Apricot, *P. armeniaca*, has been tried with fair success in this section. It grows rapidly and the single pink flowers are lovely, but frost damage is a handicap, and susceptibility to brown rot disease of the fruits is almost impossible to control. It is not recommended for ornamental plantings because the fruits, when they do mature, make an objectionable litter.

The double flowering form of the Peach has several varieties with blooms of deep red, pink, white, or white with red stripes. These trees, rarely exceeding 15 feet in height, make a spectacular color display in the early spring, especially effective in flower gardens in combination with early bulbs, annuals, and Wistarias. In foliage and form, they are not distinguished, but older specimens, heavily pruned, mutilated by attacks of borers and clinging to life by the last slender thread, are often very picturesque. They develop with remarkable speed and bloom early in life; consequently for quick effect in flower gardens these are excellent materials, albeit ephemeral. While many flowering trees and shrubs do not bloom well in the Coastal Plain, this one does make a fine show to its most southerly limits while at the same time it is also perfectly reliable throughout the Upper South.

The varieties of the Flowering Cherries of oriental origin run into the hundreds. All are small trees, but they include different forms and varying leaf and flower characters. It is beyond the purpose of this survey to do more than to mention a few characteristic forms since the group has been treated in some detail in other works. The genus *P. serrulata* includes possibly the greatest number of varieties in cultivation. "Kwanzan" is one of the very common varieties with a heavy flowering display of double pinkish blossoms coming with the foliage, a horizontal branching pattern, and rather coppery leaves. This is a favorite for flower gardens, lawns, and borders, growing to a height of about 20 feet. Grafted on trunks of uniform height, it is recommended for street and avenue plantings.

Most of the famous plants around Washington's Tidal Basin are Yoshino Cherries, *P. yedoensis*, which grow to a height of almost 40 feet, requiring ample surroundings. Another widely planted form is the Weeping Cherry, *P. subhirtella pendula*, which reaches a height of 15 feet and blooms very early with a shower of rosy single blossoms. These plants are better adapted to cooler parts of the region, and they are questionable in most of the Coastal Plain. Although they are very handsome when well grown, they might be considered inferior to such as the Dogwood, the Flowering Crab-apples, and some others because they are very liable to borer damage and often quite short lived. However, they are sometimes splendid for quick effect.

*Pyrus calleryana*, Callery Pear. In many southern farmyards and gardens from the Coastal Plain through the Upper South, spring is heralded by the early flowering of the Sand Pear, *P. pyrifolia*, or one of its hybrids such as Keiffer, Le Conte, and others. These make a bright display of white, and they are fast growing, long lived, relatively pest-free trees. But they are inferior as ornamentals because of their fruits which make a litter if not properly cared for and promptly harvested, and the frequent disfigurement caused by fire blight on occasional limbs. The Callery Pear, a newer introduction, seems to possess the good ornamental qualities of the above, producing very small fruits about ½ inch in diameter which are not a nuisance. This plant may become much sought after as a fast-growing flowering tree of rather vertical habit throughout all of this region. In the Warmer Coastal Plain some trial plantings have also been made of the Evergreen Pear, *P. kawakami*, grown in California for flower and foliage.

*Quercus acuta*, Japanese Evergreen Oak. There are several small-growing, evergreen Oaks which seem to merit a first place among the Small Trees in the Coastal Plain and in warmer parts of the Piedmont. Unfortunately they are little grown and may be found in only a few nurseries. The first of these, and possibly the best for general use, is the Japanese Evergreen Oak. This tree grows fairly rapidly, approaching 40 feet in height, and its form varies from shrubby round and lowbranching to flat topped. The foliage is olive-green in color and coarse-textured; the individual leaves are about 4 inches long, serrated, and leathery to the touch. This makes a fine screen or specimen material for open well-drained sites as far north as Atlanta.

Other species of this evergreen group which are more rare but which may be tested should be mentioned here. The Blue Japanese Oak, *Q. glauca*, is similar to the above in form, but its leaves may have a grayish cast on their undersides. It is available in at least one nursery of the Coastal Plain, as is also the Cork Oak, *Q. suber.* The latter is an interesting tree, reaching possibly to somewhat over 40 feet with rather fine-textured leaves and the coarse bark from which cork is made. It has been planted commercially in parts of this country. It is adapted better to more arid conditions than those prevailing here, but it grows nicely in well-drained sites to Southern Pines, N. C. The Holly Oak, *Q. ilex,* native to the Mediterranean region, does not seem to be grown here although it might be quite useful. Possibly it has been tried and also found to be more at home in arid sections, but it seems worth testing as a street tree. It is suggested also for those smaller city lots which the Live Oak soon outgrows, and it is said to endure the salt of the seashore very well. It takes clipping happily and it can be adapted nicely to high screens and to pleaching against buildings. *Q. myrsinaefolia* grows well in the Coastal Plain, but it does not seem to be available. It has long, graceful, lance-like leaves of dark color and a handsome ascendant branching habit with a rounded top.

Considering this group as a whole, it appears that *Q. acuta* is one of the most refined and handsome species of the entire Small Tree list for general use in the Coastal Plain and, to a lesser extent, in the Piedmont. *Q. glauca* and *Q. suber* are satisfactory for more limited use although they are interesting and colorful subjects. Both *Q. ilex* and *Q. myrsinaefolia* deserve wider trial, and the latter may prove to be one of the very best in this classification. The use of all of these is limited because they are rare. Only the first species has any general distribution.

*Sabal palmetto,* Cabbage Palmetto. This is the one Palm which is listed with the best trees for the Coastal Plain, probably the only one which is thoroughly hardy throughout the section. It occurs in native stands near the shore as far north as Cape Fear, N. C., and it is planted inland to Columbia, S. C., and Macon and Columbus, Ga. This species may reach 50 feet or more in height, but since such height is unusual it is placed arbitrarily here among the smaller trees. The stout stiff trunk and the comparatively small round tuft of coarse-textured leaves are well known. The plant has no flowers or fruits of note, and its value comes from the fact that it lends an exotic and picturesque character to the landscape. It is not good for shade or for screening. It is easy to grow and easy to transplant even in large sizes. It has no pests of consequence, and it is well adapted to the sandy soils and the exposure of the seacoast. This is a favorite material for giving a tropical look to gardens of this region. It is also of some economic importance. The wood is employed in pilings because it does not split and because it resists worm attacks and decay for some time. The fresh, folded foliage of the crown bud was formerly used like the cabbage for food.

*Sapium sebiferum,* Chinese Tallowtree. This has been planted somewhat in the Coastal Plain and to Macon, Ga., for its quick effect and its easy disease-free culture. It also makes a rather good showing in early winter with its numerous waxy white seeds from which the Chinese extract a material for candles. The foliage is deciduous, medium to coarse in texture, and the form is open, irregular, and often graceful, reminiscent of a Birch in appearance. This tree is not one of the best, as it is short lived, but it is useful for its rapid growth in unfavorable spots.

*Sassafras albidum,* Common Sassafras. The Sassafras is a well-known native tree from the north central states to the Gulf, common in thickets on cutover uplands and along fence rows. It is not often seen in landscape work, but it does become a fine specimen tree, usually to 40 feet in height but capable of reaching considerably higher with a low to upright oval form. The foliage is deciduous and coarse-textured, dense and heavy, the leaves showing great variety on a single specimen from entire to deeply lobed, and the fall color is as fine as that of nearly any species. The entire plant is aromatic; the twigs are pleasant to chew and make good flavoring spits for roasting wieners. The dried roots used to be employed in making tea. There are numerous but not very showy greenish flowers in early spring before the leaves unfurl. These are followed by a colorful display on mature female plants of green and then black fruits borne in bright scarlet candelabra-like receptacles. The Sassafras is somewhat subject to borers and bagworms, and is difficult to transplant in any size. However, it is well suited to most dry poor soils throughout the South, and it is a most interesting and beautiful tree which probably is not planted as much as it ought to be.

*Sorbus americana,* American Mountainash. *Sorbus aucuparia,* European Mountainash. There are two species of Mountainash of some value in cooler parts of the Upper South. They are small trees to about 30 feet in height with attractive fine-textured foliage, white flowers in flat clusters in June, and an exceptionally handsome display of orange-red fruits in autumn. However, these plants are almost restricted to the cooler localities or higher elevations, and even here they prove rather short-lived. The American Mountainash is native throughout the mountain section and is desirable chiefly for naturalizing, but it is not found in the nurseries. The European Mountainash has several varieties, and it is the species usually grown. It is good for borders and more general use, but its range is limited and its life often short because of borer infestations that are almost impossible to control.

*Syringa amerunsis japonica,* Japanese Tree Lilac. On rare occasions and only in the cooler localities, this might be selected for a small tree of about 20 feet in height. It has a flat-topped and rather interesting structure, coarse dark green deciduous foliage, colorful bark resembling that of the Cherry, and large showy foam-like heads of white flowers in June well after other Lilacs have ceased blooming. This plant has some character and grows with little maintenance, but it is somewhat liable to borer and scale damage. In general it is inferior to other small trees of this class.

*Thuja occidentalis*, Eastern Arborvitae. The Arborvitaes should be used infrequently, and then only in cooler sections. There are several species available here, but for all practical purposes the Eastern Arborvitae is the only one which need be considered. It is a native of the northeastern states, chiefly in wet or boggy places, of ornamental value for its upright columnar form and its evergreen foliage. This plant probably retains its lower branches better than the similar Redcedar; it makes a good hedge material, but it does not have much character as a specimen. It is quite restricted in its range. There are many named varieties distinguished by a selection of forms from globular to columnar, or by foliage colors ranging from bluish through green to gold and bronze. Many of these are only distortions of the original species.

*Ulmus parvifolia*, Chinese Elm. *Ulmus pumila*, Siberian Elm. Two Asiatic Elms are widely distributed in the Southeast for the purpose of providing a fast-growing small tree. The more common of these is the less desirable. Usually the plant sold under the name of Chinese Elm is one which should be called the Siberian Elm, *U. pumila*. It develops rapidly, and endures dry windy sites quite well. However, its unattractive grayish foliage, persisting without color until late autumn, is attacked by many leaf-eating insects. The habit is characterless and the soft wood is liable to early breakage. Use of this tree should be limited to wind breaks in severe, cold, windy exposures. The blooming and the seed formation take place on this species in the spring, and thus it is easily distinguished from the true Chinese Elm, *U. parvifolia*, which blooms in late summer and develops its often quite decorative seeds in autumn. The small leaves are deep green in color. There seem to be different forms of this variety. One bears leaves which persist, in warmer parts of the Coastal Plain at least, until deep in the winter. This may be listed as the Evergreen Elm, *U. p. sempervirens*. Another has exfoliating bark which adds much interest. These trees are adaptable to all parts of the Southeast; but, in view of the unchecked spread of two Elm diseases to which they may be subject, planting them is hardly advisable if something else is available which will satisfy the requirements of the design.

*Viburnum prunifolium*, Blackhaw Viburnum. This plant has been discussed in some detail among the Large Shrubs of Group VI, but it is widely adapted to Small Tree uses from the Coastal Plain through the Upper South. It is often too low in its branching to permit circulation under its spread, but it is a vigorous, pest-free, hardy material for places in which its horizontal character will fit. Through much of this region one may encounter a form called *V. rufidulum*, the Southern Blackhaw, which some botanists consider a variety of the above. It is equally desirable in landscape quality. These plants display beautiful dark green, glossy deciduous foliage which in autumn makes a fine color effect in dull red; they also furnish edible blue-black fruits in autumn; in late spring there are white flowers in conspicuous flat heads.

## VIII. Large Trees for the SOUTHERN COASTAL PLAIN

*Botanical Name*                                    *Common Name*

### RECOMMENDED FOR GENERAL USE

| | |
|---|---|
| Acer rubrum | Red Maple |
| Celtis laevigata | Sugar Hackberry |
| Liquidambar styraciflua | American Sweetgum |
| Magnolia grandiflora | Southern Magnolia |
| Pinus caribaea | Slash Pine |
| Pinus palustris | Longleaf Pine |
| Quercus falcata | Southern Red Oak |
| Quercus phellos | Willow Oak |
| Quercus virginiana | Live Oak |

### RECOMMENDED FOR RESTRICTED USE

| | |
|---|---|
| Acer floridanum | Florida Maple |
| Aesculus octandra | Yellow Buckeye |
| Ailanthus altissima | Treeofheaven Ailanthus |
| Carya glabra | Pignut Hickory |
| Carya illinoensis | Pecan |
| Cedrus atlantica | Atlas Cedar |
| Cedrus deodara | Deodar Cedar |
| Cedrus libani | Cedar-of-Lebanon |
| Diospyros virginiana | Common Persimmon |
| Fraxinus americana | American Ash |
| Ginkgo biloba | Ginkgo |
| Gleditsia triacanthos inermis | Thornless Honeylocust |
| Liriodendron tulipifera | Tuliptree |
| Nyssa sylvatica | Black Tupelo |

| *Botanical Name* | *Common Name* |
|---|---|
| Paulownia tomentosa | Royal Paulownia |
| Pinus echinata | Shortleaf Pine |
| Pinus taeda | Loblolly Pine |
| Platanus occidentalis | American Planetree |
| Platanus orientalis | Oriental Planetree |
| Populus alba | White Poplar |
| Quercus alba | White Oak |
| Quercus coccinea | Scarlet Oak |
| Quercus laurifolia | Laurel Oak |
| Quercus nigra | Water Oak |
| Salix species | Willow |
| Sophora japonica | Japanese Pagodatree |
| Taxodium distichum | Common Baldcypress |
| Ulmus americana | American Elm |
| Zelkova serrata | Japanese Zelkova |

## VIII. Large Trees for the SOUTHERN PIEDMONT
### RECOMMENDED FOR GENERAL USE

| | |
|---|---|
| Acer rubrum | Red Maple |
| Celtis laevigata | Sugar Hackberry |
| Liquidambar styraciflua | American Sweetgum |
| Magnolia grandiflora | Southern Magnolia |
| Pinus echinata | Shortleaf Pine |
| Pinus taeda | Loblolly Pine |
| Quercus borealis | Northern Red Oak |
| Quercus coccinea | Scarlet Oak |
| Quercus falcata | Southern Red Oak |
| Quercus phellos | Willow Oak |

### RECOMMENDED FOR RESTRICTED USE

| | |
|---|---|
| Acer floridanum | Florida Maple |
| Acer saccharum | Sugar Maple |
| Aesculus octandra | Yellow Buckeye |
| Ailanthus altissima | Treeofheaven Ailanthus |
| Carya glabra | Pignut Hickory |
| Carya illinoensis | Pecan |
| Catalpa bignonoides | Southern Catalpa |
| Cedrus atlantica | Atlas Cedar |
| Cedrus deodara | Deodar Cedar |
| Cedrus libani | Cedar-of-Lebanon |
| Diospyros virginiana | Common Persimmon |

| *Botanical Name* | *Common Name* |
|---|---|
| Fagus sylvatica | European Beech |
| Fraxinus americana | American Ash |
| Ginkgo biloba | Ginkgo |
| Gleditsia triacanthos inermis | Thornless Honeylocust |
| Liriodendron tulipifera | Tuliptree |
| Nyssa sylvatica | Black Tupelo |
| Paulownia tomentosa | Royal Paulownia |
| Phellodendron amurense | Amur Corktree |
| Pinus caribaea | Slash Pine |
| Pinus palustris | Longleaf Pine |
| Pinus strobus | White Pine |
| Platanus occidentalis | American Planetree |
| Platanus orientalis | Oriental Planetree |
| Populus alba | White Poplar |
| Prunus serotina | Black Cherry |
| Quercus alba | White Oak |
| Quercus laurifolia | Laurel Oak |
| Quercus nigra | Water Oak |
| Quercus palustris | Pin Oak |
| Quercus virginiana | Live Oak |
| Robinia pseudoacacia | Black Locust |
| Salix species | Willow |
| Sophora japonica | Japanese Pagodatree |
| Taxodium distichum | Common Baldcypress |
| Tilia americana | American Linden |
| Tilia cordata | Littleleaf Linden |
| Tsuga canadensis | Canadian Hemlock |
| Ulmus americana | American Elm |
| Zelkova serrata | Japanese Zelkova |

## VIII. Large Trees for the UPPER SOUTH

### RECOMMENDED FOR GENERAL USE

| | |
|---|---|
| Acer rubrum | Red Maple |
| Acer saccharum | Sugar Maple |
| Celtis laevigata | Sugar Hackberry |
| Ginkgo biloba | Ginkgo |
| Liquidambar styraciflua | American Sweetgum |
| Pinus echinata | Shortleaf Pine |
| Pinus strobus | White Pine |
| Quercus borealis | Northern Red Oak |

| *Botanical Name* | *Common Name* |
|---|---|
| Quercus coccinea | Scarlet Oak |
| Quercus phellos | Willow Oak |
| Tsuga canadensis | Canadian Hemlock |

### RECOMMENDED FOR RESTRICTED USE

| | |
|---|---|
| Abies fraseri | Fraser Balsam Fir |
| Aesculus octandra | Yellow Buckeye |
| Ailanthus altissima | Treeofheaven Ailanthus |
| Carya glabra | Pignut Hickory |
| Catalpa bignonoides | Southern Catalpa |
| Cedrus atlantica | Atlas Cedar |
| Cedrus libani | Cedar-of-Lebanon |
| Diospyros virginiana | Common Persimmon |
| Fagus sylvatica | European Beech |
| Fraxinus americana | American Ash |
| Gleditsia triacanthos inermis | Thornless Honeylocust |
| Gymnocladus dioicus | Kentucky Coffeetree |
| Juglans nigra | Black Walnut |
| Liriodendron tulipifera | Tuliptree |
| Magnolia acuminata | Cucumbertree Magnolia |
| Magnolia grandiflora | Southern Magnolia |
| Nyssa sylvatica | Black Tupelo |
| Paulownia tomentosa | Royal Paulownia |
| Phellodendron amurense | Amur Corktree |
| Phellodendron sachalinense | Sakhalin Corktree |
| Picea abies | Norway Spruce |
| Picea rubens | Red Spruce |
| Pinus virginiana | Virginia Pine |
| Platanus occidentalis | American Planetree |
| Platanus orientalis | Oriental Planetree |
| Populus alba | White Poplar |
| Prunus serotina | Black Cherry |
| Quercus alba | White Oak |
| Quercus palustris | Pin Oak |
| Robinia pseudoacacia | Black Locust |
| Salix species | Willow |
| Sophora japonica | Japanese Pagodatree |
| Taxodium distichum | Common Baldcypress |
| Tilia americana | American Linden |
| Tilia cordata | Littleleaf Linden |
| Tsuga caroliniana | Carolina Hemlock |
| Ulmus americana | American Elm |
| Zelkova serrata | Japanese Zelkova |

## RANGE CHART FOR GROUP VIII. LARGE TREES

| | Coastal Plain | | Piedmont | | Upper South | |
|---|---|---|---|---|---|---|
| Acer rubrum | x x x | x x x | x x x | x x x | x x x | x x x |
| Acer saccharum | | | - - - | x x x | x x x | x x x |
| Celtis laevigata | x x x | x x x | x x x | x x x | x x x | x x x |
| Ginkgo biloba | | | - - - | x x x | x x x | x x x |
| Liquidambar styraciflua | x x x | x x x | x x x | x x x | x x x | x x x |
| Pinus caribaea | x x x | x x x | - - - | | | |
| Pinus echinata | | - - - | x x x | x x x | x x x | x x x |
| Pinus palustris | x x x | x x x | - - - | | | |
| Pinus strobus | | | - - - | x x x | x x x | x x x |
| Pinus taeda | - - - | x x x | x x x | x x x | x x x | - - - |
| Magnolia grandiflora | x x x | x x x | x x x | x x x | x x x | - - - |
| Quercus borealis | | | - - - | x x x | x x x | x x x |
| Quercus coccinea | - - - | x x x | x x x | x x x | x x x | x x x |
| Quercus falcata | x x x | x x x | x x x | x x x | - - - | |
| Quercus phellos | x x x | x x x | x x x | x x x | x x x | x x x |
| Quercus virginiana | x x x | x x x | x x x | - - - | | |
| Tsuga canadensis | | | - - - | x x x | x x x | x x x |

All of the Large Trees shown here are natives of the Southeast save the *Ginkgo* which, as far south Augusta, Ga., grows reasonably well although it seems to lack vigor. *Acer rubrum, Celtis, Liquidambar,* and *Quercus phellos* seem to be equally at home in any part of the region, showing a remarkable adaptability. The two broad-leaved evergreens, *Magnolia grandiflora* and *Quercus virginiana,* are Coastal Plain species which show considerable tolerance to cold. They are more shrubby along the upper limits of their range, failing to come up to the Large Tree size beyond the zones indicated by the solid bars. However, they are still valuable here in spots as tall shrubs for screening even if they may not be entirely dependable. The coniferous evergreens listed are of great importance locally, but the *Pinus strobus* stands out for its adaptability to transplanting in large sizes. *Pinus strobus* and the *P. echinata* will succeed in the limestone regions of Kentucky and Tennessee. The deciduous Oaks are characteristic trees of the Southeast, and this list is necessarily shortened, omitting mention of some species of outstanding local value such as the *Quercus* nigra of the Deep South and *Q. palustris* of the Upper South limestone areas.

*Abies fraseri,* Fraser Balsam Fir. The Firs include a number of handsome coniferous evergreens, but they are best suited generally to cool, moist climates. On the whole they are not important in the Southeast except in the mountains where the Fraser Fir, a local variant of the Balsam Fir of the North, is a common native. This species makes a handsome pyramidal specimen or screen plant, with aromatic bright green foliage in this restricted section.

Other Firs may be mentioned for rare trial. Exceptionally handsome old specimens are found in the Washington area which may be *A. cephalonica* or *A. nordmanniana*. Both of these come from the Mediterranean area and may be tried here. *A. homolepis,* the Nikko Fir from Japan, grows well on dry uplands of West Virginia too severe for the Balsam. *A. concolor,* the White Fir, is sometimes seen but it is only fair.

*Acer floridanum,* Florida Maple. *Acer rubrum,* Red Maple. *Acer saccharum,* Sugar Maple. The Red Maple is native to all parts of the Southeast. In the Coastal Plain it is common along streams and in swamps, but farther north it also inhabits dry hillsides in combination with Ash and Oak. It is a softwood tree of rather rapid growth, but it is also long-lived, clean, free of disease, and not overly aggressive so that it is one of the most desirable species in all sections that have good soils and favorable moisture conditions. It provides an excellent color note in early spring with its red flowers and fruits, and again in autumn with its rose-red foliage. When this tree is grown in woodlands the form is loose, open, and vertical, reaching 100 feet in height, but in open sites it is much lower, round-headed, and compact. The leaves are medium in texture and medium green in color, but the undersides are silvery giving a somewhat grayed over-all effect. The twigs and branches also are silvery gray in color, most attractive in winter. There are several form varieties of this species, both columnar and round-headed, which should be selected for street tree planting where uniformity may be desirable.

The Sugar Maple is more limited in its range, being really well adapted only to the Upper South although it may be found in cooler woodlands and in stream valleys in the Piedmont. In the southern part of this range one encounters the Southern Sugar Maple, *A. floridanum,* quite similar in most ways to the above, differing only in details of size and pubescence of the leaves. This may be sold in southern nurseries as *A. saccharum.* In form, it is an opulent, round-headed, upright oval tree, with low branches. Its deciduous foliage is heavy, dense, coarse in texture, dark green in color, turning in autumn to tones of orange and yellow which are usually outstanding. This is a permanent, long-lived, slow-growing, pest-free tree which thrives only in rich, well-watered soils, either alkaline or acid. It does not take well to severe wind exposure nor to drought or crowded city conditions. Its shallow root system, heavy foliage, and low branching compete with nearby turf or shrubs. It is at its best as a specimen in spacious settings for it is truly an aristocrat of its class. This tree also has form varieties, columnar, oval, etc., which should be studied for particular locations and uses.

Other Maples of this size class are inferior and merit little if any use. Probably the best of these is the Norway, *A. platanoides*. Indeed, this is a favorite street tree in many cities, and it has many interesting forms in growth habit and in popular colored foliage varieties ("Crimson King" and "Schwedler"). It also has effective yellow flowers in early spring before the leaves. It is, however, low branched, a gross feeder which starves out grass or other plants under its spread, and is altogether a coarse material with little character to be used seldom except in a location where few plants will survive. The Silver Maple, *A. saccharinum*, is widely planted for quick growth. This is its only virtue, however, for it is a weed which speedily grows outsize and ungainly in effect, and raises problems in upkeep with its brittle branches and greedy roots, infamous for penetrating and clogging sewers. Similar comments apply to the Boxelder, *A. negundo*. The latter does have some value, however, in the very dry sites of city streets or the western plains where little else will grow.

*Aesculus octandra*, Yellow Buckeye. In the past the Horsechestnut, *Aesculus hippocastanum*, was a prized ornamental because of its dense symmetrical, formal shape, its rich coarse foliage, and its June showing of garish flowers. This type of plant, for better or for worse, is out of fashion now; and this particular species is objectionable for its steady production of litter, its liability to leaf disease, and its detrimental competition with turf. A double-flowering variety is called "Baumann." Somewhat more desirable is the Yellow Buckeye, native to rich well-watered soils of the Piedmont and the Upper South. It reaches imposing proportions and bears beautiful five-fingered, coarse-textured foliage of great richness. The flowers too are showy in late spring; the fruits are of interest although they are objectionable for litter, and they are said to be poisonous if eaten. This tree may be a fair choice for variety in parks and along highways where ample space, good soils, and moisture are provided.

*Ailanthus altissima*, Treeofheaven Ailanthus. For the few places where it seems impossible to find anything else which will grow, this may offer a last resort. It appears to thrive in the poorest soils in the most crowded urban environments to give a rapid and welcome shade and a cool display of lush rich foliage. The sexes are separate in the Ailanthus, and only female plants should be grown because of the disagreeable odor of the male flowers. The numerous seeds borne on the female trees will not germinate to spread the plant unless they have been fertilized with pollen from a male tree. These seeds make a colorful display as they mature in late summer. This tree can be adapted to small patios by cutting back its trunk to the ground whenever it grows too large. It is said to be able to withstand salt water very well. It has many excellent qualities, but it cannot be recommended for any except the most adverse sites because it tends to spread rapidly, becoming a serious weed in favorable environments.

*Carya glabra*, Pignut Hickory. *Carya illinoensis*, Pecan. Several species of Hickory are native to the Southeast, and they offer some exceedingly handsome ornamental stock. The Pignut is selected as a typical and widespread species with a fine upright form, good coarse-textured foliage which is colorful in autumn, and a strong and disease-free constitution. It is quite slow growing, however, and so difficult to transplant that one should literally start with the nut if he wants a Hickory in his garden. None of the species is at home in the sandy reaches of the lower Coastal Plain, but they are common on higher land from Florida over the hills of the Piedmont and into the mountain area, generally occupying dry, sunny, wind-swept slopes. In cooler areas on good soils the Shagbark Hickory, *C. ovata*, is a handsome tree especially valued for its sweet, thin-shelled nuts. Named varieties can be secured from nurseries where the plants are root pruned so that they can be transplanted successfully.

The Pecan is, of course, a valuable crop tree; and if there is space, there is much to be said for including at least one in every home grounds planting scheme throughout its range from the upper Coastal Plain, throughout the Piedmont, and into the warmer parts of the Upper South. Native forms will grow well on fertile bottom lands to the Ohio River Valley, but the improved nut-bearing varieties do not perform satisfactorily so far north. The purely ornamental value of this tree is not outstanding. There is some litter and often the nuts are not good if spraying is neglected. Local agricultural agents should be consulted on the selection of varieties and their care. It is sometimes said that certain ornamentals, and the Camellias in particular, will not grow under or near Pecans. This common belief is, however, unfounded.

*Catalpa bignonoides*, Southern Catalpa. This tree is native to lower parts of this region, but it is hardy throughout. It makes a gorgeous display of white flowers in early summer, and the long seed pods, often called Indian Stogies, are interesting in autumn. It is a strong, long-lived tree, but its generally coarse effect, like that of the Horsechestnuts, will be admirable only rather rarely and at some distance as in park or parkway landscapes. In the Deep South it is rather constantly infested with worms which make it more valuable to fisherman than to any others. A dwarf form, *C. b. nana*, is seen rather frequently as a formal, umbrella-shaped specimen grafted on a bole of about 5 feet. This may be listed as *C. bungei* and is another tree altogether, a native of China. The Northern Catalpa, *C. speciosa*, is a larger growing species which may be native to the northwest part of this region. It is similar to, but possibly less attractive than, its southern counterpart. The wood of these trees is said to stand weather well and to make good fence posts.

*Cedrus atlantica,* Atlas Cedar. *Cedrus deodara,* Deodar Cedar. *Cedrus libani,* Cedar-of-Lebanon. Of the three Cedars, the Deodar is the most planted in this region and the least attractive with its droopy weak character and inharmonious blue-gray foliage. It is very common in front yards and even in foundation plantings where it quickly grows outsize. The Deodar is fairly hardy to Memphis, Atlanta, and Washington, but it may freeze out in Nashville. The Atlas and Lebanon Cedars are slightly more hardy and a few may be seen in Louisville, Ky., in the Ohio Valley. These trees make splendid specimens, but they have a stiff individual and positive habit of growth which is in strong contrast with the character of most plants. Hence they must be composed in the landscape with some care. Where they are properly placed they are plants of stunning character. All of the Cedars are subject to damage by borers which may kill back the leader and damage the symmetry of the tree. In most of this region, if not all, Cedars possibly should be handled as Small Trees, for they will only rarely exceed 40 feet in height.

*Celtis laevigata,* Sugar Hackberry. This is one of the very common and dependable native trees of the Southeast, where in many places it is considered a weed. It performs well in the tight street quarters of Charleston, S. C., or Nashville, Tenn., and it appears to be one of the best for a large, high-headed shade and street tree. It is a member of the Elm Family, and it may succumb eventually to the Elm diseases which are making such disastrous inroads among American Elms. But at the moment the Hackberry still seems a good choice, tolerant of the heat and drought of much of the area, generally long-lived, of good form, and resistant to insects and the Witchesbroom disease so common on northern Hackberries. The foliage is not outstanding, yellow-green in summer and dull yellow in autumn, but it is often quite a beautiful olive-gold as it opens in early spring. There are red berry-like fruits in summer, but these are well hidden by the leaves and soon eaten by birds. The bark on older specimens is silver gray and often warty, and attractive through the winter. Young trees are frequently open and awkward in branching habit and may benefit from some corrective pruning.

*Diospyros virginiana,* Common Persimmon. Persimmons grow in numbers in the native woodlands and along edges of fields throughout this region. They are among the smaller major trees, rarely reaching over 50 feet in height. The foliage is deciduous, and in autumn the tree is colorful when the leaves turn orange and the branches are loaded with the yellow to orange fruits. Because of the latter this tree may not be planted in neat areas; but for naturalistic areas and along roadsides, it is an excellent, easily grown material, much appreciated by children and wildlife. Varieties of the Persimmon have been selected for fruit production, but they are rare and of little importance.

*Fagus sylvatica*, European Beech. The Beeches are not suited to the warmest parts of this region, and they do not thrive anywhere under severe exposures to sun, wind, and drought. But with shelter, good soils, moisture, and plenty of space in which to spread, they are magnificent as specimens, in clumps, or as woodland trees. Their rich, dark green glossy foliage turns gold in autumn; their smooth gray bark and picturesque forms are fine design qualities. Usually they cast such a dense shade and the feeding roots are so close to the ground surface that it is difficult if not impossible to grow a lawn under them. They resent heavy foot traffic, as in park picnic sites, over their root area. Sometimes the tiny nuts mature to provide a spare but tasty treat; more often they fail to develop because of poor pollination. The American Beech, *Fagus grandifolia*, is found growing wild in cool, moist, fertile spots in the Upper South and along stream valleys in the Piedmont. It is said to be difficult to transplant, and is rarely offered by the nurseries. On the other hand, the European Beech is generally available. Some of its varieties are especially choice as "horticultural gems"; though slow to develop, they are immensely rewarding in such places as parks and institutional grounds where some permanence may be expected. Among these are several purple to red-leaved forms, weepers, cut-leaved types, etc., of high value as specimens, best located in open lawn areas where their branches may be left to sweep to the ground. The European Beech, set on one- to two-foot centers, can be developed into one of the finest of hedges ranging in height from 8 to 15 feet.

*Fraxinus americana*, White Ash. Approximately five species of Ash grow naturally in this region, and they are usually considered weeds and probably not appreciated as ornamentals as much as they should be. However, since the American Elm is so endangered, this genus will almost certainly receive greater attention because it is disease free and a fast sturdy grower which forms a high-headed shade tree. There are no flowers or fruits of consequence. The compound, medium-textured foliage is light green, becoming colorful in most species in autumn. This plant should be nursery grown because it suffers a severe setback when moved from the wild in larger sizes, and it may then easily fall victim to the stem borer which is its deadly enemy in youth. The Ash will not fit into crowded, hot, city situations as well as the Hackberry, nor will it thrive in the lower Coastal Plain, but given reasonable space, it will do well in the most severe exposures, as a street or park or residential shade tree. Of the native species, the White Ash will probably be the most generally useful. Under local conditions, one of the other species may be collected and found very successful. These include the Red Ash (*F. pennsylvanica*), Green Ash (*F. p. lanceolata*), Blue Ash (*F. quadrangulata*), and Black Ash (*F. nigra*). There are also European species, but these are rare and of little value.

*Ginkgo biloba*, Ginkgo. Often listed as the Maidenhair Tree, the Ginkgo is a botanical curiosity. The only surviving member of an ancient family, which comes to us from the monastery gardens of China, it is becoming known as one of our best shade trees. It may with time reach 100 feet in height with a broadly rounded symmetrical form, but it is rather slow in developing. It is characterized in its younger stages by long, straight, awkward appearing branches which may give it an ungainly appearance for a time. The dark green, medium-textured foliage casts a light shade favoring grass under its spread; in autumn the leaves turn a bright clear yellow. They fall with surprising speed; within a day or two the skeleton is entirely naked. The inconspicuous flowers are of separate sexes on separate trees, and one avoids planting the females, as they produce in late summer quantities of fleshy round fruits which litter the ground and smell bad as they rot. The Ginkgo is prized especially because it has no known insect or disease troubles, and it is tolerant of the crowded, dirty, and inhospitable environments of city streets and parking lots. It has several horticultural varieties, the most useful of which may well be the Sentry Ginkgo, *G. b. fastigiata*, a columnar type most appropriate for narrow spaces. In buying this variety, however, one should be familiar with the source of the stock because there are wide lapses from the true Sentry form sold under that name.

*Gleditsia triacanthos inermis*, Thornless Honeylocust. This tree is a selection of the formidable spiky native species of meadows and pastures of most of this region. For some years it has been recommended as a nearly ideal shade tree because it endures poor soils and drought; it is hardy, fast growing, and long lived; it casts a light shade encouraging turf; and the leaves are so small and fine that they need not be raked up in autumn. Further selections have been made, chiefly for the purpose of stabilizing forms for growth habit, and of eliminating the unattractive bean-like seed pods. This work has resulted in patented varieties such as the "Moraine Locust," the "Imperial," and the "Sunburst," with yellow new growth. These are fine types and the plant still possesses most of the advantages it ever had; but its pest resistance, once rated so high, has broken down with the spread of a web worm which attacks the foliage in early summer and sometimes again in August, making an unsightly nuisance unless spraying is rigorously attended to. For city planting and for park work, where adequate spray equipment may be available, the Honeylocust is still a good material. For the average homeowner, however, this choice is open to question, at least wherever the web worm is common. It is well suited to the Upper South, the Piedmont, and cooler parts of the Coastal Plain. It is particularly fine for limestone sections.

*Gymnocladus dioicus,* Kentucky Coffeetree. This tree is closely related to the Honeylocust and is similar in its open, irregular, and horizontal growth habit. But its compound foliage is heavier in texture, and it probably is not as well suited to warmer sections. In the Upper South it is long lived and pest free, a good selection as a small lawn tree. The litter of its large seed pods may be objectionable. This tree is not widely available, but probably ought to be grown more often than it is.

*Juglans nigra,* Black Walnut. There will be few uses for the Walnuts as ornamentals, but they do have value for naturalizing and for nut production. Of these the Black Walnut is best known. Although the litter of nuts and their husks can be undesirable in some places, the Black Walnut becomes a fine tree of some beauty in rich, well-watered bottom lands in the Upper South. Numerous selections have been made so that grafted named varieties such as "Thomas," "Ohio," etc., are available from certain nut tree nurseries. These are well worth planting when this species is desired. Turf usually thrives under Walnuts, but some plants such as Rhododendrons are said to be unable to tolerate them in proximity. The Butternut, *J. cinerea,* is a native of inferior value, and it will hardly ever be planted. The Heartnut, *J. sieboldiana cordiformis,* is something of a curiosity — an attractive small tree. While all of these suit cooler sections, the Persian Walnut, *J. regia,* will also grow in the Coastal Plain. However, despite trials here, it is not considered a reliable or profitable species in this section.

*Liquidambar styraciflua,* American Sweetgum. One of the common deciduous native trees of this region, the American Sweetgum is usually found on deep damp soils along streams; it likes favorable spacious environments such as might be found in cultivated home grounds of generous size, parks, cemeteries, and along highways. It is usually pyramidal and rather vertical in form in youth, but it becomes more round-headed with age, reaching a height of 100 feet or more. The foliage is coarse in texture, dark green and glossy, clean and free of disease, and has a fine rose, or sometimes yellow to purple autumn color. The flowers are not showy, but the seed pods, spiky balls about the size of a half dollar, are interesting on the bare branches in winter although they do cause some litter. The bark is rough, and on the twigs it expands into broad wings which are pronounced and decorative on occasional specimens. This tree is said to be difficult to transplant except in small sizes, but it is long-lived and a rather fast grower. Generally pest free, the Sweetgum is said to be suffering in some localities from a blight, which should be watched. As suggested above, this is not particularly good for crowded dry streets in the city, but it is excellent for more favorable spacious quarters in all parts of the Southeast. The Formosa Sweetgum, *L. formosana*, is another species of attractive quality which may be equally adaptable.

*Liriodendron tulipifera*, Tuliptree. One of the magnificent forest trees of the Southeast is the Tuliptree or Yellow Poplar. It is valued for its upright form, its yellow tulip-like flowers of late spring, and for its rather coarse foliage of glossy green through the summer and bright yellow in autumn. Normally this tree grows in good, well-watered soils, and, although it will take an exposed dry and less hospitable site in cooler sections, it is best set in parks or other places with ample space. It cannot be recommended for narrow city streets as it will not thrive in tight sites and is subject to wind breakage. Neither is it a good choice for the average garden because it grows to so large a size and because it is often infested with aphids which drop a gummy excretion that is objectionable on both furniture and other plants. For early effect it is quite good because, although it does not move well in larger sizes, it grows very rapidly. A few nurseries carry an upright pyramidal form called *L. t. fastigiatum*.

*Magnolia acuminata*, Cucumbertree Magnolia. *Magnolia grandiflora*, Southern Magnolia. The Cucumbertree is a large forest tree of cool woods and good well-watered soils. It has coarse, deciduous leaves, a rather narrow upright oval form, and small greenish flowers which are followed by the cucumber-like fruits that are red in autumn. Although it is not transplanted easily and consequently is not common in the nurseries, it is a good, clean, long-lived tree for cooler sections and favorable environments.

The Southern Magnolia is one of the most characteristic and individual ornamentals of the South. Its lush evergreen foliage of coarse rich texture and deep color and its great white fragrant blooms are familiar to all. In this species there are a surprising number of variations. Some specimens have large flowers, up to 10 or 12 inches in diameter, while others bear much smaller blossoms; the petals may be broad and overlapping or they may be quite narrow; and the leaves, of several different forms, may be smooth and green underneath or the undersides may be covered with a heavy red-brown wool. Normally the Magnolia grows to a height of about

80 feet in an upright oval which appears to best advantage when the lower branches are retained and allowed to sweep the ground. Therefore it needs space and it is not at its best as a canopy tree. It is used satisfactorily as a specimen or in a high screen or windbreak. It is well adapted to all parts of the Coastal Plain and the Piedmont. It will grow well as far north as the Ohio Valley, but in cooler parts of the Upper South it is likely to remain under 40 feet in height, and it may suffer damage or defoliation from winter winds and snow or sleet storms. The tree is quite free of diseases and insect pests, but it is somewhat objectionable for tidy areas because it is always shedding some kind of litter—either the leaves or flowers in spring and early summer, or the cones and seeds in autumn. When the limbs come to the ground, this litter collects under the tree's spread where it is not such a nuisance. Since the Magnolia grows naturally in the swamps, it prefers deep, well-watered soils of good quality. It is slow in developing, and it is difficult to transplant in large sizes although transplanting can be done with care. In any garden where space is ample it is a permanent asset, always increasing in value.

*Nyssa sylvatica*, Black Tupelo. This tree is known also as the Black or Sour Gum, and it is native from Maine to Florida, mostly along creek and river bottoms in warmer sections. It is a handsome long-lived tree of upright oval or pyramidal form to 100 feet in height. The branching habit is interesting, and the clean deciduous foliage of medium texture has a dark glossy green color which turns bright red and is truly outstanding in autumn. The inconspicuous flowers are followed by dark blue fruits that are hidden by the foliage. This is an excellent tree for planting in damp places in the lower South, or in any normal well-watered sites in the Upper South. It is difficult to transplant in any but very small sizes, and probably for this reason it is not usually grown in nurseries nor planted as much as it deserves to be. In the swampy sections of the Coastal Plain, it may be confused with the Water Tupelo, *N. aquatica*.

*Paulownia tomentosa*, Royal Paulownia. Anywhere in the Southeast one's attention may be caught in early spring by the great purple bloom spikes of this tree, which is often called the Empress Tree. The decorative brown seed pods which persist through the winter and the newly formed flower buds for the following spring add a further note of interest as well as material for dried flower arrangements. Despite these attractive qualities, however, the Paulownia is not suggested for widespread planting, because of its weedy and soft wooded growth. Its appearance is very coarse with its great round deciduous leaves often a foot across. It stands drought, it is pestfree, and it survives inhospitable growing conditions as well as almost anything. For a quick bold effect in such environments, this

is a material worth remembering. It is often handsome in farmyards or along railroad tracks or riverbanks where it has escaped
and has space to develop.

Phellodendron amurense, Amur Corktree. Phellodendron sachali-
nense, Sakhalin Corktree. Within recent years the two Asiatic Cork-
trees have been introduced to rather wide use, and they give promise
of maintenance-free performance in dry sites in acid or alkaline
soils. Both are low (about 50 feet), wide-spreading, low-branching
trees, and this form may limit their usefulness as street trees. The
compound leaves are deciduous and medium in texture. In autumn
on female plants there are small clusters of black berries which
follow the inconspicuous greenish flowers. The Amur Corktree may
be the more interesting of the two because of its showy corky bark,
yellowish twigs, and picturesque branch formation. The Sakhalin
Corktree has smooth bark and reddish branchlets. These trees are
probably best suited to the Upper South.

Picea abies, Norway Spruce. Picea rubens, Red Spruce. The
Spruces are not well suited to the warmer, lower parts of this
region, but for cooler areas they include several excellent needle-
type evergreens. Generally, they retain a stiff, symmetrical, conical
form, and until they are quite old they hold their branches to the
ground, so that they are fine for screening, for borders, and for
specimens. They can be clipped to make excellent hedges or topiary.
While they prefer good soils and moisture, they will adapt well to the
exposure of higher elevations. They are easily transplanted in almost
any size. Spruces may generally be considered pest resistant and
maintenance free, but in some sections they are damaged by gall-
forming aphids which require spraying. Of the several species and
varieties that can be grown here, only a few can be mentioned. The
common native species of the higher mountains is the Red Spruce, not
often seen in the nurseries, good only for higher cooler sites. More
vigorous and more widely adaptable into cooler parts of the Piedmont is the Norway Spruce, which is the most common species in
cultivation. The Norway Spruce has many varieties, including dwarfs,
which are choice specimen plants of unusual interest (see Group
IV). The Colorado Spruce, P. pungens, is also widely planted. The
species may vary in foliage color from green to grayish, but it has
several varieties (Koster Blue, etc.) which many people consider
very choice for stronger color variations. The stature of the Colorado
Spruce may not reach over 50 feet, but the plant is often mistakenly
located as if it would not exceed 10 feet. The Serbian Spruce, P.
omorika, appears to be one of the most attractive usable forms with
weeping branchlets, growing well in West Virginia. The Oriental
Spruce, P. orientalis, thrives in Louisville, Ky., where it is considered

much superior to the Norway Spruce. Both of these latter species should be tested more widely in the Upper South.

*Pinus caribaea*, Slash Pine
*Pinus echinata*, Shortleaf Pine
*Pinus palustris*, Longleaf Pine
*Pinus strobus*, White Pine
*Pinus taeda*, Loblolly Pine
*Pinus virginiana*, Virginia Pine

The six Pines listed here are natives of various parts of this region. While most of them are prominent and characteristic features of Southeastern landscapes, the list does not cover all the native species which, for local situations, might be first choice, nor does it attempt to evaluate the numerous foreign species which can be grown here. None of the latter is superior to the natives, although some of them are interesting to include in special collections, and several are very useful in the Upper South. For most situations a satisfactory solution will be found in this list.

The Longleaf and the Slash Pines are the important species for the Coastal Plain. Both grow to 100 feet or more in height with a high branching habit. Both are important timber trees, much planted for forest products. Differentiation between the two is based on the cones, which are short stalked in the Slash Pine and stemless in the Longleaf. Further, the leaves are from 8 to 18 inches long and the cones from 6 to 10 inches on the Longleaf Pine while the leaves are from 8 to 12 inches and the cones from 3 to 6 inches on the Slash Pine. The high, airy, fragrant canopy of a mature stand of these trees makes fine shade for the home grounds. On new, bare lots it is not out of the question to plant the seedlings, as they grow with amazing rapidity when given even the least care. These Pines cannot be recommended generally for planting along streets or in crowded city quarters, but they are fine for suburban areas, school grounds, parks, estates, and roadsides. They tolerate almost any soil conditions except the very swampy or extremely droughty. In many ways these Pines are a symbol of the conservation idea in the Deep South, and because of the ease with which they may be grown, their great utility, and their equally great beauty, they can hardly be overplanted.

Most of the same comments can be made of the Loblolly and Shortleaf Pines in the Piedmont where fine old stands are common on the well-drained slopes and uplands. In planting, these are usually set out as seedlings of 12 to 18 inches in height since in larger sizes they are difficult to move, hardly ever recovering from the shock. These do grow with such remarkable speed, however, that planting them is not impractical for landscape purposes. The leaves of the

Loblolly range from 6 to 10 inches in length and occur in threes to the bundle, while those of the Shortleaf are less than 6 inches long in twos per bundle. Both species pass through an awkward stage of ungainly form in their youth, but later they become rather round-headed, usually high branched, sometimes picturesque as free standing specimens. Since they show great endurance in the poorest subsoils and the most exposed situations, they are extremely valuable for reclaiming eroded lands and protecting fresh slopes along roadsides. Both trees are subject to borer infestations if they are pruned or otherwise injured in the spring or early summer. They are suitable for planting on drier upland sites in the Coastal Plain, but the Longleaf and Slash Pines are not highly successful in this region, largely because they are liable to bad breakage in the sleet storms which are not uncommon here.

Possibly the finest of this genus in the Upper South is the White Pine which is also excellent throughout cooler parts of the Piedmont. This is a vigorous grower in almost all parts of the area, reaching ultimately to a great height with at first a symmetrical pyramidal form, becoming irregular, high branching and picturesque with age. Its gray-green foliage of fine, soft effect is particularly notable in the landscape. It is well adapted to most well-drained soils in the region although it does not thrive under crowded conditions in cities or among taller trees. It makes a good screen as a young tree until it loses its lower branches, it makes a fine specimen, and it is excellent woodland or forestry material. It can be clipped into a tall hedge rather successfully. Unlike the species discussed above, this has a fibrous root system which enables it to be balled and transplanted successfully in sizes up to 25 feet in height, and it is thus valuable for building immediate landscape effects. It is very hardy, but it is subject to the White Pine Blister Rust disease which may be common in localities where native or introduced species of Gooseberries are grown.

The Shortleaf Pine is just as valuable and just as adaptable in the Upper South as in the Piedmont. Closely related to it and possibly just as common is the Virginia Pine, often called the Scrub Pine. This is usually somewhat smaller and, with its thin and straggling habit and yellowish winter color, not so attractive, but it grows well on the poorest stony, dry sites to make a good cover. The Pitch Pine, *P. rigida*, is similar in character, becoming picturesque with age, and it also is good for dry exposed positions in the Upper South. Both of these trees are difficult to move except as seedlings. In the Upper South both the Scotch and the Austrian Pines are fairly common (*P. sylvestris* and *P. nigra*). Both are natives of Europe, and the former, with its bluish green foliage and its reddish branches of striking form, is often handsome. The latter has long needles of dark green color and it also takes on a picturesque habit with age. Both are easily transplanted in almost any size, and they will do well on dry exposed sites. Unfortunately the former is short-lived and rather subject to infestations of needle scales. Both are occasionally attacked by a tip blight disease and by bud moths. Altogether they seem inferior to the native species.

*Platanus occidentalis*, American Planetree. *Platanus orientalis*, Oriental planetree. The Oriental Planetree, adaptable to all but the lower extremes of the Coastal Plain, is suggested here for possible further planting in cities of this region. It is one of the most common street trees in the urban areas of southern Europe, and it seems to endure this type of condition very well. This species is fairly disease resistant and very long-lived. It is also very colorful, especially in winter, when its bright olive bark is displayed to the best advantage. It lends itself well to clipping and pollarding to make highly decorative forms for urban settings and period gardens. Equally good and similar in effect is the London Planetree, *P. acerifolia*, which is a hybrid of the Oriental. The American Plane or Sycamore is common along river bottoms throughout the region from the Coastal Plain to the Ohio River, and, with its chalky white bark, it also makes a colorful, handsome specimen in parks and along highways. However, this can be damaged by a twig blight to which the others are resistant, and it is recommended with reservations. All of the Planes grow to very large size with considerable speed. They are considered somewhat dirty because of their litter of leaves and bark, and they are also somewhat coarse in effect for many situations.

*Populus alba*, White Poplar. Poplars may be planted for quick effects and to hold soil, but they are generally short-lived, brittle, and possessed of rapacious root systems which severely limit their desirability. Possibly the best of them all is the White or Silver Poplar. The leaves are rather small and fine in texture, gray-green above and silvery beneath. These have the characteristic Poplar stem structure which causes them to flutter in the lightest breeze. Seen from a distance, these trees seem to glitter with an almost metallic luster. The bark too is silver-gray on the younger branches, becoming black and heavily ridged with age. The flowers appear in early spring in catkins, and the falling of these and the cottony tufted seeds causes some litter. The tree is quite free of disease and insect damage. It reaches a height of 75 feet with a broad-spreading rounded crown. Of all the very fast-growing, softwooded deciduous trees, this seems to be one of the most resistant to the ice storms of this region and one of the most amenable to the heat and glare of paved areas of cities where shade may be needed in a hurry. There is an upright growing variety called the Bolleana Poplar, *P. a. pyramidalis*, which is desirable for narrow places and generally superior to the older and more popular Lombardy Poplar, *P. nigra pyramidalis*. The Eastern Poplar, *P. deltoides*, is common along the river banks of the region, a rapid, weedy grower of little landscape value. The Carolina Poplar, *P. canadensis*, has been used somewhat as a street tree but it, along with others of its genus, probably should be banned from any location where the roots can get into sewer lines or the brittle twigs and branches can raise a maintenance and clean-up problem.

*Prunus serotina*, Black Cherry. This is probably the only Cherry of real significance among the Large Trees, and even its use is limited to a large extent to naturalistic plantings for wildlife, to soil reclamation projects, or possibly to provide shade for new sub-divisions. The tree is a fast weedy grower on poor soils in severe exposures, with medium-textured deciduous foliage casting a light shade, and with white flowers in early summer, and small fruits maturing from red to black in late summer. The latter are edible, a favorite bird food. Although it can reach great size, the tree is usually cut down by borers before it is very old. The foliage is favored by tent caterpillars and other insects. Altogether this is not a choice ornamental.

*Quercus alba*, White Oak
*Quercus borealis*, Northern Red Oak
*Quercus coccinea*, Scarlet Oak
*Quercus falcata*, Southern Red Oak
*Quercus laurifolia*, Laurel Oak
*Quercus nigra*, Water Oak
*Quercus palustris*, Pin Oak
*Quercus phellos*, Willow Oak
*Quercus virginiana*, Live Oak

Throughout the Southeast the Oaks are easily among the most valuable of all shade trees. Probably twenty species grow wild in this region and their identification is complicated often by only slight differences and by the tendency to interbreed and to produce numerous hybrids of mixed characters. In a general way, they are divided into two large classes: (1) the White Oaks, including those having leaves with rounded lobes, and (2) the Red Oaks, having leaves with pointed lobes. Again generally speaking, the White Oaks are slower growing, more difficult to transplant, and less useful for landscape work than the Red Oaks, which grow quite rapidly and which as a rule can be transplanted in large size with relative ease. One disease of the genus poses a threat which should be watched although it does not as yet appear so serious that Oak plantings should be abandoned. The Oak Wilt disease appeared in the northern

Midwest a few years ago, and it has been spreading slowly with no means yet discovered for checking it. It is said to be somewhat more destructive among the Red Oaks than among the White. However, it is fatal to all as yet, and its spread throughout the region can be hardly contemplated with any comfort. There are, of course, other pests of Oaks including scales, borers, and gall-forming insects, but these are not too serious, and these trees are generally considered clean, healthy, and long-lived.

The White Oak is well adapted to all parts of the Southeast, generally growing on high ground, but it is confined in the Coastal Plain portion of the region to well-drained elevations with a heavy subsoil. It is one of the most beautiful and enduring of the tall trees, but it is not highly important in cultivation because it is difficult to handle, is slow in growth, and demands a spacious area for perfect development of its spreading form.

The Northern and the Southern Red Oaks overlap in their ranges. In the Piedmont they may be used interchangeably, but in subregions north and south of it the differentiation should be recognized. Both of these varieties are large trees of broad spread, robust habit, and rapid growth. The leaves of the Northern Red Oak are larger and heavier, but both are rather coarse in texture; the foliage turns dull red or brown before falling in autumn. Both are important in landscape design because they are easily transplanted in large size and generally available in the nurseries of the region.

The Scarlet and the Pin Oaks are discussed together because their leaves are similar in appearance and because in landscape design both are valuable materials of the Oak genus for slightly smaller stature and finer texture, becoming excellent shade trees for average home grounds and suburban streets. For most purposes the Scarlet Oak is the more desirable species. As a young tree it is upright oval in form, eventually becoming high-branching and round-headed. In autumn the rich red of the foliage is most beautiful. A native of high ground and poor dry soils from the upper Coastal Plain to the Ohio Valley, it is not widely grown in the nurseries because it is said to be difficult to move. This objection could be overcome with root pruning, however. This tree should be more widely grown because it is one of the finest in many ways. The Pin Oak is much more common, and, being easily transplanted in large sizes, it has long been used in landscape problems. A native of the moist rich bottoms of the Ohio Valley, it adapts easily to all average growing situations in the cooler Piedmont and the Upper South. It cannot be grown successfully, however, on thin soils over a limestone base because here the foliage yellows for lack of iron (chlorosis). For many places the Pin Oak is slightly less desirable than the Scarlet

Oak because it has no fall color although it often holds its brown leaves through the winter, and also because it tends to be low branching, retaining the declining lower branches in the characteristic manner which necessitates steady pruning for circulation under its spread. Set in a broad lawn where the branches may sweep the ground, this habit may become a virtue, of course, in the formation of a fine specimen.

The Willow Oak and the Water Oak may be considered together as two distinctly southern species of similar form. Both are large-growing, high-branching, round-headed trees of fine foliage texture. The leaves of the former are lance-like, entire, not at all typical of the Oaks, while those of the latter are slightly lobed. Both are well suited to all well-drained sites in the Coastal Plain and the Piedmont where they are native, but the Willow Oak is also thoroughly reliable throughout the Upper South and as far north as New York City. These trees can be employed successfully in all kinds of shade tree and street tree plantings where space is generous and a large form is required; they are easily transplanted in very large sizes and are fast growing. Of the two the Willow Oak is slightly the better because it has a good bright yellow fall color, and it seems not quite so brittle nor so subject to the scale infestations which are sometimes severe on the Water Oak. Both are, however, superior shade trees for warmer parts of the region.

The Laurel Oak is a large round-topped tree to about 80 feet in height, best known in cultivation in the form called the "Darlington" Oak, originally found in the South Carolina Coastal Plain. It is called evergreen, but generally this is not entirely true, and the leaves drop in the late winter or early spring. The foliage and general habit are somewhat similar in appearance to those of the Live Oak although the form is not so broad. The Laurel Oak is considered comparatively weak and short-lived and therefore inferior to the Live Oak. It is useful chiefly for quick effect in the Coastal Plain and it is fairly common in street tree work.

The Live Oak is the one true evergreen of this group, and it is a characteristic plant of the Coastal Plain. Its low and broadly spreading form, richly draped in Spanish Moss, is so familiar that little description or comment is needed. The foliage is medium in texture and dark in color, but the new growth of spring is often a bright olive which is pronounced in effect. This is one of the most handsome of all trees, disease free and long-lived, for parks, highways, and more spacious quarters. In certain sections the growths of Spanish Moss, which seem to be especially luxuriant on this species, are quite a nuisance, a consideration which makes the Pines, for example, somewhat more desirable for areas very near houses.

The Live Oak is difficult to move in large sizes but it grows quite rapidly considering the hardness and toughness of the wood. Nursery grown specimens properly pruned and balled with trunk diameters up to six inches are commonly moved. This species is apparently quite variable and it may be found growing in many different forms in such different environments as seashore, open fields, river bluff, and woodland. It is not much seen in the upper reaches of the Coastal Plain, but it is perfectly hardy throughout. It may also be planted in warmer parts of the Piedmont, but here it should be treated as a small tree chiefly for screening, as it may be damaged by ice storms.

*Robinia pseudoacacia*, Black Locust. This is hardly an important ornamental because (1) it is thorny, (2) in most sections its life is cut short by borer activities, and (3) its foliage is sometimes turned brown and unsightly in late summer by leaf beetles. Still, in poor dry soils, and especially in alkaline regions, the Black Locust is useful for a quick cover and as a nurse tree for other permanent species. In the limestone soils of the Upper South it sometimes makes large and rather valuable specimens. Usually rather narrow, upright, and irregular in form, it has a light foliage of fine texture which does not require raking in autumn. The small weeping clusters of white flowers in early spring are often showy and are highly prized for their delicious fragrance. The wood is weather resistant, hard, and tough, valuable for rough outdoor construction. Because of their non-fibrous root system, Locusts are set out as small seedlings. They grow so rapidly that they can be very useful, chiefly in the Upper South, for reforestation and the protection of raw slopes, and they could very well be introduced into new subdivisions which lack tree growth of any kind. A variety called the Shipmast Locust is said to grow to one straight trunk, is especially fine for posts, and is rated highly resistant to borers.

*Salix* species, Willow. The Willows are fast growers of rather short life and they harbor numerous pests. In spite of these faults, the various weeping forms are still great favorites. In the sentimental landscapes of Victorian taste, they were often associated with lakes and ponds. The names of these trees are confused in the nurseries. The Babylon Weeping Willow, *S. babylonica*, is a common form, but the Thurlow, *S. elegantissima*, and the Yellowstem, *S. alba vitellina pendula*, are possibly better. The latter has golden yellow twigs for winter color. Where their greedy rooting and general untidiness can be tolerated, the upright Willows always contribute a picturesque charm to the landscape with their billowy soft forms and gray-green color. There are many species of varying size and character. The native Black Willow, *S. nigra*, common along watercourses throughout the region, and the White Willow, *S. alba,* from Europe, are imposing species. The Yellowstem White Willow, *S. alba vitellina,* contributes golden winter twig color. Although it is considerably smaller, the Contorted Hankow Willow, *S. matsudana tortuosa,* makes a fantastic specimen at all seasons with its twisted twigs and foliage. All of these are suited to damp soils through most of this region.

*Sophora japonica,* Japanese Pagodatree. Although it is not widely distributed in this region, this promises to be one of the best shade trees throughout the Southeast. Growing to a height of just over 50 feet, it is not too large for many residential streets and lots. The deciduous foliage is compound, fine in texture, and dark green. In late summer there are small white flowers borne in showy clusters, said to yield quantities of honey. The succeeding fruits develop in yellowish pods which are occasionally effective in winter after the leaf fall. The bark of the trunk is black and fissured, but smaller branches are smooth and dark green all year. This tree seems well suited to all parts of this region, and, belonging to the Pea Family, it may be recommended for limestone soils, adapting to low fertility and drought as well as any. It is a reasonably fast grower, seems to be quite clean and free of pests, and makes a light shade which favors turf under its spread. It may be somewhat brittle, but it appears to be most worthy of further testing in the Southeast.

*Taxodium distichum,* Common Baldcypress. This is native to the swamps of the Coastal Plain, but it is quite hardy and grows well under normal soil conditions throughout the Southeast, becoming 50 to a 100 feet in height with a spread of 20 feet. With its symmetrical conical form, characteristic of young specimens, and its light green, fern-like foliage, it makes an exotic and unusual feature, possibly difficult to harmonize in the landscape but always interesting when well placed. It is slow growing and resents moving, but it is quite pest free except for occasional depredations of bag worms which are not often serious. Closely related to the Pine Family, this tree is similar to the cone-bearing evergreens in form and seed production, but the foliage is deciduous, turning golden brown in autumn. It can be a useful material for poorly drained sites.

*Tilia americana,* American Linden. *Tilia cordata,* Littleleaf Linden. Best suited to cooler areas, the Linden species, including several important hybrids and varieties, offer some superior shade trees, rather fast growing and fairly trouble free, for the Upper South and parts of the Piedmont. Only two of the more common species are mentioned here although there are others worth testing. The American Linden is a coarse-growing giant of cool, moist woodlands of the Upper South. It will be somewhat useful in parks and parkways, and it has been planted along broad streets. Commonly known as the Basswood, this is well known for its fragrant small flowers of early summer and for its white wood. The Littleleaf Linden is smaller growing, more refined, and often very effective in flower. It is probably better in most cases as a street tree, and it is fine for small lawns although its dense shade discourages turf growth. All of the Lindens may be damaged occasionally by leaf insects, but they are usually quite clean and desirable for urban surroundings.

*Tsuga canadensis,* Canadian Hemlock. *Tsuga caroliniana,* Carolina Hemlock. The Canadian Hemlock is native to moist acid soil uplands of the Upper South and cool slopes of the Piedmont. It is successful in shaded locations as far south as Memphis, Birmingham, and Atlanta. It has a fine texture, a rich dark color, and a graceful, rather weeping habit of branching in its upright conical form. It is restricted in its normal range to cooler, well-watered, sheltered sites. Although it will stand thin soils and a good bit of shade, it will not thrive in severe exposure to wind and sun or heat and drought. Becoming a forest giant in its native stands, the Canadian Hemlock also is an exceedingly useful material for many landscape problems requiring a hardy evergreen material of smaller size since it is so readily adaptable to either formal shearing or to less obvious pruning to reduce size without destroying the natural informality of habit. This is one of the best plants for hedges of from 5 to 10 feet in height, keeping its foliage to the ground well with proper shaping. For boundaries, screens, and informal clumps, again because it holds its lower branches well, and also because it stands shade and some crowding, this tree can be kept at almost any height with an occasional nipping back of the leaders. This Hemlock has many varieties which, although scarce, are very interesting as garden specimens. These include dwarfs, cone or ball forms, and weepers.

The Carolina Hemlock is more restricted in its range to the mountains of the Upper South, and it is less adaptable to general use. It differs from the above in the arrangement of the leaves on the twigs, having a more bushy, full appearance. It is not widely available, but it makes a handsome specimen in its limited range.

*Ulmus americana,* American Elm. Because of the Elm diseases which are sweeping most of the eastern states still unchecked, this and its sister species are not recommended for general planting. There is no real substitute for the American Elm's beautiful vase-like form, its rapid but sturdy growth, ease of handling, and its wide tolerance. However, years of research have not revealed effective measures for either control or prevention of the Dutch Elm Disease or *phloem necrosis.* Spray and pruning programs have been worked out as city projects in a few communities where Elms are considered essential to real estate values or where such a maintenance program might be less costly than the enormous task of the removal and replacement of many giant trees. The success of such programs depends on their being executed on a city-wide scale to eliminate all sources of infection, and on the availability of adequate spray equipment and competent workmen. Where such programs are in effect, some replanting of Elms is being done, but for general conditions at this time these trees seem a questionable choice if a fair substitute can be found.

*Zelkova serrata*, Japanese Zelkova. Belonging to the same family as the American Elm but also apparently resistant to disease, this tree might often be planted as a substitute for the Elm. It has been used little in this region and is not widely available, but still there are a few specimens which demonstrate its adaptability to these climatic and soil conditions from the sandy Coastal Plain to the Ohio River. This is a medium-large tree, growing to about 80 feet in height with a vase-like form. The deciduous foliage, medium to fine in texture, is similar to that of the Elm. There are a delicate branching tracery and a faint orange-red cast to the bark to add beauty to the winter scene. On further testing this might prove widely useful as a shade tree for streets and for home landscapes.

# Appendix A

## PLANT MATERIALS FOR THE NEW ORLEANS AREA

WILLIAM S. WIEDORN, LANDSCAPE ARCHITECT
NEW ORLEANS, LOUISIANA

Editor's Note: Growing plants in this area presents peculiar problems which are highlighted by some of Mr. Wiedorn's comments. "I hesitate to compose any list without notes inasmuch as New Orleans is in the Great Mississippi River Flood Plain with its predominantly alkaline soil and poor drainage conditions. Most of the plants grow taller here than in almost any other region, and a few remain smaller."

The asterisk placed beside some of the plant names indicates generally a requirement for special soil or spray treatment. However, Mr. Wiedorn adds this note: "Perhaps under the asterisk we should add 'needs protection,' as some plants, such as Furry Jasmine, are not always hardy except in protected places such as enclosed patios."

### Group I - Vines

| Botanical Name | Common Name |
|---|---|
| Antigonon leptopus | Mountainrose Coralvine |
| Clytostoma callistegioides | Argentine Trumpetvine |
| Doxantha unguis-cati | Catclaw Funnelcreeper |
| Ficus pumila | Climbing Fig |
| Hedera canariensis | Algerian Ivy |
| *Jasminum multiflorum | Furry Jasmine |
| Lantana sellowiana | Trailing Lantana |
| Rosa banksiae | Banks Rose |
| Rosa bracteata var. "Mermaid" | Mermaid Macartney Rose |
| Rosa laevigata | Cherokee Rose |

244

*Botanical Name*                    *Common Name*

| Botanical Name | Common Name |
|---|---|
| Solanum jasminoides | Jasmine Nightshade |
| Trachelospermum jasminoides | Chinese Starjasmine |
| Wistaria sinensis | Chinese Wistaria |

### Group II - Groundcovers - Height to 1 foot

| | |
|---|---|
| Aspidistra elatior | Common Aspidistra |
| Cyrtomium falcatum | Holly Fern |
| Hedera canariensis | Algerian Ivy |
| Hemerocallis varieties | Daylily (Evergreen varieties) |
| Liriope muscari | Bigblue Liriope |
| Mondo jaburan (M. or Ophiopogon japonicum) | Dwarf Lilyturf |
| Nephrolepis exaltata bostoniensis | Boston Fern |

### Group III - Dwarf Shrubs - Height 1 to 4 feet

| | |
|---|---|
| *Ardisia crispa | Coral Ardisia |
| *Buxus harlandi | Harland's Box |
| Ilex vomitoria nana Stokes | Stokes Dwarf Yaupon |
| Malpighia glabra | Babados Cherry Malpighia |
| Punica granatum nana | Dwarf Pomegranate |
| Raphiolepis indica | India Raphiolepis |
| *Rhododendron (Azalea) species | Macrantha Azalea |
| Serissa foetida | Serissa |

### Group IV - Small Shrubs - Height 4 to 6 feet

| | |
|---|---|
| Jasminum humile | Italian Jasmine |
| *Rhododendron (Azalea) obtusum japonicum | Kurume Azalea |
| Rosa chinensis "Louis Philippe" | Louis Philippe Rose |
| Spiraea cantoniensis lanceolata | Double Reeves Spiraea |

### Group V - Medium Shrubs - Height 6 to 10 feet

| | |
|---|---|
| *Abelia grandiflora | Glossy Abelia |
| Buxus microphylla japonica | Littleleaf Japanese Box |
| Jasminum mesnyi | Primrose Jasmine |
| Nerium oleander | Common Oleander |
| *Rhododendron (Azalea) indicum | Indica Azalea |
| Viburnum suspensum | Sandankwa Viburnum |

### Group VI - Large Shrubs - Height over 10 feet

| | |
|---|---|
| *Camellia japonica in variety | Common Camellia |
| *Camellia sasanqua in variety | Sasanqua Camellia |
| Cocculus laurifolius | Laurelleaf Snailseed |
| Elaeagnus pungens | Thorny Elaeagnus |
| Eurya japonica | Japanese Eurya |

| *Botanical Name* | *Common Name* |
|---|---|
| Feijoa sellowiana | Feijoa |
| *Ilex cornuta burfordi | Burford Chinese Holly |
| Ilex vomitoria | Yaupon Holly |
| Ligustrum lucidum (japonicum) | |
| | Glossy Privet (Waxleaved Ligustrum) |
| Myrica cerifera | Southern Waxmyrtle |
| Myrtus communis | True Myrtle |
| Myrtus communis microphylla | Littleleaf True Myrtle |
| Pittosporum tobira | Tobira Pittosporum |
| Pyracantha koidzumi (formosana) | Formosa Firethorn |
| Viburnum odoratissimum | Sweet Viburnum |

## Group VII - Small Trees - Height 10 to 40 feet

| | |
|---|---|
| Eriobotrya japonica | Loquat |
| Koelreuteria formosana | Formosa Goldenraintree |
| Lagerstroemia indica | Common Crapemyrtle |
| Michelia fuscata | Bananashrub |
| Osmanthus fragrans | Sweet Osmanthus |
| Conifers | |
| Juniperus chinensis japonica | Japanese Juniper |
| Juniperus virginiana | Eastern Redcedar |
| Podocarpus macrophyllus maki | Shrubby Yew Podocarpus |
| Palms | |
| Butia capitata (Cocos australis) | Brazilian Butiapalm |
| Rhapidophyllum hystrix | Needlepalm |
| Sabal Palmetto | Cabbage Palmetto |
| Bamboo | |
| Bambusa multiplex | Hedge Bamboo |
| Bambusa multiplex var. Alphonse Karr | Alphonse Karr Hedge Bamboo |

## Group VIII - Large Trees - Height over 40 feet

| | |
|---|---|
| Carya illinoensis | Pecan |
| Cinnamomum camphora | Camphortree |
| Liquidambar formosana | Formosa Sweetgum |
| Magnolia grandiflora | Southern Magnolia |
| Quercus nigra | Water Oak |
| Quercus virginiana | Live Oak |
| Conifers | |
| Taxodium distichum | Common Baldcypress |
| Palms | |
| Phoenix canariensis | Canary Island Palm |
| Washingtonia robusta | Mexican Washington Palm |

# Appendix B

PLANTS ADAPTED TO LANDSCAPE USE FOR SEASIDE AND
SHORE AREAS OF GEORGIA, NORTH FLORIDA,
AND THE GULF COAST

T. Miesse Baumgardner, Landscape Architect
Sea Island, Georgia

The selection of materials for seaside planting is limited by the many severe growth-inhibiting factors existing along the seashore. These factors usually include poor sandy soil containing very little, if any, organic matter; extreme winds, sometimes laden with salt spray; and drainage conditions, which may vary from "high and dry," such as found on the slopes of sand dune formations, to areas which may be water-logged during rainy periods, such as the prevalent low flats and inter-dune areas, which are often underlaid with hardpan strata. Here, experience and keen observation are prerequisites to successful plantings.

On the credit side, the very factors mentioned above which may tend to limit the selection of plants have, at the same time, been largely responsible for creating the rare and beautiful natural subtropical landscape found only along a narrow strip of land adjacent to these coasts. The climate tempering effect of the sea and the prevailing humidity permit the growing of many subtropical plants not found in the same latitudes farther inland.

Here also the preparation of the planting soil is of far greater importance than it is under more favorable conditions of soil, drainage, and exposure. The plant beds or planting pits generally must be adequate in size, deep, and raised in elevation when necessary to provide drainage; the natural sandy soil should be fortified with a high percentage of humus provided by incorporating good muck topsoil, peat moss, compost, well-rotted straw manure, or a combination of these materials. The incorporation of a small percentage of coarse sand or gravel in the soil mixture is often found to be beneficial in improving soil aeration and promoting deep rooting in coastal regions where the natural sands are very fine in texture.

The number of plants of ornamental value which will survive full onslaught of beach winds is extremely limited. Many more can be grown (particularly among the evergreen trees and shrubs) with some extra care and precaution a little farther back from the beach line when protection from the full sweep of winds and salt spray is provided, either by natural or artificial barriers.

## First Zone Exposure

The following plants have been chosen for their ability to bear up under the most rigorous conditions of winds, salt spray to a limited extent, and, in some instances, moderate amounts of salt in the soil. These are among the very few plants which will persist in the teeth of the winds a short distance back from the shore line with a minimum of burning and searing. The plants are listed roughly in sequence as to their degree of wind tolerance.

### Trees

| Botanical Name | Common Name |
|---|---|
| Sabal palmetto | Cabbage Palmetto |
| Washingtonia robusta | Mexican Washington Palm |
| Cocos australis (Butia capitata) | Pindo Palm |
| Phoenix canariensis | Canary Date Palm |
| Tamarix (native variety) | Tamarisk |
| Casuarina cunninghamia | Beef Wood (Australian Pine) |
| | (usually frozen back every few seasons) |
| Parkinsonia aculeata | Jerusalemthorn |
| Bumelia (native variety, probably tenax) | Bumelia |
| Myrica cerifera | Southern Waxmyrtle |
| Acacia farnesiana | Opopanax |

### Shrubs

| | |
|---|---|
| Yucca aloifolia | Spanish Bayonet |
| Yucca filamentosa | Adam's Needle |
| Yucca gloriosa | Moundlily Yucca |
| Sabal minor | Dwarf Palmetto |
| Serenoa repens | Saw Palmetto |

*Botanical Name*                          *Common Name*

| Nerium oleander | Common Oleander (in variety) |
| Pittosporum tobira | Tobira Pittosporum |
| Raphiolepis indica | Indian Hawthorn (dwarf type) |
| Raphiolepis indica rosea | Pink Indian Hawthorn (dwarf type) |
| Raphiolepis japonica | Japanese Hawthorn (upright type) |
| Juniperus conferta | Shore Juniper |
| Ligustrum japonicum | Japanese Privet (Glossy or Waxleaf Privet—compact spreading type) |
| Ligustrum coriaceum (L. j. rotundi-folium) | Roundleaf Japanese Privet (Curly-leaf Privet) |
| Ligustrum japonicum erectum | Upright Japanese Privet |

NOTE: Ligustrum should be grafted on Nematode (rootknot) resistant understock.

| Elaeagnus pungens fruitlandi | Fruitland Elaeagnus |
| Myrica cerifera | Southern Waxmyrtle |
| Ilex vomitoria | Yaupon (Christmas Berry) |
| Ilex vomitoria nana | Dwarf Yaupon |
| Baccharis halimifolia | Eastern Baccharis (Salt Myrtle) |
| Severinia buxifolia | Chinese Boxorange |
| Agave | Century Plant |
| Ruscus aculeatus | Butchersbroom |

### Groundcover Plants and Vines

| Ipomea Pes-caprae | Soilbind (Beach) Morning Glory |
| Lantana sellowiana | Trailing Lantana |
| Liriope muscari | Big Blue Liriope |
| Liriope spicata (Mondo or Ophiopogon japonicum) | Little Blue Liriope (Dwarf Lilyturf) |
| Vinca major | Bigleaf Periwinkle |
| Smilax lanceolata | Lanceleaf Greenbrier (native variety-vine) |
| Lonicera japonica halliana | Hall's Japanese Honeysuckle (vine) |
| Lonicera heckrotti | Goldflame Honeysuckle (vine) |
| Uniola paniculata | Seaoats |

### Second Zone Exposure

Plants in the following list are being grown satisfactorily in various seaside areas of the region in locations with some protection from direct sea winds. This partial protection may be provided by such natural features as a sharp indentation of the coast line, high protecting sand dune formations, the shelter of established plantings or other windbreaks such as walls, fences, buildings, etc.

## Trees

| *Botanical Name* | *Common Name* |
|---|---|
| Celtis laevigata | Sugar Hackberry |
| Cinnamomum camphora | Camphortree |
| Eriobotrya japonica | Loquat |
| Ilex cassine | Dahoon |
| Ilex opaca | American Holly |
| Ilex vomitoria | Yaupon |
| Juniperus virginiana | Eastern Redcedar (type native to the region) |
| Ligustrum lucidum | Glossy Privet |
| Liquidambar styraciflua | Sweetgum |
| Magnolia grandiflora | Southern Magnolia |
| Magnolia virginiana (glauca) | Sweetbay Magnolia |
| Olea europaea | Common Olive |
| Pinus (in variety) | Slash Pine and Native Shortleaf Pines |
| Platanus orientalis | Oriental Planetree |
| Prunus caroliniana | Carolina Laurelcherry |
| Quercus virginiana | Live Oak |
| Sapium sebiferum | Chinese Tallowtree |
| Ulmus parvifolia sempervirens | Chinese Elm (Evergreen Elm) |

## Shrubs

| | |
|---|---|
| Bambusa multiplex | Fernleaf Hedgebamboo |
| Bambusa multiplex argentea | Greenstem Hedgebamboo |
| Brunfelsia calycina | Brazilian Raintree |
| Buxus harlandi | Harland's Box |
| Buxus microphylla japonica | Littleleaf Japanese Box |
| Calliandra guildingi | Trinidad Calliandra |
| Callistemon lanceolata | Lemon Bottlebrush |
| Callistemon rigidus | Stiff Bottlebrush |
| Cassia splendida (berriana) | Goldenwonder Senna |
| Cleyera japonica | Japan Cleyera |
| Cocculus laurifolius | Laurelleaf Snailseed |
| Cortaderia sellowiana | Pampasgrass |
| Cycas revoluta | Sago Cycas |
| Eurya japonica | Japanese Eurya |
| Fatsia japonica | Japan Fatsia |
| Feijoa sellowiana | Feijoa |
| Gardenia jasminoides | Cape Jasmine |
| Hibiscus rosa-sinensis | Chinese Hibiscus |
| Ilex crenata convexa (bullata) | Convexleaf Japanese Holly |
| Ilex crenata helleri | Heller's Japanese Holly |

| *Botanical Name* | *Common Name* |
|---|---|
| Ilex crenata latifolia (rotundifolia) | Roundleaf Japanese Holly |
| Illicium anisatum | Japanese Anisetree |
| Illicium floridanum | Florida Anisetree |
| Jasminum floridum | Showy Jasmine |
| Jasminum mesnyi (primulinum) | Primrose Jasmine |
| Malvaviscus arboreus (grandiflora) | South American Waxmallow (Turk's Cap) |
| Michelia fuscata | Bananashrub |
| Photinia glabra | Japanese Photinia |
| Photinia serrulata | Chinese Photinia |
| Plumbago capensis | Cape Plumbago |
| Podocarpus macrophyllus maki | Shrubby Yew Podocarpus |
| Podocarpus nagi | Japanese Podocarpus |
| Punica granatum nana | Dwarf Pomegranate |
| Pyracantha koidzumi (formosana) | Formosa Firethorn |
| Pyracantha nana | Low Dense (Dwarf) Pyracantha |
| Rosa chinensis "Louis Philippe" | Louis Philippe Rose |
| Rosa odora (varieties) | Tea Rose |
| Serissa foetida | Serissa |
| Tetrapanax papyriferus | Ricepaperplant |
| Thryallis glauca | Goldenshower Thryallis |
| Viburnum odoratissimum | Sweet Viburnum |
| Viburnum suspensum | Sandankwa Viburnum |

## Fruits

The following fruits are recommended for limited use in well-drained locations protected from the winds where they can be given year-round care:

Citrus Fruits (Citrus fruits for this region should be grafted only on Citrus trifoliata understock)

Calamondin

Grapefruit - Duncan

Kumquat - (in variety)

Lemon - Meyer

Limequat

Satsuma Orange

Sweet Orange - only the most cold resistant varieties such as Hamlin, Lu Gim Gong, Parson Brown, Washington Navel.

## Miscellaneous Fruits

Banana - Orinoco

Fig

| *Botanical Name* | *Common Name* |
|---|---|
| Grapes - Muscadine varieties | |
| Guava - Red and Yellow Cattley | |
| Sand Pear | |

Groundcovers (Including vines suitable for groundcover use)

| | |
|---|---|
| Gelsemium sempervirens | Carolina Jessamine |
| Hedera canariensis | Algerian Ivy |
| Hemerocallis | Daylily |
| Jasminum multiflorum (pubescens) | Furry Jasmine |
| Juniperus conferta | Shore Juniper |
| Neomarica (Marica) | Slender Falseflag (Walking Iris) |
| Plumbago capensis | Cape Plumbago |
| Santolina chamaecyparissus | Lavender Cotton |
| Serissa foetida | Serissa |
| Zamia integrifolia | Coontie |

The following Bulbs and Perennial Plants are recommended for use in groundcover and shrub beds and as edgings or borders for seasonal color effects where year-round care can be provided:

| | |
|---|---|
| Agapanthus orientalis | Blue Lily-of-the-Nile |
| Alstroemeria | Leopard Lily |
| Amaryllis hybrids | Fancyleaf Caladium |
| Caladium picturatum | Amaryllis |
| Crinum (in variety) | Crinum |
| Gerbera Jameson Hybrids | Flameray Gerbera |
| Gloriosa rothschildiana | Rothschild Glorylily |
| Gloriosa superba | Malabar Glorylily |
| Hedychium coronarium | Common Gingerlily |
| Hymenocallis | Spiderlily |
| Leucojum vernum | Spring Snowflake |
| Lycoris radiata | Red Spiderlily |
| Ornithogalum arabicum | Arabian Star-of-Bethlehem |
| Oxalis | (Winter blooming varieties including Bermuda Buttercup and Grand Duchess varieties) |
| Scilla peruviana | Peruvian Squill |
| Sprekelia formosissima | Azteclily |
| Viola odorata | Sweet Violet |
| Watsonia iridifolia | Buglelily |
| Zephyranthes (in variety) | Zephyrlily (Rainlily) |

## Vines

| | |
|---|---|
| Antigonon leptopus | Coralvine |
| Bignonia capreolata | Crossvine |

| *Botanical Name* | *Common Name* |
|---|---|
| Bignonia chamberlayni (Anemopaegma) (Doxantha unguis-cati) | Goldentrumpet (Catsclaw) |
| Bignonia speciosa (Clytostoma callistegioides) | Lavender Trumpet |
| Clematis paniculata | Sweetautumn Clematis |
| Fatshedera lizei | Fatshedera |
| Ficus pumila | Climbing Fig |
| Gelsemium sempervirens | Carolina Jessamine |
| Hedera canariensis | Algerian Ivy |
| Hedera helix | English Ivy |
| Jasminum multiflorum (pubescens) | Furry Jasmine |
| Lonicera heckrotti | Goldenflame Honeysuckle |
| Lonicera japonica halliana | Hall's Japanese Honeysuckle |
| Lonicera sempervirens | Trumpet Honeysuckle |
| Passiflora | Passionflower (native Maypop) |
| Tecomaria capensis | Cape Honeysuckle |
| Trachelospermum jasminoides | Chinese Star Jasmine |
| Rosa banksiae | Banks Rose |
| Rosa bracteata | Macartney Rose |
| Rosa bracteata "Mermaid" | Mermaid Rose |
| Rosa laevigata | Cherokee Rose |
| Rosa chinensis (climbing) "Louis Philippe" | Climbing Louis Philippe Rose |
| Smilax lanceolata | Lanceleaf Greenbrier |

# Appendix C

## PLANT MATERIALS FOR THE SOUTHEASTERN MOUNTAIN AREA

DOAN R. OGDEN, LANDSCAPE ARCHITECT
ASHEVILLE, NORTH CAROLINA

### Group I - Vines

| *Botanical Name* | *Common Name* |
|---|---|
| Akebia quinata | Fiveleaf Akebia |
| Campsis radicans | Common Trumpetcreeper (for bird lovers) |
| Celastrus orbiculatus | Oriental Bittersweet |
| Clematis hybrids | Hybrid Clematis |
| Gelsemium sempervirens | Carolina Jessamine (better in Piedmont) |
| Hydrangea petiolaris | Climbing Hydrangea (very slow) |
| Lonicera varieties | Honeysuckle (too common for interest) |
| Parthenocissus quinquefolia | Virginia Creeper (fall color) |
| Rosa hybrids | Climbing Roses |
| Vitis varieties | Garden Grapes |
| Wistaria sinensis | Chinese Wistaria (hard to control) |

### Little Used Vines

| | |
|---|---|
| Ampelopsis brevipedunculata | Amur Ampelopsis (Turquoise Berry) |
| Aristolochia durior | Dutchmanspipe |
| Celastrus scandens | American Bittersweet |
| Dioscorea batatas | Cinnamonvine |
| Lonicera japonica halliana | Hall's Honeysuckle |
| Lycium halimifolium | Matrimonyvine |

| *Botanical Name* | *Common Name* |
|---|---|
| Passiflora species | Passionflower |
| Polygonum auberti | Silvervine Fleeceflower |
| Pueraria thunbergiana | Kudzuvine |

## Group II - Groundcovers

| | |
|---|---|
| Ajuga reptans | Carpet Bugle |
| Bamboo species | Dwarf Bamboo |
| Euonymus f. coloratus | Purpleleaf Wintercreeper |
| Galax aphylla | Galax |
| Gaultheria procumbens | Checkerberry Wintergreen |
| Hedera helix | English Ivy |
| Heuchera varieties | Alumroot |
| Hypericum calycinum | Aaronsbeard St. Johnswort |
| Iberis sempervirens | Evergreen Candytuft |
| Juniperus varieties | Creeping Junipers |
| Leiophyllum buxifolium | Box Sandmyrtle |
| Mitchella repens | Partridgeberry |
| Pachistima canbyi | Canby Pachistima |
| Pachysandra terminalis | Japanese Pachysandra |
| Phlox subulata | Creeping Phlox |
| Polystichum acrostichoides | Christmasfern |
| Shortia galacifolia | Oconeebells |
| Thymus species | Creeping Thyme |
| Veronica repens | Creeping Speedwell |
| Vinca major and minor | Bigleaf and Common Periwinkle |

## Little-used Groundcovers

| | |
|---|---|
| Arctostaphylos uva-ursi | Bearberry (soil too heavy) |
| Cotoneaster species | Creeping Cotoneasters (should be used more) |
| Convallaria majalis | Lilyofthevalley (becomes too shabby) |
| Dianthus species | Pinks (soil too heavy) |
| Lysimachia nummularia | Moneywort (Creeping Buttercup) |
| Rosa species | Creeping Roses (too brambly) |
| Sedum species | Stonecrop (used occasionally) |
| Xanthorhiza simplicissima | Yellowroot (poor in winter) |
| Yucca filamentosa | Adamsneedle Yucca (too foreign) |

## Group III - Dwarf Shrubs - 1 to 3 feet

## Evergreen Dwarf Shrubs

| | |
|---|---|
| Berberis julianae nana | Dwarf Wintergreen Barberry |
| Buxus sempervirens suffruticosa | Truedwarf Box (some winterburn) |

| *Botanical Name* | *Common Name* |
|---|---|
| Calluna species | Heather (fairly short-lived) |
| Daphne odora | Winter Daphne (shelter from wind) |
| Erica carnea | Spring Heath |
| Ilex crenata helleri | Heller Japanese Holly |
| Jasminum floridum | Showy Jasmine |
| Jasminum nudiflorum | Winter Jasmine |
| Leucothoe catesbaei | Drooping Leucothoe (needs moisture) |
| Pachistima canbyi | Canby Pachistima |
| Pieris floribunda | Mountain Pieris |
| Rhododendron varieties | Dwarf Evergreen Azaleas |

### Little-used Dwarf Evergreen Shrubs

| | |
|---|---|
| Daphne cneorum | Rose Daphne |
| Euonymus f. carrieri | Glossy Wintercreeper |
| Euonymus f. vegetus | Bigleaf Wintercreeper (Euonymus scale) |
| Gardenia jasminoides radicans | Dwarf Gardenia (semi-hardy, better in Piedmont) |
| Skimmia species | Skimmia (should be used more) |
| Teucrium chamaedrys | Germander |

### Deciduous Dwarf Shrubs

| | |
|---|---|
| Caryopteris variety | Bluebeard |
| Deutzia gracilis | Slender Deutzia |
| Hypericum species | St. Johnswort (Hidcote and Sungold) |
| Prunus glandulosa | Almond Cherry (Flowering Almond) |
| Rosa floribunda | Floribunda Rose |
| Spiraea bumalda Anthony Waterer | Anthony Waterer Spiraea |
| Spiraea froebeli | |
| Symphoricarpos orbiculatus | Indiancurrent Coralberry |
| Viburnum opulus nanum | Dwarf European Cranberrybush |

### Little-used Deciduous Dwarf Shrubs

| | |
|---|---|
| Cotoneaster species | Dwarf Cotoneasters (should be used more) |
| Fothergilla gardeni | Dwarf Fothergilla (should be used more) |
| Hydrangea macrophylla (hortensis) | Bigleaf Hydrangea (wood kills in winter) |
| Lespedeza bicolor | Shrub Lespedeza (should be used more) ? |
| Philadelphus variety | Dwarf Golden Mockorange |
| Rhus aromatica | Fragrant Sumac - ? |
| Rosa carolina | Carolina Rose |
| Ulex species | Gorse |

## Group IV - Small Shrubs - 4 to 6 feet

*Botanical Name*                                    *Common Name*

### Evergreen Small Shrubs

| | |
|---|---|
| Abelia grandiflora | Glossy Abelia |
| Aucuba japonica | Japanese Aucuba |
| Berberis julianae | Wintergreen Barberry |
| Berberis sargentiana | Sargent Barberry |
| Buxus sempervirens | Common (American) Box |
| Camellia (hardy varieties) | Camellias (height range here — most Sasanquas are fine — wood and foliage of Japonicas also hardy but flowers winter kill) |
| Ilex crenata convexa | Convexleaf Japanese Holly |
| Ilex crenata hetzi | Hetz Japanese Holly |
| Ilex crenata rotundifolia | Bigleaf Japanese Holly |
| Mahonia bealei | Leatherleaf Mahonia |
| Nandina domestica | Nandina |
| Osmanthus fortunei | Fortune's Osmanthus |
| Osmanthus ilicifolius | Holly Osmanthus |
| Pieris japonica | Japanese Pieris |
| Rhododendron species | Evergreen Azaleas |

### Little-used Evergreen Small Shrubs

| | |
|---|---|
| Cyrilla racemiflora | American Cyrilla |
| Cytisus species | Brooms (all) |
| Lyonia (Pieris) lucida | Fetterbush Lyonia |
| Mahonia aquifolium | Oregongrape Mahonia (winter damage to leaves) |
| Myrica gale | Sweetgale |
| Osmanthus fragans | Sweet Osmanthus (semi-hardy) |
| Rhododendron minus | Piedmont Rhododendron |

### Deciduous Small Shrubs

| | |
|---|---|
| Berberis thunbergi | Japanese Barberry |
| Callicarpa species | Beautyberry |
| Clethra alnifolia | Summersweet |
| Cornus varieties | Yellow and Coralstem Dogwoods (keep to 6 feet) |
| Enkianthus perulatus | White Enkianthus |
| Euonymus alatus compactus | Dwarf Winged Euonymus |
| Forsythia suspensa | Weeping Forsythia |
| Hydrangea arborescens grandiflora | Snowhill Hydrangea |
| Kerria japonica | Japanese Kerria |

| *Botanical Name* | *Common Name* |
|---|---|
| Rhododendron roseum | Roseshell Azalea |
| Rhododendron vaseyi | Pinkshell Azalea |
| Rhododendron viscosum | Swamp Azalea |
| Rhodotypos scandens | Black Jetbead |
| Rosa setigera | Prairie Rose |
| Spiraea arguta | Garland Spiraea |
| Spiraea vanhouttei | Vanhoutte Spiraea |
| Spiraea prunifolia | Bridalwreath Spiraea |

### Little-used Deciduous Small Shrubs

| | |
|---|---|
| Amelanchier stolonifera | Running Shadbush |
| Cotoneaster divaricata | Glossy Cotoneaster |
| Deutzia lemoinei | Lemoine Deutzia |
| Diervilla sessilifolia | Southern Bushhoneysuckle |
| Fothergilla major | Large Fothergilla (should be used more) |
| Hypericum aureum | Golden St. Johnswort (spreads by seeding) |
| Ribes alpinum | Alpine Currant (drops leaves too early) |
| Rubus odoratus | Fragrant Thimbleberry |
| Stephanandra incisa | Cutleaf Stephanandra (should be used more) |
| Symphoricarpos a. laevigatus | Garden Snowberry |
| Viburnum acerifolium | Mapleleaf Viburnum (marvelous fall color) |

### Group V - Medium-sized Shrubs - 6 to 10 feet

### Evergreen Medium-sized Shrubs

| | |
|---|---|
| Euonymus kiautschovicus (patens) | Spreading Euonymus |
| Ilex varieties | Holly (in this height range) |
| Kalmia latifolia | Mountainlaurel |
| Ligustrum japonicum (lucidum) | Japanese (Glossy) Privet |
| Prunus l. schipkaensis | Schipka Laurelcherry |
| Prunus l. zabeli | Zabel Laurelcherry |
| Pyracantha species | Firethorn |
| Rhododendron carolinianum | Carolina Rhododendron |
| Rhododendron catawbiense | Catawba Rhododendron |

### Little-used Evergreen Medium-sized Shrubs

| | |
|---|---|
| Escallonia species | Escallonia |
| Illicium anisatum | Japanese Anisetree |
| Laurus nobilis | Grecian Laurel |
| Leucothoe axillaris | Coast Leucothoe |
| Ligustrum lucidum (japonicum) | Glossy (Japanese) Privet |

*Botanical Name*                          *Common Name*

Loropetalum chinense                          Loropetalum
Myrica pennsylvanica (carolinensis)       Northern Bayberry
Pittosporum tobira              Tobira Pittosporum (semi-hardy,
                                            not in mountains)

### Deciduous Medium-sized Shrubs

Buddleia davidi hybrids              Orangeye Butterflybush
Calycanthus floridus                        Sweetshrub
Chaenomeles lagenaria     Japanese Floweringquince (red and white)
Deutzia species                               Deutzia
Euonymus alatus                        Winged Euonymus
Exochorda species                            Pearlbush
Forsythia intermedia                    Border Forsythia
Hibiscus syriacus                         Shrubalthaea
Hydrangea paniculata grandiflora      Peegee Hydrangea
Kolkwitzia amabilis                        Beautybush
Lagerstroemia indica                       Crapemyrtle
Lindera benzoin                      Common Spicebush
Lonicera fragrantissima              Winter Honeysuckle
Lonicera species                      Zabel Honeysuckle
Prunus triloba                      Flowering Plum (fair)
Rhododendron species                   Native Azaleas
Ribes aureum                          Golden Currant
Syringa vulgaris         Common Lilac (late frost damages bloom —
                              French hybrids almost entirely)
Weigela species                               Weigela
Vaccinium species                           Blueberries
Viburnum species            Viburnums (in this height range)
Vitex agnuscastus                      Lilac Chastetree

### Little-used Deciduous Medium-sized Shrubs

Acanthopanax sieboldianus            Fiveleaf Acanthopanax
Amorpha                               Leadplant Amorpha
Aronia                                 Red Chokeberry
Cephalanthus occidentalis           Common Buttonbush
Corylopsis species              Winterhazel (should be used more)
Cotoneaster species             Cotoneaster (in this height range)
Euonymus yedoensis and others   Yeddo Euonymus, and others (scale)
Hippophae rhamnoides          Common Seabuckthorn (soil not right)
Lonicera species                       Bushhoneysuckles
Philadelphus species             Mockorange (some planted)

| *Botanical Name* | *Common Name* |
|---|---|
| Photinia villosa | Oriental Photinia (should be used) |
| Physocarpus opulifolius | Common Ninebark |
| Prunus tomentosa | Manchu Cherry (short-lived) |
| Rhamnus species | Buckthorn |
| Sambucus canadensis | American Elder |
| Staphylea trifolia | American Bladdernut |
| Tamarix species | Tamarisk |

## Group VI - Large Shrubs - over 10 feet

### Evergreen Large Shrubs

| | |
|---|---|
| Bambusa species | Tall Golden Japanese Bamboo Cane |
| Elaeagnus pungens | Thorny Elaeagnus |
| Elaeagnus pungens fruitlandi | Fruitland Elaeagnus |
| Ilex species | Hollies (English, Chinese, Japanese, American in this height range) |
| Magnolia grandiflora | Southern Magnolia |
| Photinia glabra | Japanese Photinia |
| Photinia serrulata | Chinese Photinia |
| Prunus caroliniana | Carolina Laurelcherry |
| Pyracantha species | Firethorn (in this height range) |
| Rhododendron maximum | Rosebay Rhododendron |
| Viburnum rhytidophyllum | Leatherleaf Viburnum |

### Little-used Evergreen Shrubs

| | |
|---|---|
| Myrica pennsylvanica | Northern Bayberry |

### Deciduous Large Shrubs

| | |
|---|---|
| Viburnum tomentosum | Doublefile Viburnum |
| Viburnum prunifolium | Blackhaw Viburnum |
| Syringa chinensis | Chinese Lilac |
| Syringa a. japonica | Japanese Tree Lilac |

### Little-used Deciduous Shrubs

| | |
|---|---|
| Aralia spinosa | Devils-Walkingstick (spread badly) |
| Caragana species | Peashrub |
| Corylus americana | American Filbert (should be used) |
| Hamamelis virginiana, mollis, vernalis | Common Witchhazel (Chinese, Vernal) |
| Ligustrum vulgare | European Privet |

## Group VII - Small Trees

*Botanical Name*                                    *Common Name*

| | |
|---|---|
| Acer palmatum in variety | Japanese Maples |
| Albizzia julibrissin | Silktree Albizzia |
| Amelanchier canadensis | Shadblow Serviceberry — |
| Carpinus species | Hornbeam (American and European species) |
| Cercis canadensis | Eastern Redbud — |
| Chionanthus virginicus | White Fringetree |
| Cladrastis lutea | Yellowwood |
| Clerodendron trichotomum | Harlequin Glorybower |
| Cornus florida | Flowering Dogwood — |
| Cornus kousa | Kousa Dogwood |
| Cotinus coggygria | Common Smoketree |
| Franklinia alatamaha | Franklinia — |
| Halesia carolina | Carolina Silverbell (also H. monticola) |
| Koelreuteria paniculata | Panicled Goldraintree |
| Laburnum species | Laburnum (Goldenchain) (poor in foliage) |
| Lagerstroemia indica | Common Crapemyrtle — |
| Malus species | Flowering Crabapples — |
| Oxydendrum arboreum | Sourwood — |
| Prunus species | Wild Plum |
| | Japanese Flowering Cherries |
| | Flowering Peach |
| Salix species | Pussywillow — |
| Sassafras albidum | Sassafras — |
| Sorbus species | Mountainash — |

### Little-used Small Trees

| | |
|---|---|
| Ailanthus altissima | Treeofheaven Ailanthus |
| Asimina triloba | Common Pawpaw |
| Catalpa species | Catalpa |
| Cercidiphyllum japonicum | Katsuratree |
| Crataegus species | Hawthorns (danger to children) |
| Davidia involucrata | Dovetree (scarce) |
| Elaeagnus angustifolia | Russianolive (seeds all over) |
| Fraxinus ornus | Flowering Ash (should be used) — |
| Magnolia soulangeana | Saucer Magnolia (late frost on flowers) |
| Magnolia stellata | Star Magnolia (late frost on flowers) |
| Prunus species | Purple-leaved Plums (hard to blend) |
| Ptelea trifoliata | Common Hoptree (Wafer Ash) |
| Robinia viscosa | Clammy Locust (poor form) |
| Sophora japonica | Japanese Pagodatree |

| *Botanical Name* | *Common Name* |
|---|---|
| Stewartia species | Stewartia (should be used) |
| Styrax species | Snowbell (should be used) |
| Zanthoxyllum americanum | Common Pricklyash |

## Group VIII - Large Trees

### Evergreen Large Trees

| | |
|---|---|
| Abies balsamea | Balsam Fir |
| Abies fraseri | Fraser Balsam Fir |
| Abies nordmanniana | Nordmann Fir |
| Cedrus deodara | Deodar Cedar (danger of top dying) |
| Chamaecyparis | Falsecypress (all species except pisifera) |
| Cryptomeria species | Cryptomeria |
| Cunninghamia lanceolata | Common Chinafir |
| Juniperus chinensis varieties | Chinese Junipers in variety |
| Picea abies | Norway Spruce |
| Pinus strobus | White Pine (very good) |
| Thuja species | Arborvitae (all kinds) |
| Tsuga species | Hemlocks (all kinds) |

### Little-used Evergreen Large Trees

| | |
|---|---|
| Abies concolor | White Fir (unfortunately) |
| Larix species | Larch |
| Picea species | Spruce (all but Norway) |
| Pinus nigra | Austrian Pine |
| Pinus sylvestris | Scotch Pine |
| Pseudotsuga taxifolia | Common Douglasfir (very poor here) |

### Deciduous Large Trees

| | |
|---|---|
| Acer species | Maples (all except Silver and Boxelder) |
| Betula species | Birch (all except white-stemmed varieties) |
| Carya species | Hickory (hard to transplant) |
| Fagus species | Beech (American and European varieties) |
| Gleditsia triacanthos inermis | Thornless Honeylocust (all forms) |
| Liquidambar styraciflua | American Sweetgum |
| Liriodendron tulipifera | Tuliptree |
| Magnolia species | Magnolia (native species) |
| Nyssa sylvatica | Black Tupelo (hard to transplant) |
| Platanus species | Planetrees (all species) |
| Quercus species | Oak (all species except Q. coccinea, Scarlet) |
| Salix species | Weeping Willows |

## Little-used Deciduous Large Trees

| *Botanical Name* | *Common Name* |
|---|---|
| Aesculus species | Horsechestnut |
| Celtis species | Hackberry |
| Diospyros virginiana | Persimmon |
| Fraxinus species | Ash |
| Ginkgo biloba | Ginkgo (should be used) |
| Gymnocladus dioicus | Kentucky Coffeetree |
| Juglans cinerea | Butternut (drops leaves early) |
| Juglans nigra | Black Walnut (drops leaves early) |
| Morus species | Mulberry (for bird lovers only) |
| Ostrya virginiana | American Hophornbeam |
| Paulownia tomentosa | Royal Paulownia (dirty) |
| Phellodendron species | Corktree |
| Populus species | Poplar (very few used) |
| Robinia species | Locust (poor foliage) |
| Tilia species | Lindens |
| Ulmus species | Elms |

# References

American Horticultural Society, *Azalea Handbook* (1952), *Holly Handbook* (1957). Washington: American Horticultural Society.

American Joint Committee on Horticultural Nomenclature, *Standardized Plant Names*. Harrisburg, Pa.: J. Horace McFarland Company, 1942.

Bailey, L. H., *Manual of Cultivated Plants*. New York: Macmillan Company, 1949.

Brooklyn Botanic Garden, Horticultural Handbooks Series: No. 5 *Flowering Shrubs*, No. 14 *Vines and Groundcovers*, No. 22 *Broad-leaved Evergreens*, No. 25 *100 Finest Trees and Shrubs*, Vol. 16-1 *Trees and Shrubs—Where to Buy Them*. New York: Brooklyn Botanic Garden.

Cloud, Katharine M. P., *Evergreens for Every State*. Philadelphia-New York: Chilton Company, 1960.

Coker, W. G. and H. R. Totten, *Trees of the Southeastern States*. Chapel Hill: University of North Carolina Press, 1945.

den Boer, Arie F., *Flowering Crabapples*. Washington: American Association of Nurserymen, 1959.

Hastings, Louise and Donald, *The Southern Garden Book*. New York: Doubleday and Company, 1948.

Hudson, Charles J., Jr., *Southern Gardening*. Atlanta: Tupper and Love, 1953.

Hume, H. H., *Gardening in the Lower South* (1929), *Azaleas and Camellias* (1931), *Azaleas, Kinds and Culture* (1948), *Camellias, Kinds and Culture* (1951), *Hollies* (1953). New York: Macmillan Company.

Lawrence, Elizabeth L., *A Southern Garden*. Chapel Hill: University of North Carolina Press, 1942.

Loundsberry, Alice, *Southern Wild Flowers and Trees*. New York: Frederick A. Stokes Company, 1901.

Mason, Hamilton, *Your Garden in the South*. Princeton, N. J.: Van Nostrand Company, 1961.

Wyman, Donald, *Shrubs and Vines for American Gardens* (1949), *Trees for American Gardens* (1951). New York: Macmillan Company.

# Index